C000217325

The Theory of Computer Scie

A Programming Approach

The Theory of Computer Science

A Programming Approach

J. M. BRADY

Department of Computer Science
University of Essex

LONDON

CHAPMAN AND HALL

A Halsted Press Book
John Wiley & Sons, New York

First published 1977
by Chapman and Hall Ltd
11 New Fetter Lane, London EC4P 4EE

© *1977 J. M. Brady*

Typeset by Alden Press, Oxford,
London and Northampton
and printed in Great Britain by
Richard Clay (The Chaucer Press) Ltd,
Bungay, Suffolk

ISBN 0 412 14930 3 (cased edition)
ISBN 0 412 15040 9 (Science Paperback edition)

This title is available in both hardbound and paperback editions. The
paperback edition is sold subject to the condition that it shall not, by way
of trade or otherwise, be lent, re-sold, hired out, or otherwise circulated
without the publisher's prior consent in any form of binding or cover
other than that in which it is published and without a similar condition
including this condition being imposed on the subsequent purchaser.

All rights reserved. No part of this book may be reprinted, or reproduced
or utilized in any form or by any electronic, mechanical or other means,
now known or hereafter invented, including photocopying and recording,
or in any information storage and retrieval system, without permission in
writing from the Publisher.

Distributed in the U.S.A. by Halsted Press,
a Division of John Wiley & Sons, Inc., New York

Library of Congress Cataloging in Publication Data

Brady, J   M
  The theory of computer science.

  (Science paperbacks)
  "A Halsted Press book."
  Bibliography: p.
  Includes index.
  1. Programming (Electronic computers) 2. Machine
theory. 3. Computable functions. I. Title.
QA76.B697   001.6'4'01   77-729
ISBN 0-470-99103-8

TO
NAOMI, SHARON AND CAROL

Contents

Preface

The first electronic digital computer was constructed as recently as the 1940s. In the thirty or so years that have elapsed since then, the use of computers has spread to the point where there can now be very few people in Western society whose lives are not affected by computation. The vast majority of companies, government departments, and institutes of tertiary education have their own computer centres, as does a large and growing number of secondary schools.

Although we can hardly begin to conjecture what computers will be used for after another thirty years have gone by, we can safely predict applications such as automated traffic lights, assembly lines, self-piloted vehicles for planetary exploration, automated timetable and route planning services, and machines to work autonomously in environments, such as the ocean bed, which are hostile to man. In fact, prototypes for most of these activities already exist. Equally, the rapidly decreasing cost of computers will mean that, as is already the case with television, a substantial proportion of the population will own one or more computers, whose power will match that of current large machines. We can hardly begin to estimate the impact this will eventually have on the dissemination of information, the quality of life, and the organisation of society.

To date, the development of computers has had an essentially engineering or technological flavour. Spurred on by massive backing from industry and government, new designs and components for machines, and new programming languages, constructs and applications have been developed at an incredible pace. Currently the pace seems not so much to be slowing down as increasing.

Meanwhile, the normal scientific process has been at work. A growing number of workers have sifted and abstracted the many concepts which have been suggested, and have developed models for the analysis of computing phenomena, the explanation of observed regularities, and the suggestion of new lines of development. As the title suggests, this book is an introduction to the theory of using computers. One of the impressions which I hope to convey concerns the vitality, relevance and immediacy of computing theory to computing practice. Chapter 1 explains how the theory is sampled in various ways in the second part of the book in chapters covering the pioneering work of John McCarthy (Chapter 6), attempts to make software reliable (Chapter 7), and ideas regarding the meaning of programming languages (Chapter 8). An introductory text should not aim to be exhaustive in its coverage of the field but should select according to explicitly stated criteria. Two topics which pressed for inclusion in part two, but were eventually excluded, were finite automata and complexity theory. The former was excluded on the grounds that several excellent texts are already available. The latter was excluded because I felt that current work was more inspired by the ideas of Part 1 than by computing practice.

One interesting anomaly in the development of computer science concerns the fact that the study of precise definitions of 'computable' predated the actual construction of computers! This came about because mathematicians also postulated the notion of 'effective procedure' (what we nowadays call a program) in connection with conjectures about numbers and logic, and sought to make their intuitions precise. Part 1 of the book discusses what we call 'meta' computer science. We shall find that the idea of computability is intimately related to some of the oldest paradoxes of philosophy and the foundations of mathematics. In particular, it is closely related to Gödel's theorem, one of the most remarkable intellectual advances of the twentieth century, which essentially states that there is a limit to what can be proved using formal languages such as second-order predicate logic.

However, the excitement of working in computer science is not of itself sufficient reason for writing a book! There are so many books being produced nowadays that any author ought reasonably to justify adding his contribution. There were, I believe, three main reasons why this book was written, and which distinguish it from most others covering similar material.

Firstly, I strongly believe that the theory of computing must relate directly to a student's intuitions, which are gained from computing practice. These refer to programming, data structuring, machine design, and so on. Thus in Chapter 3 for example we view theorems in recursive function theory as programming problems, and exhibit the surprisingly limited stock of programming techniques which have been developed to date for such proofs. Similarly, Chapter 5 views the problem of proving the equipollence of Turing's formalism and the general recursive functions (GRF) as a computer problem, and thereby exhibits a shortcoming in the GRF.

This approach, especially to the material present in Part 1, should be contrasted with the more usual abstract mathematical treatment, which ignores computing science intuitions, and which results from the historical 'accident' referred to above. One exception to this criticism is Marvin Minsky's (1967) machine-based account. Indeed, this book can be seen as bearing the same relation to Minsky's as programming does to computer hardware design, an observation which finally explains the title of the book.

One notable consequence of taking a programming approach to the theory of computation is that I deny that the main prerequisite for reading the book is a familiarity with modern pure mathematical ideas such as set theory, algebraic structures, and formal logic. Certainly, a familiarity with such ideas would make parts of the material easier to assimilate, but my experience has been that Appendix A contains sufficient mathematical background. The main prerequisite is *computing* experience, and appeals to computing intuitions and practice pervade the book.

The second distinctive feature of the book is closely related to the first. Over the years I have detected what I believe to be a confusion amongst my fellow computer scientists about the relationship between the theory and metatheory of computer science. I shall argue in Chapter 1 that theory and metatheory are very different ventures, so that to criticise Turing machines, for example, on the grounds that their architecture is not at all like that of von Neumann computers is, quite simply, beside the point.

Finally, I have tried, in Part 2 of the book, to correct the enormous mismatch between what is commonly taught as theory (usually the Part 1 metatheory), and the issues with which computer science theorists concern themselves. Very few computer scientists actively work in recursive function theory. They do work on formal semantics of programming languages, correctness of programs, and so on. At the risk of displaying bias, I have tried to tease out some of the presuppositions underlying models of meaning and correctness, to get the reader to think about their possible shortcomings, and to be aware of the as yet primitive state of computer science.

The approach to the theory of computation outlined in this book developed over five years of teaching an introductory course at the University of Essex. Roughly speaking, it has been used for a two-semester (second year) under-graduate, and a one-semester graduate, course. The course was always accom-panied by two projects. The first required the students to implement a Universal Turing Machine (see Checkpoint 2.24) in a suitable high level programming language. The second required students to read about a half dozen research papers on a topic such as lambda calculus models or complexity hierarchies, and to write an essay expressing their understanding and assessment of the material. I have found the latter project particularly valuable for convincing science students, who, as passive consumers, all too often are taught various aspects of Absolute Truth, that controversy, consensus and value judgements are endemic to science.

Finally, I gratefully acknowledge the inspiration, criticism, and encourage-ment I have received while developing this book. Firstly, some of the workers whose ideas most inspired me to think about the theory of computer science in the first place: John McCarthy, Peter Landin, Rod Burstall, Christopher Strachey, Tony Hoare, John Reynolds, Robin Milner, David Park, David Luckham, Peter Lauer and Bob Floyd. Secondly my colleagues at Essex: Richard Bornat, Pat Hayes, Ray Turner, Bernard Sufrin, John Laski, Tony Brooker, Lockwood Morris, Cliff Lloyd, and Barry Cornelius. Ray Turner, Tony Brooker, and Naomi Brady read various drafts and suggested a great many improvements. Pam Short did a marvellous job of typing. Most of all I acknow-ledge the support I received from my family.

October, 1976   J. M. Brady

1 Overview

1.1 Introduction

Computer science has emerged over the past twenty or so years as a discipline in its own right. During that time, a host of new ideas, such as process, data structure, and timesharing, have been established. The primary activity of computing is writing *programs* in *programming languages* which when executed on a *computer* manipulate *data* in such a way as to solve *problems*. The theory of computation chronicles the attempt to establish a theory to account for all of these phenomena in much the same way that classical dynamics attempts to explain the motion of objects.

Any scientific theory is primarily concerned with representing in the abstract realm of mathematics the real-world entities that comprise its subject matter. The representation should facilitate the discovery of mathematical relationships in the form of equations or laws. Thus, in the case of classical dynamics, where the real-world entities include distance, speed, force, and acceleration, distance is usually represented by a function of time, and speed as the derivative of such a distance function. The basic relations are Newton's laws of motion and his laws of gravitation. The relationships discovered within the theory can be interpreted in terms of real-world entities to predict or explain observed real-world phenomena. Alternatively one may be concerned to extend the range of applicability of the theory to accommodate further observations.

Any theory increases our understanding of, and systematizes our knowledge about, the subject domain. But a more immediate reason for constructing theories derives from the fact that it is usually the case that the theory also leads to significant practical advances. So it is with the theory of computer science. Section 1.3, which introduces Part 2 of the book, describes several shortcomings of today's computer science practice in which the theory of computation can be expected to make major contributions.

To each theory there is a corresponding metatheory (Greek: meta = about) which is concerned with analysing the theory itself, for example by precisely defining the concepts used in the theory and in discovering the theory's limitations. Thus, the metatheory of mathematics, naturally called metamathematics, formalizes the notions of set, proof, and theorem, and attempts to discover their limitations. A major result of metamathematics, the undecidability of predicate logic, implies that it is impossible to write a single program that decides for all legal sentences in the logic which are theorems and which are not.

This situation is typical. The theory is concerned with establishing useful *positive* results; the metatheory consists largely of results, often of a *negative* nature, which define and delimit the subject matter of the theory. Part 1 of the book, introduced in the following section, is an introduction to meta computer science. The major goals are to define precisely what is meant by 'computable' and to establish meta-results such as the unsolvability of the Halting problem for Turing machines, which implies that it is impossible to write a single program P that will decide for any other program Q input to it (in the same way that programs are often submitted as data to a compiler program) whether or not Q will terminate its computation in a finite time. On the other hand, Part 2 of the book will introduce some of the areas in which computer scientists have worked towards the discovery of positive results.

The differing goals of the theory and metatheory of computer science are reflected in the differing approaches to computability which they suggest. Thus the systems we shall meet in Part 1 of the book – Turing machines and the General Recursive Functions – enable results of meta computer science to be proved easily, but are very inconvenient to use. Conversely, systems like McCarthy's which we shall meet in Part 2 (Chapter 6) are much more convenient and practical for proving results *in* but are correspondingly harder to prove theorems *about*. It is unreasonable to indict the formalisms of Part 1 (as many people within computer science do) on the grounds of their impracticality or lack of similarity to modern computers or programming languages; that is simply not their purpose.

As a matter of fact, meta computer science, under its more usual name of Recursive Function Theory, pre-dated the actual construction of computers by several years! For example, Turing machines, which we shall meet in Chapter 2, were introduced in 1936. This apparently paradoxical situation arose largely because (meta)mathematicians had for many years worked on problems which called for 'effective processes' or 'algorithms' (or, as we would now say, 'programs'). In 1900, one of the greatest mathematicians of the century, David Hilbers (1862–1943), delivered a very famous and seminal lecture to the Second International Congress of Mathematicians, in which he posed 23 problems, some of which remain unsolved to this day. The tenth of these problems asked whether it is possible to write a program to decide whether an arbitrary polynomial in a finite number of variables with integral coefficients has integral roots. It was proved by Matyasevich in 1971 that there can be no such program.

One of the distinguishing features of this book is the computer science viewpoint which we adopt, particularly regarding the material in Part 1, which is more usually considered to be a part of mathematics that is somehow relevant to computer science. Instead, we consider the material to be the *metatheory of computer science*. Thus we shall be concerned at all times to relate the ideas we introduce to computer science. We shall rely on intuitions about programming etc., and we will draw our examples from computer science. This is particularly true of Chapter 3, in which we discuss *non*-computable functions or unsolvable problems. The examples to which we give pride of place come from the work of Luckham, Park, and Paterson (1970) and from the theory of formal grammars.

The point about these examples, as opposed to the more usual ones of mathematics or logic (which we also give but not so prominently), is that they were discovered in the course of answering problems posed *in* computer science.

There is one particular idea which we want to promote, that forms the basis of our treatment of the material in Chapters 3, 4, and 5; it can be best introduced via an example. In Chapter 3 we shall be concerned with the question of whether or not various sets S are enumerable. One way to define enumerability is in terms of a computable function $f: N \rightarrow S$ from the natural numbers onto S. An alternative viewpoint, less formal but more intuitively appealing to computer scientists, is that a set S is enumerable if there is a program that successively prints the elements of S in such a way that each element of S is listed within a finite time from the start of the process. Accordingly, our 'proofs' of enumerability will usually consist of sketching a program to carry out the enumeration. We thus arrive at the idea of a *program as a constructive proof*. This idea is developed much more fully in Chapters 4 and 5, where we shall show how a programming approach can give real insight into what has traditionally been considered a difficult proof. We will try to convince the reader that he can most usefully approach the Theory of Computation by applying his extensive skill for constructing programs. Hoare and Allison (1972) seem to argue along much the same lines, and we shall refer to their paper several times.

In the final analysis, it will be the richness or poverty of the theory of computation that will determine the scope and standing of computer science. The author will try to convince the reader that the theory is not, as one respected professor of computer science once avowed to him, "as dry as sawdust", but is vital, vibrant, and fascinating.

The remainder of this introductory chapter consists of more detailed overviews of the material to be covered in Parts 1 (Chapters 2–5) and 2 (Chapters 6–8).

1.2 PART 1: Meta computer science

We saw in the preceding section that the two major goals of meta computer science are: (i) to define 'computable' precisely, and (ii) given such a precise definition, to discover what (if any) are the theoretical limitations of computability, thus delimiting the subject matter of computer science.

1.2.1 *Defining 'computable'*

Computer scientists have a deep intuitive grasp of the notion of 'computable' in terms of one or more of 'algorithm', 'effective process', 'program', 'procedure', and 'routine'. However, while we strongly believe that the theory of computation should be presented so as to relate to the intuition of the computer science student, we nevertheless wish to issue a cautionary note against placing too heavy a reliance on intuition at the very basis of the theory of computer science.

In case the experience of set theory and Russell's paradox (see Appendix A, Section A.5.2) does not convince the reader, we have included in the last part of this section a number of comments that expose the limitations of our intuition.

For a computer scientist, the most obvious way to define 'computable is to say that something is computable precisely in the case that it can be programmed in a programming language L, where candidates for L might include FORTRAN, ALGOL 60, and so on. Such a suggestion must be rejected for meta computer science, since, as we saw in the preceeding section, a hallmark of systems in metatheories is that they should be sufficiently *simple* to enable the proofs of metatheorems to be given easily. However, this does not rule out the possibility that the suggestion could profitably be taken up as part of computer science. It turns out that there is a problem with the scheme. We clearly have to be able to deduce for any program exactly what it computes, and this problem – the so-called semantics problem – is far from trivial (see Chapter 8).

As we saw in the preceeding section, since at least 1900, mathematicians and logicians had attempted to give a precise definition of 'computable'. These efforts culminated in 1936 with the simultaneous (independent) publication by Turing in England and Church in the United States of America of suggested definitions which are nowadays accepted as correct.

Church's paper introduced the λ-calculus as a uniform way of denoting computable functions (see Sections 6.1 and 8.2) and he went on to prove the undecidability of predicate logic mentioned above. Nowadays the relevance of Church's work to computer science is seen in its use as the basis of the approach to representing procedures in programming languages as different as LISP (McCarthy *et al.*, 1962) and ALGOL 68 (van Wijngaarden *et al.*, 1969), and its use in establishing a formal definition of the meaning of computing constructs (see Chapter 8).

Turing approached the problem of giving a formal definition of 'computable' directly, by making precise what he argued as his 'intuitive notion'. In a truly remarkable paper he presented an *intuitively-appealing* development of a class of 'abstract machines' which we nowadays call Turing machines (from now on abbreviated to TM). The main point of his paper was to defend the following claim:

> (Turing's thesis) The processes which could naturally be called algorithms are precisely those which can be carried out on Turing machines.

It is important to realize that Turing's thesis cannot be proved or disproved. Rather is embodies a fundamental tenet or law of computer science. The reasonableness or otherwise of this belief can be debated but not proved. (An analogous situation is presented by Newton's 'laws' of motion, which were believed unquestionably until Einstein's theory of relativity suggested a refinement.)

We now present two arguments in favour, and two against, Turing's thesis.

FOR-1 It is difficult to fault Turing's intuitive development of his notion of computable. An alternative intuitive development is presented in Chapter 2.

FOR-2   Since 1936 many great logicians, mathematicians, and computer scientists have framed alternative definitions of 'computable'. All of them have come up with the *same* solution in the sense that the set of computable functions is the same in all cases. The consensus suggests that Turing did indeed discover the correct notion.

AGAINST-1 Turing's system is not rich enough. The fact that Turing machines are so primitive suggests that there are likely to be functions that one would 'naturally' want to accept as computable, but which no Turing machine is capable of computing. (It is probably fair to say that very few people would now advance this argument; however, consider its force in 1936.)

AGAINST-2 Turing's system is far too rich. There are functions that a Turing machine can *in theory* compute but which it is *unrealistic* to accept as computable. For example, it is surely not realistic to call a function 'computable' if any Turing machine to compute it (even if it executes a computational step every microsecond) still would take ten times the life of the universe to calculate an answer.

On balance, Turing's claim is today accepted, despite the misgivings many people have regarding the second argument against it. Indeed, this argument is one of the motivations behind the study of 'complexity' of programs (see Section 1.3).

Broadly speaking, there have been two main approaches to framing a definition of 'computable', which we may call the 'abstract machine approach', and the 'functional' or 'programming' approach.

The former approach, which includes the work of Turing (1936), Wang (1957), Shepherdson and Sturgis (1963), Elgot and Robinson (1964), and Minsky (1967), consists of developing mathematical models of executing mechanisms (processors) on which computations may be 'run'. 'Computable' is then defined to mean 'computable on one of the abstract machines'. The abstract machine approach is illustrated in Chapter 2, which consists of an intuitive development of the Turing machine (TM) model, a discussion of 'Universal' machines, and Shannon's suggested notion of complexity of machines. The chapter ends with a brief look at some other abstract machine approaches.

The functional or programming approach, which includes the work of Church (1941), Herbrand–Gödel–Kleene (see Hermes 1965, Chapter 5), Hilbert–Kleene (the General Recursive Functions), Kleene (1936), and McCarthy (1963), essentially consists of developing mathematical systems of functions for 'programming in'. We shall illustrate this in Chapter 4, by describing the General Recursive Functions and Grzegroczyk's (1953) notion of complexity.

One instance of the second argument (the 'concensus' argument) in support of Turing's thesis is that a function belongs to the General Recursive Functions (GRF) precisely when it is computable according to Turing. Since we are advocating viewing the GRF as a programming language, it is reasonable to ask what the equivalence of the GRF and Turing machines amounts to *in programming terms*. On the one hand we have a linguistic approach GRF, and on the other a machine approach TM. We have proofs that to each GRF there corresponds a TM, and vice versa. Clearly this suggests a pair of programs: A TM 'simulator' in the GRF, and a 'compiler' from GRF to TM. The main features of such a pair of programs are described in Chapter 5. In particular, it is shown how such a programming approach brings out shortcomings in a system (GRF) apparently intended as part of meta computer science. This view of the equivalence problem as an example of the compiler problem, which we know to be rather difficult, helps us to understand why it was not considered 'obvious' in 1936 that Church and Turing had equivalent notions. (I thank Professor George Barnard for this piece of historical information.)

1.2.2 *The limitations of computability*

Given a precise definition of what it means for a function to be computable, we may ask whether all functions are computable or whether there are some well-defined functions that we can prove are not computable. Put another way, we ask whether there are any well-defined problems that we can prove it is not possible to program a solution to. It is important to realize that by 'possible' we mean 'possible in theory' as opposed to 'financially possible given current resources' or 'possible given the current state of the art of programming'. We devote Chapter 3 to this issue and will see that, as we pointed out in the preceding section, there are indeed problems that we can prove cannot be solved algorithmically. We shall see that the theoretical limitations on what we can program solutions to are extremely subtle; indeed Minsky notes (1967, page vii): "There is no reason to suppose machines have any limitations not shared by man". To get a feel for the limitations of computability, we consider two topics in computer science that give rise to unsolvable problems, namely the equivalence of programs and formal grammars.

1.2.3 *The limitations of our intuition*

To round off this section we present two observations to point up the need for a precise notion of 'computable' on which to build a theory of computer science. Hoare and Allison (1972) present a variant on the same basic theme.

(1) *Descriptions*
An algorithm can be thought of as an unambiguous description of how an executing mechanism is to proceed from step to step. In the final analysis, an algorithm is a description, so it is reasonable to suppose that any algorithm can be described in any powerful enough language, say English. Indeed, many descriptions we find in everyday life can be interpreted as algorithms: Knitting patterns, recipes, instructions from a manual, route-finder maps, and so on. Given that a description is a list of English words, we may order descriptions by saying that a description d_1 precedes description d_2 if either d_1 has less letters than d_2 or, if

they have the same number, d_1 precedes d_2 in dictionary order. Given any set of descriptions we can talk about the shortest (since any totally-ordered set has a least element). Now consider the following description:

The smallest number whose shortest description requires more than eleven words.

No such number can exist! For if it did, the above *description* would describe it but would take only eleven words! The problem is that we did not impose any restrictions on lists of words that form acceptable descriptions. For more in this direction see Hermes (1965, Chapter 1).

(2) *Self-application* (following Scott, 1970)
Some functions take other functions as arguments; an example is the following general summation function, which is easily programmed in Algol 60:

$$\text{sum}(f, m, n) = f(m) + \ldots + f(n)$$

Another example is the function twice, whose result is also a function:

$$(\text{twice}(f))(x) = f(f(x))$$

so that $(\text{twice}(\text{sq}))(3) = 81$. More interesting though is the fact that twice can be applied to itself, for example:

$$\text{twice}(\text{twice})(\text{sq})(2) = 256$$

Unfortunately, we cannot allow functions to be applied to themselves quite generally, since consider the function selfzero defined (cf. Russell's paradox) by:

$$\text{selfzero}(f) = f(f) = 0 \rightarrow 1, 0$$

It is all too easy to show that:

$$\text{selfzero}(\text{selfzero}) = 0 \text{ iff selfzero}(\text{selfzero}) \neq 0$$

The solution to this paradox lies in realizing that selfzero is allowed to take *any* function as an argument. It turns out that there is no problem if selfzero is only applied to computable functions. Selfzero can in fact be programmed in many programming languages; the self-application just does not terminate.

This is not quite as irrelevant as might appear at first glance. Firstly, we would like to be able to program self-applying functions, or at least functions like sum which take *any* computable function as an argument. Secondly, the same problem arises in giving a simplified idealized model of computer storage. Suppose we consider memory to be a set L of locations, each capable of holding any of a set V of values. A state of memory can be modelled by a contents function:

$$\text{cont} : L \rightarrow V$$

which gives the value cont (l) contained in the location l. Now one sort of value that compilers often plant in memory is commands. A command cmd is executed in order to change the state of memory, and so it can be modelled by a state-change function:

$$\text{cmd} : (L \to V) \to (L \to V)$$

Suppose now that cont is a state of memory, and that cont(l) is a command cmd. We can clearly execute cmd in state cont to get a new state cmd(cont). That is, we can execute:

$$\text{cont}(l)(\text{cont})$$

which is just one step away from the self-application problem. Hoare and Allison (1972) also discuss the self-application problem in terms of Grelling's formulation of the Russell paradox. They suggest that one way round the problem is to prevent it from occurring by emulating Russell's set theory solution consisting of a precise theory of types; such a solution is implemented in heavily typed programming languages such as ALGOL 68. Section 8.2 outlines a different, and typeless, solution due to Scott (1970).

1.3 PART 2: Towards a theory of computer science

Part 1 established a framework into which any theory of computation must fit. The *essentially negative* results presented in Chapter 3 *about* the theory show that there is a theoretical limit to what can be computed and to what *positive* results can be achieved *within* the theory. Unfortunately, the metatheory offers hardly any suggestions about the kinds of problem areas that the theory might profitably address, about the kinds of results achievable within those areas, or about the techniques by which those results might be achieved. As we shall see in Chapter 6, even the formalisms of the metatheory are not especially useful when it comes to developing a theory. For example, whereas Part 1 tells us that it is *impossible* to write a single program to determine *for all* programs P and *all* inputs d to P whether or not the computation of P on d terminates, it is nevertheless often *possible* to be convinced about the termination or nontermination for many *individual* pairs P,d; the metatheory remains silent regarding how we might approach the question for a particular pair P,d.

Part 2, consisting of Chapters 6–8, introduces some of the work that has been carried out in the past twenty or so years aimed at filling out the theory with positive results about a number of problem areas. We list below some of the problems that have attracted the most attention to date, and then describe in greater detail the plan of Part 2.

For a theory which is so young, computer science displays a quite remarkable richness, breadth, and vigour, which makes it all the more surprising that there is a widespread opinion that most theoretical studies are esoteric game-playing of no real or lasting value. There seem to be two main reasons for this phenomenon (although they should really be argued more closely and at greater length than the curren context allows).

Firstly, most current workers in computing are not computing science graduates; rather they were attracted into the subject either from an engineering/industrial background or from pure mathematics/logic. These two groups bring with them very different attitudes, skills, and methodologies; these differences can be seen quite clearly in the different kinds of work done on grammars for describing programming languages during the 1960s. It may be conjectured that this methodological difference will disappear in the near future with the establishment and institutionalization of a shared (Kuhnian) paradigm for computer science; it may, on the other hand, crystallize into the kind of applied/pure split that currently disfigures mathematics.

Probably more significant for the past, present, and future development of computer science are its obvious financial/military implications. This is an issue largely because of the way research is funded. The extent to which such pressures have affected the long-term development of computer science, and scientific effort and judgement, because of an overemphasis on projects likely to be rich in short-term yield, is an issue that the author would like to pursue elsewhere.

It is agains this background that the author feels it necessary to supplement the following description of some of the problem areas that have so far occupied theorists with an assessment of their potential short-to-medium term impact on the practice of computing. We base our presentation on the idea that computing practice centres on one or more aspects of the phenomenon of programs being developed in order effectively to solve some previously given problem on a computer. Programs are representations of algorithms in programming languages and transform data structures.

This characterization of computing practice hopefully suggests to the reader that the 'theory' of computer science is in fact the *whole* of computer science. What has come to be called the 'theory' of computer science relates to studies of abstract mathematical models of computing phenomena. Not surprisingly, most such studies are the work of people in the mathematical/logic camp of computing science referred to above. We now briefly discuss problems, programming languages, data structures, program correctness, termination and equivalence, complexity of algorithms, and computers in turn, with reference to this characterization of computing practice.

1.3.1 *Problem solving*

Problem solving occupies an important position within computer science. Much of the development of computer science has stemmed from the demonstration that a particular class of problems is amenable to solution by computer. Currently, data processing, integer programming, and numerical analysis are often regarded as examples of problem areas *internal* to computer science, as opposed to applications of computers to *externally* posed problems in fields as diverse as chemistry (e.g. analysis of the structure of large molecules), physics (e.g. studies of subnuclear structure), archaeology (e.g. the analysis of data gleaned from ancient burial sites), and psychology (e.g. the analysis of problem-solving protocols and seriation behaviour). Of course, the internal/external distinction has no non-institutional validity; indeed we may well ask whether data processing problems are internal to computer science, or are the (external) application of computers to business information handling. Similarly, it is frequently (pointlessly) debated whether numerical analysis more properly belongs to mathematics or computer science.

The point we wish to make is that (the theory of) computer science interacts significantly with many subjects; in particular, advances in computer science are likely to have an impact beyond computer science. As a simple illustration, developments in programming languages have often led to the more effective deployment of computers in a wide range of fields; engineering design studies have leaned heavily on APT, and psychological modelling on IPL, LISP, and production systems.

The idea that computers can be programmed to solve problems previously believed to require human intelligence has given rise to the idea of a computer-based artificial intelligence. [See Raphael (1976), Winston (1975), and Jackson (1974) for introductions to this fascinating subject.] As an example of the contributions alluded to above, one of the earliest, simplest models of human problem solving, GPS (Newell and Simon, 1963), has recently been applied at Carnegie-Mellon University to a variety of automated design problems, and has led to significant advances in the automatic design of chemical engineering plants.

1.3.2 *Programming languages*

A program is a written representation of an algorithm in a programming language. By analogy with the study of natural language, it is usual to distinguish syntax and semantics. Syntax, or grammatical analysis, refers to the study of the written form of a program, as far as possible independently of its meaning; in particular it concerns the legality or well-formedness of a program relative to a set of grammatical rules, and (parsing) algorithms for the discovery of the grammatical structure of such well-formed programs. Semantics refers to the study of the meaning of programs. In order to run programs it is also necessary to implement the language on some computer, and the way in which it is implemented determines for the programmer one of a number of very different environments in which he will use it. It is clear that syntax and semantics cannot be clearly demarcated for natural languages, as is shown by sentence pairs such as:

"Time flies like an arrow"
"Fruit flies like a banana"

and
> "The city councilmen refused to give the demonstrators a permit because they feared violence"
>
> "The city councilmen refused to give the demonstrators a permit because they advocated violence"

It may be supposed that such problems do not arise with 'artificial' programming languages; indeed it may be supposed that programming languages are expressly designed to avoid such problems. In fact, it is generally not possible to give a (context-free) grammar that specifies only legal programs. For example:

begin integer x; $x := 3$ **end**

is a legal ALGOL 60 program, while:

begin integer x; $y := 3$ **end**

is not, despite the fact that they have the same grammatical structure. We now discuss syntax, semantics, and the user-environment in turn.

Most programs assume the written form, as does English, of a linear sequence of tokens or words, made out of strings of characters. Notice that this is not necessarily the case, and that there are 'picture' languages whose written forms are constructed out of two- or even three-dimensional components, such as grammars for flowchart programs. What is important is that there should be a set of rules governing the construction of allowed or legal forms. For early languages such as FORTRAN, these rules were expressed in English. This served perfectly well for most purposes; however, once FORTRAN was implemented on a wide variety of machines it became evident that there were a number of ambiguities and shortcomings in the English formulation, and a mathematical formalism for the precise specification of grammatical structure was sought. Such a formalism, nowadays popularly known as BNF, was developed by Backus and Naur as part of the IAL project which produced ALGOL 60. Studies of grammars and of specific parsing algorithms occupied much of the attention of computer scientists during the 1960's.

In the ALGOL 60 report (Naur, 1963), syntax was specified by a set of BNF productions. Corresponding to each syntactic construct, such as ⟨if-statement⟩ and ⟨block⟩, was a paragraph of English describing the intended interpretation or meaning. It was soon discovered that there were a number of semantic ambiguities, places where the English descriptions were incomplete, and places where the proposed meanings were (unconsciously) extremely difficult to implement. Thus the problem was formulated of doing for semantics what BNF had done for syntax, namely giving a precise specification. The work which resulted is introduced in Section 6.5 and Chapter 8. We shall observe there how such formal studies have had an impact on programming practice by suggesting better programming languages and programming constructs, such as dynamic lists, escapers, and closures.

Both FORTRAN and ALGOL 60 were developed at a time when computers processed programs in batch mode. In such systems, the programmer conceives of, and writes, his program in its entirety before submitting it to the machine. Stylistics for program writing such as structured programming (Dahl, Dijkstra, and Hoare, 1972) seem to assume implicitly that such is still (or should still be) the case. Timesharing systems meant that the programmer could interact with his program if only to the extent of shortening the test-edit cycle. Immediate effects were the development of incremental compilers (LISP, POP-2) and error recovery facilities. More significantly perhaps, it has been realized that the order in which decisions are taken during the design of a program need not be the same as the order in which the program statements will in the end be executed, and furthermore that the computer could be used to keep a track of decisions taken to date, work out automatically a number of consequences of those decisions, and run partially specified programs. Probably the first system to explore these ideas was a theoretical language project known as ABSET (Elcock *et al.*, 1971). More recent systems such as INTERLISP (Teitelman *et al.*, 1974) have gone some way beyond this toward the goal of creating a language implementation assuming the form of a programmer's assistant (see Winograd, 1974). We shall argue in Chapter 7 that much of the work currently being done on program correctness will in fact contribute significantly to the realization of such helpful assistants.

1.3.3 *Data structures*

Data structuring refers to the way in which the entities conceptually manipulated by a program are represented within a program language. Differing choices of data structure can significantly affect program efficiency because of the different efficiencies with which the operations on the data called for in the program can be carried out. Such choices also affect the effectiveness with which the programmer works by enabling differing degrees of natural articulation of his conceptual program. Since a good deal of computing practice is concerned with the design of data structures optimizing these two considerations, any theoretical contributions are sure to have significant short-term impact. Most of our understanding of data structures consists of a set of techniques such as Illiffe vectors or array descriptors (dope vectors) for the implementation of abstract mathematical entities. Attempts to give a semantics of data structures have tended to be either extremely mathematical and unrelated to the needs of programmer (for example, graph theory), or hopelessly tangled with implementation issues. There have however been a number of theoretical studies that have tried to design a formal semantics related to programmer's needs, for example, Hoare's recursive data structures (1973), Reynolds's functional data structures (1971), and Gimpel's (1973) theory of discrete patterns.

The representation of a problem and its associated data can have a profound effect on the way in which it can be solved; but we currently have little more than elegant demonstrations of the fact, such as Amarel's discussion (1970) of the missionaries and cannibals problem.

1.3.4 *Program correctness*

How can we be sure, or at least reasonably sure, that a program really does solve the problem that was intended? We might expect a guarantee, or at least solid evidence, that any program we use (or buy) always behaves as it should. Now, it is by no means clear what is meant by 'always', 'behave', or 'should', but it is a fact that much of the software currently produced is highly unreliable. It has been estimated that half of the cost and time of a large programming project is taken up with debugging, although this is scant comfort, since debugging is such a haphazard affair. Broadly speaking, there have been two main approaches to the problem of developing methods for making programs more reliable. They embody rather different notions of 'behave', 'always', and 'should':

(1) Systematize testing, so that the reliability of a program is inductively in-ferred from a relatively small number of test behaviours.

(2) Attempt to prove in an appropriate mathematical system that a program is consistent with it specifications.

However, there are many problems that cloud the issue, such as the fact that a programmer's understanding of the problem to which he is trying to program a solution usually develops only with the program. There is no absolute demarca-tion between the testing and proving approaches. We shall discuss the whole sub-ject of reliable software much more thoroughly in Chapter 7, and shall argue in particular that many recent developments in formal correctness should be con-sidered not so much as 'oracles' that pronounce "yea" or "nay" on any program submitted to the system, but as suggestions for the design of better, more in-telligent, programming systems.

It was suggested by McCarthy in 1963 that, even if it was not practically pos-sible to develop programs capable of automatically verifying other programs, it might at least be possible to develop programs capable of checking programmer-supplied proofs. The ideas has evolved of interactive proof checkers, which help a programmer to develop a proof, by checking individual steps, keeping tabs on what remains to be done, simplifying expressions, and, occasionally, offering ad-vice about the kind of proof that might be appropriate. See Milner (1973) and Weyrauch and Thomas (1975) for example systems.

1.3.5 *Program termination*

Many of the remarks made in Section 1.3.4 about program reliability apply also to attempts to prove that programs actually terminate. Indeed, Manna has shown that the problems of correctness and termination are closely related, a result we sketch in Section 7.4.

1.3.6 *Effectiveness of program solution*

The 'effectiveness' with which a program solves a given problem is only understandable in terms of the spending of computational resources such as time
(which can to a first approximation be measured by the number of processor
steps needed to execute it), use of primary or secondary memory, or use of
input–output (since the latter will usually require the spending of a physical resource such as cards or line printer paper). Functions involving the amount of
each such resource spent, and the cost per unit resource, have long been developed for accountancy purposes in computer systems. The theoretical study
of such measures in known as *complexity theory*, and is touched on briefly in
Chapters 2 and 4. Such studies give formal expression to the intuitive idea of
trade-off, for example between space and time, and set lower bounds on the
spending of certain resources (such as time) for particular algorithms like
addition, matrix inversion, and sorting; [See Arbib (1969, Chapter 7), Hopcroft
and Ullman (1969, Chapter 10), or Knuth (1971a) for an introduction to complexity theory.]

An alternative approach is to prove that an otherwise satisfactory program,
which is modified so as to make it more efficient, is *equivalent* to the original
version, for example in the sense of meeting the same specifications. Studies
aimed at proving the equivalence of programs are introduced in Chapters 3 and
6. An example of a pair of equivalent procedures, one of which is considerably
more efficient than the other both in terms of space and time, is given by
McCarthy's 91-function:

$$\text{let } f(x) = x > 100 \to x - 10, f(f(x + 11))$$

which the reader should convince himself (how!) is equivalent to:

$$\text{let } g(x) = x > 100 \to x - 10, 91$$

1.3.7 *Computers*

Programs describe processes to be run on processors. The notion of processor is
meant to generalize the idea of a single central processor unit to include anything that runs process descriptions. For example, input and output may be considered to be mediated by processors, which are particularly evident in the case
of graphics terminals, disc controllers, and effectors such as robot arms. Processor design has been highly responsive to developing technology; for example
the idea of computer 'generations' refers to the changing physical logic from
valves to transistors to integrated circuits to medium-to-large scale integrated cir-
cuit technology. However, an equally important influence on machine design has
been the attempts to implement in hardware (for reasons of efficiency) various
programming concepts of proven importance such as floating point arithmetic,
paging, read-only memories, stack machines, bus structures, and machines based
on non-redundancy coding. This is not meant to suggest that the contributions

have all gone one way, from software to hardware, as microprogramming, interrupt handling, and parallel processing show.

In fact, what these examples point out very forcibly is that there is no absolute demarcation between process and processor, and that ideas such as debugging and the interfacing of sub-components appear in both settings. It is therefore reasonable to argue that any theoretical contribution to hardware or software is in fact a contribution to both, i.e. to all.

PLAN OF PART 2

The theory of computation is introduced in Part 2 of the book, comprising Chapters 6–8. Since it is neither feasible, nor desirable, to present an exhaustive account of the current state of the theory in an introductory text, choices of material must necessarily be made. In the remainder of this section, we give the reasons underlying our choice of the contents of Chapters 6–8.

We observed above that most computer science theorists have a background in mathematics or logic. Not surprisingly, one of the major concerns of the theory of computation to date has been to prove that a (class of) program behaviour(s) has certain properties such as being finite (the program terminates), necessarily involves a minimal number of steps (complexity theory), or is consistent with its specifications (correctness). Since one of the major problems in computing practice is program reliability, we discuss in Chapter 7 studies based on testing and proving correctness, aimed at making programs more reliable.

In order to prove that a program behaviour has a certain property, one first has to define what constitutes a program behaviour. Ultimately, this is bound up with the problem of giving a mathematical model of the meaning of a programming language, which is a problem we introduced above with reference to the inadequacy of the specification of semantics in the ALGOL 60 report. Chapter 8 introduces various models that have been proposed as the meaning of programming languages.

The observant reader will have noted that we have omitted mention of Chapter 6. Our reasons for including it are rather different from those given above for Chapters 7 and 8.

Kuhn (1962) has hsown how the early development of a science is indelibly marked by the contributions of a small number of workers. Two of the major contributions which these workers make are the *formulation* of the set of problems with which the science is initially concerned, and the *methods* which they use in their preliminary analyses of these problems. In particular, the interrelationship between the various problems and the transferability of methods between problems is usually stressed. A great deal of subsequent early work accepts the problem formulations and methods, and concentrates on developing the analyses. Consequently, chronological accounts of progress on problems, and detailed accounts of the contributions of the pioneers, figure largely in discussions of emergent sciences, but hardly at all in more traditional sciences such as mathematics, physics, and chemistry. We may consider in this light the sciences of psychology and sociology, both of which emerged long before computer science but within the last century. Most contemporary introductions to sociology discuss the contributions of Durkheim, Weber, Marx, and others, while psychology students become familiar with the writings of James, Helmholtz, Freud, and so on.

So it is with computer science. Although there are many claimants to be included, the outstanding pioneering contributor to the theory of computation has been John McCarthy, who, in a series of papers written between 1958 and 1963, formulated and analysed most of the problems listed above. For the reasons given above, we believe that the account of his work which we give in Chapter 6 provides a context in which much subsequent work in the theory of computation can best be understood, and in that way it introduces and complements the discussions in Chapters 7 and 8.

Meta Computer Science

2 The Abstract Machine Approach

2.1 Introduction

An early synonym for 'algorithm' was 'mechanical procedure'. This expresses
the intuition that any computation should be capable of being specified in such
precise detail as to require negligible intelligence to carry in out – indeed should
be capable of being carried out automatically by a machine. Our major aim in
this chapter is to develop this idea and arrive in three stages at Turing's formulation of 'computable'. We shall repeatedly relate to the reader's understanding
of real (calculating) machines: adding machines, computers, and, more generally,
switching circuits.

Some machines, for example (mechanical) adding machines and the adder of
a computer's central processor, embody essentially similar processes for computing the same function (addition) but are physically very different. This suggests
that the theory should largely ignore such physical considerations as being
essentially irrelevant to an understanding of a machine's computing capabilities
(which explains the qualifier 'abstract' in the title of this chapter). Physical considerations of real machines do however affect the theory in one crucial way:
there is an overall finiteness assumption which reflects the fact that any machine
should be constructed out of a finite number of parts.

We begin by considering a basic machine model. This is quickly rejected and
refined to the finite state machine (FSM) model. Eventually, the FSM model is
also rejected and refined to give the Turing machine (TM) model. It is important
to realize that these rejections take place in the context of an intuitive development of a formal definition of 'computable' and in no way constitute a value
judgement in *all* contexts on the merits of the model in question. The FSM
model in particular has a central importance in computing science in modelling
the hardware components out of which computers are built (see Minsky, 1967,
Part 1).

2.2 Basic machines and finite state machines

We suggested in the preceding section that we are concerned only with *what* a
machine does, not with detailed physical considerations of how it works. It is
possible to gain some understanding of what a machine does by considering the
outputs it produces in response to the various inputs with which it can be presented. An obvious first step then in developing a theory of computing machines
is to ignore everything except the machine's input–output behaviour. We call

this the basic machine model. (Such a model is often called a 'black-box', which refers to the fact that the machine is opaque, in the sense that it does not permit

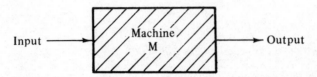

Input ⟶ Machine M ⟶ Output

Fig. 2.1

internal.analysis; see Fig. 2.1.) Mathematically, such a machine can be modelled by a function from the set I of its inputs to the set O of its outputs. The finiteness assumption mentioned in Section 2.1 implies that we should insist that I and O be finite; otherwise we have to imagine a finitely constructable machine interpreting infinitely many different input characters or producing infinitely many output characters! We can now precisely define a basic machine.

DEFINITION 2.1 A basic machine is a function mfn: $I \rightarrow O$, where I and O are finite sets respectively called the input set and the output set.

EXAMPLE 2.1 We can consider an AND gate as a basic machine. The output set is $\{1, 0\}$; the input set is the set of four pairs $\{(1,1), (1,0), (0,1), (0,0)\}$. The function mfn is defined by the following table:

I	(1,1)	(1,0)	(0,1)	(0,0)
O	1	0	0	0

EXAMPLE 2.2 We can define a basic machine that converts each character in the ASCII 7-bit character set into the corresponding three-digit octal number. Here are some instances of the function mfn:

$$\mathrm{mfn}(A) = 101, \mathrm{mfn}(*) = 052, \mathrm{mfn}(;) = 073$$

CHECKPOINT 2.1 Show how the following can be modelled as basic machines: (a) OR gate; (b) two-bit adder (hint: you can use a one-bit overflow register)

CHECKPOINT 2.2 Show that the class of computations that basic machines can carry out are precisely table lookups in finite tables. (Hint: use the notion of the graph of a function, p. 259).

The reader may object that no basic machine is capable of computing even simple functions like addition, since the input sets I are restricted to be finite. In fact, we shall show in the following section that this does not present a serious problem since *an entire sequence* of inputs to the machine can be *interpreted by the user* as a *single entity*. This is of course what we normally do in mathematics, where, for example, the sequence 194 of three digits can be interpreted as the number one hundred and ninety four.

We now consider a couple of examples which lead us to refine the basic machine model. Firstly, consider the usual process for adding two numbers $x_1 x_2 \ldots x_n$ and $y_1 y_2 \ldots y_n$ to get $z_0 z_1 \ldots z_n$. We proceed by adding pairs of digits, for example $(x_i + y_i)$, *but* we admit the possibility that a carry from the previous such addition can affect the output z_i. Consequently a basic machine function $\text{mfn}(x_i, y_i)$ would also need somehow to take account of the carry 'situation'. Secondly, consider a push-button light which has two outputs {on, off} but only one input {pressbutton}. Successive responses to the sole input are . . .on, off, on, off, ...

CHECKPOINT 2.3 Prove that no basic machine can adequately model the push-button light. What function does the push-button light compute?

Our intuition as computer scientists suggests that these examples merely illustrate the fact that the basic machine model is deficient because it omits the notion of *state*. We shall give a formal treatment of 'state' in the following section; for the moment we shall rely on our intuitive understanding of state as a description of the internal configuration of some of the parts from which a machine is constructed, e.g. the contents of (some of) the registers of a computer or the positions of (some of) the levers in an adding machine. We therefore refine the basic machine model by including a set S of states. Our overall finiteness assumption suggests that S should be a finite set. Further thought about real machines suggests that we should not only expect an input and state to generate an appropriate output, but that the state will alter also. Putting these considerations together, we get:

DEFINITION 2.2 *A finite-state machine* (FSM) consists of a pair of functions:*

$$\text{mfn} : I \times S \to 0, \quad \text{sfn} : I \times S \to S$$

where I, O, and S are finite sets respectively of inputs, output, and states. We call mfn the *machine function*; sfn is the *state-function*.

EXAMPLE 2.3 The push-button machine described above has state set {light, dark}; the machine and state functions are defined in the following tables:

$I \times S$	O	$I \times S$	S
pressbutton, light	off	pressbutton, light	dark
pressbutton, dark	on	pressbutton, dark	light
mfn		sfn	

---

* We describe on p. 257 how a function such as mfn of more than one argument can be neatly modelled by a function whose domain is a Cartesian product.

EXAMPLE 2.4 The binary adder has state set {carry, nocarry}, output set {1,0}, and input set {(1,1), (1,0), (0,1), (0,0)} of pairs of binary digits. The functions mfn and sfn are given by:

	S	
mfn	carry	nocarry
$I\begin{cases}(1,1)\\(0,1)\\(1,0)\\(0,0)\end{cases}$	1 0 0 1	0 1 1 0

	S	
sfn	carry	nocarry
$I\begin{cases}(1,1)\\(1,0)\\(0,1)\\(0,0)\end{cases}$	carry carry carry nocarry	carry nocarry nocarry nocarry

CHECKPOINT 2.4 Design a FSM model of a flip-flop

As the number of states, inputs, and outputs increases, the table representation of the FSM functions mfn and sfn becomes highly imperspicuous. Fortunately there is a much more convenient representation using what is called *circle-and-arrow* notation: to each state there corresponds a cirlce with the name of the state inscribed. An arrow connects the circles corresponding to states s_1 and s_2 if there is some input i such that $sfn(i,s_1) = s_2$. The input i and the corresponding output $o = mfn(i,s_1)$ are displayed on the shaft of the connecting arrow:

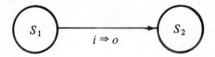

EXAMPLE 2.5 The circle-and-arrow representations of the push-button light and binary adder are:

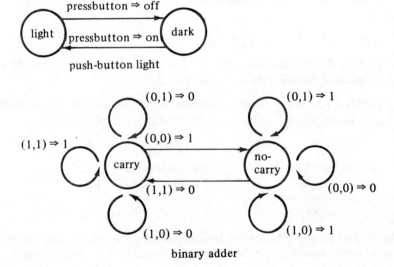

push-button light

binary adder

EXAMPLE 2.6 Despite the fact that we have not as yet made precise the idea of input sequence, we can design a FSM which remembers an input for two moments and then outputs it. If $I = \{0,1\}$, there are four possibilities for two inputs in sequence $\{00, 11, 10, 01\}$, where xy means first x and then y. Our memory machine has a state corresponding to each such sequence of two inputs.

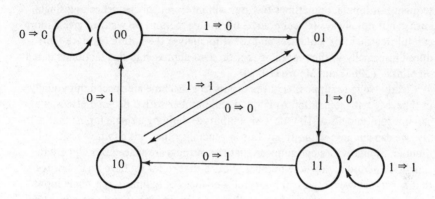

EXAMPLE 2.7 (My thanks to the M202 team at the Open University for this example.) The dial on a certain combination lock can be in on of three positions. There are six possible inputs or dial movements, A1, A2, A3, C1, C2, C3, where A2 (for example) means 'twist the dial Anticlockwise to position 2'. The other inputs are defined analogously. Only one sequence opens the door, namely $A_1,C2,A2$; all other sequences cause an alarm to ring. The output set $O = \{$alarm, click, open$\}$; the state set is $\{$locked, unlocked, 1, 2$\}$. We denote by '$*$' all inputs other than the ones shown explicitly. Notice how a sequence of moves is directly modelled by a sequence of arrows.

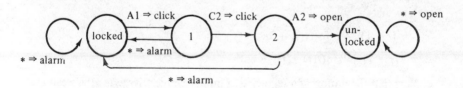

CHECKPOINT 2.5 Design a 3-moment delay FSM. Prove that an n-moment delay machine needs at least 2^n states.

CHECKPOINT 2.6 Design a FSM which 'remembers' whether it has been presented with an odd or even number of 1's. (Notice that this is an example of a machine that expects a sequence of inputs but does not interpret that sequence as a single entity.)

CHECKPOINT 2.7 Design a FSM that, when presented with a sequence of n

1's followed by an end-of-sequence marker, computes the remainder of n integer-divided by 3.

2.3 Sequence of inputs; states

We have considered several examples in which a machine expects to receive a sequence of inputs. Sometimes the user will interpret this sequence as a single entity; but not always (Checkpoint 2.6). In this section, we want to give a more careful treatment of sequences and use it to analyse the notion of 'state', introduced informally in the preceding section. Our approach in this section is based on Minsky (1967) and Moore (1956).

Clearly we may suppose that the inputs to a machine are spaced out equally in time, say with separation t_i. If t_i is a real number with d decimal places, we can interpret blocks of 10^d successive inputs as defining a single input; that is to say, we can suppose without any loss in generality that t_i is a (whole) natural number. Similarly, we can suppose that the outputs are spaced out equally in time with period t_o, a whole number. Notice that so far we have no guarantee that $t_i = t_o$. However, we can interpret sequences of t_o inputs as a single input, and t_i outputs as a single output, so that we have one input and one output per $t_o * t_i$ 'clock ticks'. Thus without loss of generality we can assume that the machine has synchronized inputs and outputs at times $0, 1, 2, \ldots$. Consequently, if an input is presented to the machine at time T it will give rise to an output at some later time $T + D$, where D is some constant delay determined by the machine. Physical considerations (the 'speed of light' problem) show that we must assume D is strictly greater than zero; that is, D is at least 1.

CHECKPOINT 2.8 Show that we may assume D equals 1. (Hint: use Example 2.6, Checkpoint 2.5.)

We shall denote the input, state, and output of a FSM at time t by $i(t)$, $s(t)$, $o(t)$, so that:

$$o(t + 1) = \mathrm{mfn}(i(t), s(t))$$

$$s(t + 1) = \mathrm{sfn}(i(t), s(t))$$

Now that the notion of a sequence of inputs is precisely defined, we can use the FSM as an *acceptor* or *recognizer* of sequences. Suppose that START and STOP are designated (different) states of the FSM; we say that a sequence x is *accepted* or *recognized* if the FSM ends up in state STOP when it is initially in state START and is presented with x. In 1956, Kleene provided a very neat characterization of the sequences called *regular sets of sequences* which can be accepted by FSMs. We do not want to break off our line of development at this point sufficiently to prove Kleene's theorem, but we will briefly describe regular sets since they appear again in Section 3.4.4.

A regular set R is completely determined by specifying which singleton base sets, or sequences of length one, are in the set. Having specified the base sets, the rest is 'automatic'; if S and T are regular sets in R, so is the union $S \cup T$ and the set ST of concatenations of an element of S followed by an element of T. Finally, the set $S*$ consisting of a concatenation of any finite number of members of S is a subset of R.

EXAMPLE 2.8 (The binary numbers.) The basic sequences are $1, 0$ corresponding to basic singleton subsets $\{1\}, \{0\}$. Consider any binary number, say $n = 10000111$. The sequence of three trailing 1's belongs to $\{1\}*$ and the sequence of four zeros to $\{0\}*$. Thus n has the form $1xy$ where $x \in \{0\}*, y \in \{1\}*$. Now xy belongs to the set $\{0\}*\{1\}*$ of concatenations, so n has the form $1z$, which then belongs to the set $\{1\}[\{0\}*\{1\}*]$ of concatenations. Hence n and similarly all other binary numbers, belongs to the regular set defined by $1,0$.

The idea of proving that a given sequence is, or is not, in a given regular set by *parsing* it, i.e. analysing its structure, turns out to be extremely important in the theory of formal languages, which is discussed further in Section 3.4.4. (We shall see that the regular sets are precisely the phrase structure languages of Chomsky type-3.) For more details on regualr sets, and a proof of Kleene's theorem, see Hopcroft and Ullman (1969, Section 3.4), Minsky (1967, Chapter 4), or Gries (1971, Chapters 2 and 3).

CHECKPOINT 2.9 Show that the set Z of integer numbers and the set I of identifiers (where, as usual, an identifier is a sequence of alphanumeric characters starting with a letter) are regular sets. Design FSMs to recognize Z and I.

Suppose that a FSM starts at time $t = 0$, and consider the state $s(t)$ at any later time $t > 0$. By definition of sequences:

$$s(t) = \mathrm{sfn}(i(t-1), s(t-1))$$
$$= \mathrm{sfn}(i(t-1), \mathrm{sfn}(i(t-2), s(t-2)))$$

Continuing in this way, we see that:

$$s(t) = \mathrm{sfn}(i(t-1), \mathrm{sfn}(i(t-2), \ldots, \mathrm{sfn}(i(0), s(0)) \ldots)) \tag{2.1}$$

This means that the state $s(t)$ at any time t is completely determined by the initial state $s(0)$ and the sequence $i(0)i(1) \ldots i(t-1)$ of inputs. Minsky (1967, Chapter 2) calls such an initial state and input sequence a *history* of the FSM.

We now define the length, first element of, and rest of, an input sequence i in the obvious way. Let $i = i_0 i_1 \ldots i_t$ be an input sequence. The *length* of i is the number $(t + 1)$ of inputs in the sequence; we write $\mathrm{length}(i) = t + 1$. The *first element* of the sequence i is i_0 and the *rest* of i is the sequence $i_1 i_2 \ldots i_t$. We write:

$$\mathrm{first}(i) = i_0, \quad \mathrm{rest}(i) = i_1 \ldots i_t$$

If i is any sequence (of inputs, outputs, or whatever) of length t, and x is any sequence element, we can make a sequence j of length $(t + 1)$ out of x and i so that:

$$\text{first}(j) = x, \quad \text{rest}(j) = i$$

We denote j by $x :: i$.

A sequence i of inputs and an initial state s_0 give rise to sequences of states and output as the FSM 'executes' the sequence i. More precisely, we can define functions:

$$\text{sfnseq} : I^* \times S \to S^*, \quad \text{mfnseq} : I^* \times S \to O^*$$

such that $\text{sfnseq}(i, s_0)$ is the *sequence* of states generated by i from s_0. In fact:

let $\text{sfnseq}(i, s_0) = \text{length}(i) = 1 \to \text{sfn}(i, s_0),$

$\quad\quad\quad$ **valof** \$(**let** $s_1 = \text{sfn}(\text{first}(i), s_0)$

$\quad\quad\quad\quad\quad\quad$ **resultis** $s_1 :: \text{sfnseq}(\text{rest}(i), s_1)$

$\quad\quad\quad\quad$ \$)

The above piece of program is written in an extension to BCPL, which is informally introduced in Appendix B.

In the definition of sfnseq, we have identified an input with the input sequence of length one of which it is the sole member. This is done merely to improve readability.

CHECKPOINT 2.10 Define the function mfnseq analogously.

CHECKPOINT 2.11 Neither of the definitions of sfnseq and mfnseq admits the possibility of a sequence of length 0. How would you extend the definitions to cover those cases?

We can now present one of the most powerful methods available for proving results about FSMs: the fact that a long enough sequence formed by repeating the same input over and over is bound to cause a state to be repeated. Suppose that M is any FSM; let n be the (finite) number of states of M. Let i be any input to M and denote by $t * i$ the sequence of length t consisting entirely of the input i.

THEOREM 2.1 (the 'FSM must eventually repeat a state' theorem) No matter what state s_0 the FSM M is started in, the state sequence $\text{sfnseq}((n + 1) * i, s_0)$ must contain at least two occurrences of some state.

The proof is very easy and will not be given. (This is a good example of something being called a 'theorem' because of its relevance to the subject as opposed to the difficulty of its proof).

CHECKPOINT 2.12 Define the function $\text{sfnafterseq} : I^* \times S \to S$ such that $\text{sfnafterseq}(i, s_0)$ is the state in which the FSM ends up *after* executing the sequence i starting from s_0.

Consider now the parity checking FSM (see Checkpoint 2.6):

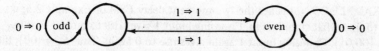

Suppose we start the machine in state even. The following sequences of length 4, 7, and 5 cause the machine to end up in state even: 1010, 1110111, 10100. Not only are all of these sequences equivalent as regrard determining the final state of the machine, but it is also the case that the state 'even' precisely expresses this equivalence. We can make this intuition precise as follows:

DEFINITION 2.3 Let s_0 be a state of a FSM M. Input sequences i_1 and i_2 to M are said to be *Equivalent* (for s_0) if

$$\text{sfnafterseq}(i_1, s_0) = \text{sfnafterseq}(i_2, s_0)$$

CHECKPOINT 2.13 Prove that Definition 2.3 really does define an equivalence relation on sequences of inputs of M, and that there is a one-one relationship between the equivalence classes and the states of M which can be reached from the chosen state s_0.

If it is possible to choose the state s_0 so that every state of the FSM M is reachable from s_0 after some input sequence i, then Checkpoint 2.13 says that there is a one-one correspondence between the states of M and the equivalence classes of input sequences. The reachability assumption seems to be implicit in Minsky's (1967, Chapter 2) treatment.

Our treatment of sequences shows that the initial state and the input sequence determine the output sequence. This suggests a way of *discovering experimentally* the state of the machine. Suppose that at time $t = 0$ the machine is in the (unknown) state s_0. If we supply input i_0, and note the response O_1, then we can pin s_0 down to belonging to the subset S_0 of S, where:

$$S_0 = \{s | \text{mfn}(i_0, s) = O_1\}$$

If S_0 has only one element s_0, we have discovered the original state; in general S_0 will have several members.

Suppose that we next supply i_1 giving rise to O_2. Then we know that s_0 belongs to S_1 where:

$$S_1 = \{s | \text{mfnseq}(i_0 i_1, s) = O_1 O_2\}$$

Clearly $S_1 \subseteq S_0$. Continuing in this way we can choose inputs $i_0, \ldots, i_n$ to define sets $S_0, \ldots, S_n$ with:

$$S_n \subseteq S_{n-1} \subseteq \ldots \subseteq S_0$$

CHECKPOINT 2.14 Prove that for all t, if S_t has more than one element, it is possible to *choose* a sequence i_{t+1} so that S_{t+1} is smaller than S_t.

EXAMPLE 2.9 Consider the two-moment delay FSM of Example 2.6; we wish to find what state it is in. Choosing input 1 gives rise to output 0; thus $S_0 = \{00,01\}$. Choosing input 1 again gives rise to 0 again. Thus $S_1 = \{00\}$; the machine was originally in state 00.

CHECKPOINT 2.15 What can you say about the choice of inputs to determine the state for: (a) the parity checker; (b) the three-moment delay machine?

CHECKPOINT 2.16 To what extent do you think it is feasible to attempt to discover the state of a digital computer, or of a human brain, by supplying a sequence of inputs?

2.4 The limitations of FSMs

This section shows that there are certain functions, for example multiplication, that are 'obviously' computable, but that we can prove cannot be computed on any FSM. In line with the overall aim of this chapter, as stated in Section 2.1, we are thus led to refine the FSM model to the more powerful Turing machine model.

The fundamental limitation of FSMs is that they have no capacity for remembering arbitrarily large amounts of information. As we saw in Example 2.5 and Checkpoints 2.5 and 2.6, a FSM *can* be made to remember information by appropriately interpreting the fact that it has assumed a certain state. We also found that, in order to remember a sequence of n inputs, a FSM would have to dedicate at least 2^n of its states for memory purposes. Since any FSM has a preset, fixed number of states, there is an *a priori* limit to the length of sequences that can be remembered. Consequently, any computation that requires the memory of arbitrarily long seuqences cannot be carried out on a FSM.

Multiplication is such a function. As we have already seen, arbitrary numbers x and y have to be presented to a FSM as sequences i and j; moreover, such sequences have to grow unboundedly large to cater for all such pairs as x,y. In multiplication, the *whole* of the sequences i and j have to be remembered. Instead of proving this formally, we will consider a simple example to gain insight into why it is the case. Suppose $i = i_1 i_2 i_3$ and $j = j_1 j_2 j_3$ both have length 3, and consider the representation $k_1 k_2 \ldots k_6$ of the product of i and j. The digit k_4 is *defined by the following expression* irrespective of the process used to compute it:

$$k_4 = i_1 * j_3 + i_2 * j_2 + i_3 * j_1 \text{ (perhaps plus carry)}$$

Thus, in order to compute the digit k_4, all of i and j have to be remembered.

We can now prove formally that multiplication cannot be carried out on any FSM. The proof is by *reductio ad absurdum*.

THEOREM 2.2 It is impossible to devise a single FSM that can multiply all pairs of numbers.

Proof. We shall suppose, contrary to the statement of the theorem, that it is in fact possible to build such a multiplier P. Suppose that P has n states. As we showed above, the input sequences i and j which represent the numbers x and y to be multiplied must be arbitrarily long; in particular there must be some number x whose corresponding input sequence i has length at least n. Since P claims to be capable of multiplying *all* pairs x,y of numbers, it must be capable of multiplying x by itself, which is presented as i and j. We saw above that this means that P has to remember all of i, which in turn requires at least 2^n of P's states. But P has only n states, and so it certainly cannot dedicate 2^n for anything.

CHECKPOINT 2.17 Use the same kind of argument to show that it is not possible to devise a FSM which accepts a sequence of left and right parentheses followed by an end-of-input marker and checks that the sequence is well-formed. The well-formed parentheses are defined by the following BNF-productions (see Section 3.4.4 if this notation is unfamiliar):

$\langle$wfp$\rangle ::= (\langle$wfp$\rangle)|$ $|\langle$wfp$\rangle\langle$wfp$\rangle$

that is, the empty sequence is well-formed.

CHECKPOINT 2.18 Prove that no FSM can decide if an input string is a palindrome, i.e. a string such as ABLE WAS I ERE I SAW ELBA which reads the same backwards and forwards.

The above theorem suggest that we should follow the precedent set in Section 2.2 and refine the FSM model to get a model on which multiplication can be computed. Presumably the refinement should consist of providing the FSM with unlimited external memory so that it can remember arbitrarily large amounts of information without using up all its precious few (control) states. This is precisely what we shall do in the following section; but before we do we should pause to consider the objection that in so doing we no longer have a 'realistic' model, since the memory of any real machine *is* limited.

In fact, it turns out that we get a *more realistic* theory by considering a computer installation as an *approximation* to a FSM augmented to have unlimited memory as opposed to a standard FSM. The point is that a computer installation can usually expand its amount of memory by acquiring extra tapes, discs, and so on to accommodate any large computation. Notice that provision of FSMs with unlimited memory means that 'the FSM must eventually repeat a state' theorem (Theorem 2.1) no longer holds. McCarthy (1963, p. 22) has commented: "Much of the work on the theory of [FSM]s has been motivated by the hope of applying it to computation. I think this hope is mostly in vain because the fact of finiteness is used to show that the [FSM] eventually repeats a state. However, anybody who waits for a modern large digital computer to repeat a state, solely because it is a [FSM], in in for a very long wait.". For example, a typical modern computer with say 100K 32 bit words of memory can be in any one of

$2^{100*2^{15}}$ states! It is for this reason that the really successful applications of FSM theory in computer science have been in connection with hardware design, where the individual components have only a few states. Even this application is threatened as the unit of construction has changed from gates to whole (micro-) processors.

2.5 Turing machines

We now want to refine the FSM model by retaining the finite state control but providing in addition an external memory capable of remembering arbitrarily long sequences of inputs. Suppose that $i = i_1 i_2 \ldots i_t$ is an input sequence to a FSM. We can imagine the sequence i being prepared on a tape and supplied to the FSM so that it first processes i_1, then i_2, and so on up to i_t. This can be depicted as follows:

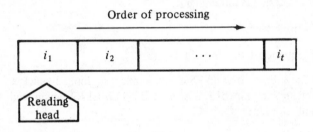

From the diagram, it can be seen that the FSM moves one tape square to the right at each step of the computation.* The 'obvious' way to refine the model to enable it always to have access to the whole of its input sequence is to allow it to 'choose' at each step of the computation whether to move left, right, or not at all.

The 'choosing' of a direction in which to move in order to read the next tape square can be achieved by supplying a third function in addition to mfn and sfn for the FSM. Thus we have a direction function:

dfn : $I \times S \rightarrow \{L, R, N\}$

where L, R, and N respectively stand for move left, move right, and no move.

This is the basic idea behind the Turing machine (TM) model: there is a finite state control or 'reading head' which can scan the squares of a tape on which the input is written. At each step in the computation, the TM stays where it is or moves one square either to the left or to the right, after first overwriting an 'output' in place of the 'input' character being scanned. The computation terminates

---

* For this reason, Arbib (1969, p. 15ff) jokingly calls FSMs "John Birch machines"! He remarks: "Teachers at more conservative campuses may [redraw the diagram to get] a suitably insidious device which always moves left."!

when the TM enters a designated 'halt' state. Since squares can be revisited, outputs can later become inputs, and so the distinction between outputs and inputs is dropped. In the sequel we shall denote the common (input–output) character set by I.

One slight problem remains to be solved before the TM can be formally defined. Suppose we start the reading head somewhere in the middle of a tape; as the computation proceeds the head will move left and right up and down the tape. It is just possible that at some point in the computation the reading head will be positioned over the left-most square of the tape and choose to move left! Analogously, it may be positioned on the right-most square and choose to move right. In either case the TM can be thought of as having exhausted the current supply of memory; this is precisely the problem discussed at the end of the preceeding section. We saw there that one solution to the problem is to suppose that in such a situation 'extra memory', in the form of an extra piece of tape, can be straightaway made available and spliced on to overcome the immediate memory shortage. An alternative solution of course is to ensure that the problem never arises by supposing that the tape stretches both ways to infinity

The reader should convince himself that so long as the tape is restricted to always having only a finite portion marked in the infinite tape solution, and so long as extra memory can be made available whenever it is needed in the finite solution, the two solutions are equivalent. It turns out that the mathematics (and programming) of Turing machines is much simpler if we adopt the infinite solution. Notice that the condition that only a finite number of squares be marked after any number of computation steps is guaranteed if there are only a finite number marked at the start of the computation. We are now in a position to define the TM model.

DEFINITION 2.4 A *Turing machine* has a finite character set I, and a finite state set S (one of whose states is 'halt'). It has a reading head which can scan any square on an infinite tape* on which initially only a finite number of squares are marked. There are three functions:

$$\mathrm{mfn} : I \times S \to I, \quad \mathrm{sfn} : I \times S \to S, \quad \mathrm{dfn} : I \times S \to \{L, R, N\}$$

called respectively the *machine*, *state*, and *direction* function.

A *Turing machine computation* consists of initializing the tape, scanned square, and state, and repeatedly executing the following cycle until the machine assumes the halt state:

---

* Students of a mathematical disposition should note that the notions of tape and reading head can be made precise by a function tape : $Z \to I$ and an integer scannedsquare.

$(**let** previousstate = state

    let move = dfn(scannedch, state)

    state := sfn(scannedch, previousstate)

    tape!scannedsq := mfn(scannedch, previousstate)

    scannedsq := scannedsq + (move = $R \rightarrow 1$, move = $L \rightarrow -1, 0$)

    scannedch := tape!scannedsq

$)

[The reader should be warned that there are almost as many variants to Definition 2.4 as there are books on the subject; Fischer (1965) is a good survey of the variants. In particular he should learn to ignore trivial differences between definitions such as whether the machine has to move left or right at every stage or whether, as here, it can additionally choose to stay where it is.]

EXAMPLE 2.10 [taken from Minsky (1967, Section 6.1.2)] Recall from Checkpoint 2.17 that no FSM is capable of checking whether a string of left and right parentheses is well-formed or not. We now show that the TM model is genuinely more powerful than the FSM model by presenting a TM that decides well-formedness.

The initial tape consists of the string to be pronounced upon bounded by semicolons; the rest of the infinite tape is not needed in this example. The initial position of the reading head, which is started in state RT, is as shown:

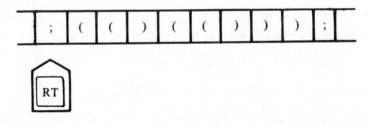

The character set I is {(,), ;, *, $\sqrt{}$, X} and the state set S is {RT, LT, LASTLT, HALT}. The functions mfn, sfn, and dfn are defined in Table 2.1.

The TM searches for and then attempts to match each right parenthesis with a corresponding left parenthesis. In more detail, RT is a 'right-moving' state that passes over left parentheses and pairs of asterisks (which mark previously matched pairs) until it finds a right parentheses. This is replaced by an asterisk and the state becomes LT – an analogous left-moving state which searches for the first left parenthesis to match with the right parenthesis found the RT search. If the left-hand tape mark ';' is found in state LT, it means that there is at least one right parenthesis too many; a failure is signalled and the TM halts. If

Table 2.1

State s	Scanned character i	Machine function mfn(i, s)	State function sfn(i, s)	Direction function dfn(i, s)
RT	(	(	RT	R
RT	*	*	RT	R
RT	)	*	LT	L
RT	;	;	LASTLT	L
LT	)	)	LT	L
LT	*	*	LT	L
LT	(	*	RT	R
LT	;	X	HALT	N
LASTLT	)	)	LASTLT	L
LASTLT	*	*	LATSLT	L
LASTLT	;	√	HALT	N
LASTLT	(	X	HALT	N

the right-hand ';' is found by the RT search, we may conclude that the string contains as many left as right parentheses. But of course there may be more, so a final leftwards scan is made in state LASTLT.

Students who eventually study a compiling techniques course will meet this algorithm again − it is the essence of a parsing algorithm for so-called 'precedence grammars'; see Gries (1971, Chapter 5).

In the above example, the TM was represented by a set of *quintuples* of the form;

$$(s, i, \text{mfn}(i, s), \text{sfn}(i, s), \text{dfn}(i, s))$$

The remark we made in connection with FSMs in Section 2.2, that such a representation soon becomes rather imperspicuous, is even more true of TMs. As a result we shall extend the circle-and-arrow representation for FSMs to cater for TMs. The obvious way to do this is to include the direction information $d = \text{dfn}(i, s_1)$ on the shaft of the arrow thus:

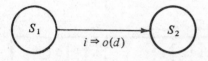

Minsky (1967, p. 123, attributing N. Rochester) has pointed out that in practice most TM states are unidirectional search states (like LT, RT, and LASTLT of the above example) so that *all* the arrows into S_2 are likely to have the same direction d associated with them. Accordingly, he suggests that d be made into a *default attribute*, placed next to the state name, and omitted from the individual arrows:

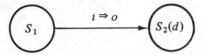

Only those (very few) state transformations whose associated direction is different from the default need be given explicitly. Moreover, arrows of the form:

which occur frequently, can also be treated as defaults and omitted. The net result of these default conventions is that circle-and-arrow diagrams only need to display the more significant state transformations.

Here is the circle-and-arrow representation of the parenthesis checking TM:

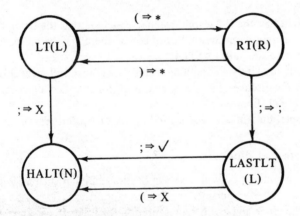

EXAMPLE 2.11   The main result of Section 2.4 was that the multiplication function cannot be computed on any FSM; we now present a TM that does the job. The numbers x and y to be multiplied are presented (in unary notation) as strings of 1's of lengths x and y:

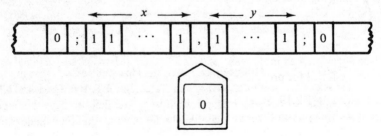

The final tape configuration is:

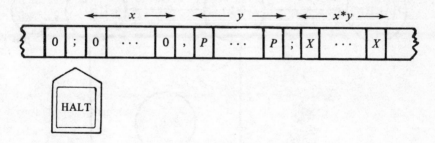

where P is used as a marker (or *pointer*) during each (repeated addition) cycle:

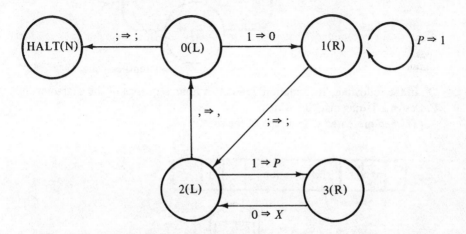

We recall that, following Example 2.7 in Section 2.2 (the combination lock FSM), we remarked how a sequence of operations was directly modelled by a sequence of arrows. The same is true of the above examples: a loop or cycle of operations in the TM is modelled by a loop in a chain of arrows from one state back to itself. In particular, if we present the circle-and-arrow diagram for the multiplier TM as follows (see overleaf), it becomes clear that the repeated addition algorithm for multiplying involves a (nested) loop within a loop.

The following three exercises are intended to give the reader practice in designing TMs. He will find that it is even more obscure than machine code programming since the facilities for controlling the computation sequence are almost non-existent. Recall the discussion in Section 1.1 that this should not by itself be considered an indictment of TMs: they are meant for reasoning *about* computations not for programming useful computations *in*.

CHECKPOINT 2.19   Suppose that $C = \{c_1, \ldots, c_n\}$ is a finite character set which does not contain the punctuation symbols ';' and ',' or the blank symbol

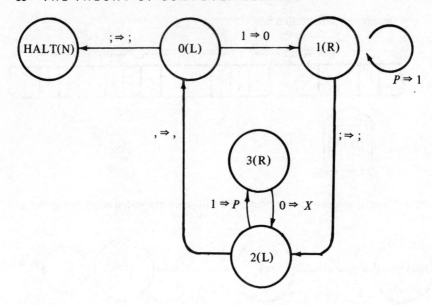

'0'. In the following, 'information' refers to a finite sequence of the characters in C. Design a Turing machine which:

(a) when presented with a tape of the form:

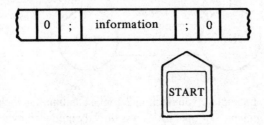

copies the information block to end up with:

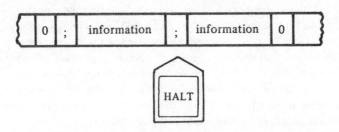

(b) when presented with a tape of the form:

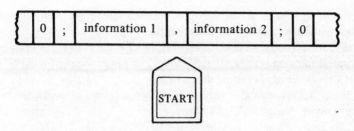

checks whether the blocks information 1 and information 2 are palindromes of each other. (Recall from Checkpoint 2.18 that this is outside the range of a FSM.)

CHECKPOINT 2.20 Devise a TM to compute the integer quotient $x \div y$ of a pair x, y of numbers.

CHECKPOINT 2.21 *Sketch* the construction of a TM to compute the greatest common divisor of a pair of numbers.

At this point we recall the the overall aim of this chapter is to give a precise formulation of the notion of 'computable' in terms of the TM model. Intuitively we might think of defining a function $f: X \to Y$ to be *Turing-computable* if there is some TM M_f such that, whenever M_f is supplied with a tape just containing a representation of an element x of X (and perhaps some punctuation), and if M_f halts after some finite number of computation steps, then there will be a representation of $f(x)$ on some part of the tape. Now, much of the point of a definition is that it should be precise and unambiguous; there are several respects in which this intuitive definition needs tightening up.

(1) The problems associated with defining sets, in particular Russell's paradox (Section A.5.2 in Appendix A), suggest that we should be very specific about what sets X and Y are to be allowed. Since we are attempting to give a precise definition of 'computable' on which to base a theory, as opposed to forming a *usable* definition, and since we expect that all information can be coded into numerical form, it seems reasonable to restrict Y to be the set N of numbers and X to be some N^r (in order to cater for functions of more than one argument). In fact, it turns out (see Section 5.4) that we could restrict X also to be N; but that is going too far!

(2) We should similarly be more specific about *how* we present an element $(x_1, \ldots, x_r)$ of $X = N^r$ to the TM. To this end we decree that an input $(x_1, \ldots, x_r)$ be presented as an *argument strip* as follows:

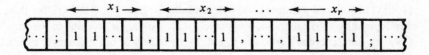

(3) We should be specific about the initial scanned square; we might decree that it is the right-hand ';' of the argument strip.

(4) Finally, we must say precisely *where* on the tape the answer $f(x)$ can be found. A typical solution is to say that M_f should halt over the right-most '1' of $f(x)$, the left-hand end of $f(x)$ being delineated by ';'

Taking these (housekeeping!) considerations into account, we refine the intuitive definition of 'computable' as follows:

DEFINITION 2.5   A function $f: N^r \to N$ is *Turing-computable* if there is a Turing machine M_f such that if $M_{f,}$ is supplied with the tape:

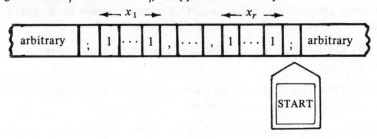

and if M_f eventually halts, it does so with the tape configured as follows:

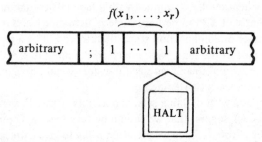

CHECKPOINT 2.22   Modify the TMs of Examples 2.10 and 2.11 and Checkpoints 2.19 and 2.20 to conform to the requirements of the above definition.

CHECKPOINT 2.23   By devising an appropriate TM, prove that the function which squares its sole argument is Turing-computable.

Before leaving this section, we observe that, according to Definition 2.5, the functions sum, product, power, and square are computable because there are different TMs to compute them. It would appear that we are suggesting a different piece of (special-purpose) hardware to effect each different computation! In practice of course we make do with a single piece of hardware which can be *programmed* to behave like any such dedicated machine. With this in mind, Knuth (1968a) introduced a simple little programming language TURINGOL for the development of TM programs. For more details see Knuth (1968b) or Knuth (1971b). Similar considerations will also figure largely in our discussion in Section 2.8 of other 'abstract machine' definitions of computable.

2.6 A universal Turing machine

In this section we shall consider a very useful and important kind of TM, a universal Turing machine. To see what 'universal' means, we consider what such a machine does.

Suppose we are presented with a representation of a TM M_f which computes a function $f: N^r \to N$. A typical representation for M_f might be a table of quintuples, a circle-and-arrow diagram, or a TURINGOL program. Suppose further that we are given an r-tuple $x = (x_1, \ldots, x_r)$ and are asked to use M_f to compute $f(x)$. We would probably proceed by first writing the argument strip for x on an otherwise blank tape, and then working step-by-step through the computation of $f(x)$, at each stage referring to the representation of M_f to see what was called for next and carrying it out. Finally we would extract the result $f(x)$ from the tape. This process seems remarkably mechanical; which suggests that we might be able to write a TM-interpreter program to do it for us. Without bothering overmuch about details of representation (but see Checkpoint 2.24) such an interpreter might be programmed as follows:

> **let** Turing(M, args) =
>
> > **valof** \$(**let** sfn, mfn, dfn = statefn(M), machfn(M), dirfn(M)
> >
> > initialize (args)
> >
> > **while** state $\neq$ halt **do***
> >
> > \$(W **let** prevstate = state
> >
> > > **let** move = dfn(scannedch, state)
> > >
> > > state := sfn(scannedch, state)
> > >
> > > tape!scannedsq := mfn(scannedch, prevstate)
> > >
> > > scannedsq := scannedsq + (move = $R \to 1$,
> > >
> > > > move = $L \to -1,0$)
> > >
> > > scannedch := tape!scannedsq
> >
> > \$)W
> >
> > **resultis** extractresult()
> >
> > \$)

In the above program, initialize is a simple routine that builds the argument strip as explained in definition 2.5, and extractresult() is a routine that counts the '1's of the answer $f(x)$ up to the preceding semicolon (see Definition 2.5). Several declarations including tape, state, scannedsq, and scannedch are omitted,

---

* Compare the program for the TM cycle given on p. 32.

together with the respective initialization. No details of the mechanism for representing the TM M as a data structure are given. The reader is strongly urged to complete the following checkpoint:

CHECKPOINT 2.24 Complete the programming of Turing, and test your program on appropriate representations of the TMs you devised as solutions in Checkpoint 2.22.

We can imagine that the program Turing computes the function turing: $TM \times N^r \to N$, where TM is the set of TMs, defined by:

$$\text{turing}(M_f, x) = f(x)$$

The function turing is surely intuitively computable, since we have just completed a program Turing to compute it! By Turing's thesis, there must exist a TM, say U, which also Turing-computes the function turing. The TM U has the following property:

Given an appropriate description of *any* TM M_f and *any* argument x for f, U halts over $f(x)$ [so long as $f(x)$ is defined]. Moreover, U computes $f(x)$ by simulating the action of M_f at every step.

Since the single TM U works *for all* pairs f and x, it is called a *universal Turing machine*.

It might be objected that by appealing to Turing's thesis our proof of the existence of a universal TM (henceforth UTM) is less satisfying than an actual construction of a UTM would be. We reject this argument by referring yet again to the point we have repeatedly made about formalisms such as TMs: they are not primarily intended to be programmed in. Indeed, we contend that *more* insight into the interpretive process embodied in a UTM is in fact gained by considering a high-level language equivalent than comes from poring over a mass of circles and arrows, even when as much care is taken over the construction as in Minsky (1967, Chapter 7).

There are a number of situations in computing science where UTMs have an important influence; for the moment we consider just three:

(1) "All our stored program computers, when provided with unlimited auxiliary storage are universal in Turing's sense. In some subconscious sense even the sales departments of computer manufacturers are aware of this, and they do not advertize magic instructions that cannot be simulated on competitors' machines, but only that their machines are faster, cheaper, have more memory, or are easier to program" [McCarthy (1962a, p. 28)].

(2) The UTM underlies interpretive implementations of programming languages. In an interpretive system (for example LISP), the interpreter (LISP's is called eval) acts as a UTM in the following way. The analogues of TMs are programs; the interpreter simulates step-by-step the behaviour called for by any such program on any data.

(3) Since a UTM is capable of interpreting any other TM, It is tempting to

think of a UTM, or, following (2), an interpreter for a programming language, as embodying the semantics for the system. This idea is developed further in Section 8.3.

There is one slight snag with the development of UTMs given above: the function turing had domain $TM \times N^r$ instead of some N^s, as demanded by Definition 2.5. This problem can be over come once we have established the existence of a function:

$$\text{code} : TM \to N$$

which codes a TM as a number. We shall explore the idea of a number as a data structure further in Section 5.4; in the meantime the reader should attempt the following:

CHECKPOINT 2.25 (answered in Section 5.4) Sketch the construction of a pair of programs that respectively code a TM as a number, and decode such a number to give back the original TM. (We shall use the computable function code in Section 3.1.)

2.7 Shannon's complexity measure for TMs

We recall from Chapter 1 that the development of measures for the complexity or difficulty of a computable function is an important topic in the theory of computation. One of the earliest such measures for TMs, roughly the product of the number of states of the TM with the number of symbols, was proposed by Shannon (1956). We introduce his work here since it is an interesting application using only the ideas of the preceding two sections. Nowadays the state–symbol product measure has been superseded by time and tape bound theorems and speed-up theorems (see Arbib, 1969, Chapter 7). These latter results are proved using the notion of crossing sequence as a way of formalizing aspects of the trace or execution sequence of a computation.

Before stating Shannon's results, we give an illustrative example of the way in which states can be 'traded' for symbols to get different Turing machines to do the same job. We shall present two TMs to solve a reverse-information-block problem analogous to the copy-block problem described in Checkpoint 2.19(a). In the reverse-block problem, we have a finite character set $C = \{c_1, \ldots, c_n\}$ and are to design a TM which when placed over the tape:

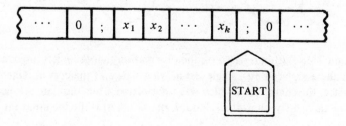

(where each x_i belongs to C) halts with the tape configured as follows:

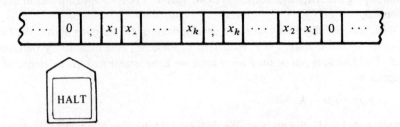

In the first solution, the input set I has $(n + 3)$ elements, namely C together with ';', '0', and a place-marker '*'. There are $(2n + 3)$ states, namely start, halt, loop, and the $2n$ states:

$$l_i, r_i \qquad 1 \leqslant i \leqslant n$$

where l_i (respectively r_i) is a left-moving (respectively right-moving) state which 'remembers' the character c_i being transmitted. Here is the circle-and-arrow diagram for the first TM:

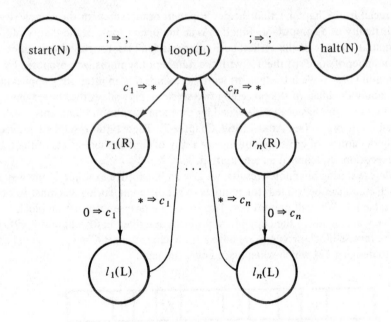

The second TM solution is based on the observation that the n left-moving states l_i can all be replaced by a single left-moving state l, at the cost of remembering, in place, the character c_i which was transmitted. Thus the state set has $(n + 4)$ elements namely {start, halt, loop, $l, r_i | 1 \leqslant i \leqslant n$} while the input set has

$(2n + 2)$ elements namely $\{c_i, *_i | 1 \leqslant i \leqslant n\}$ together with ';' and '0'. Here is the circle-and-arrow diagram:

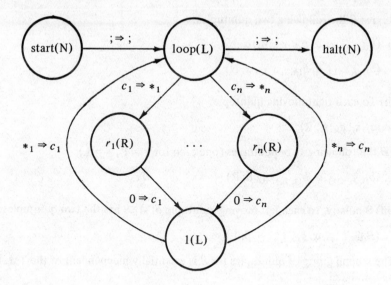

Here is the first of Shannon's theorems:

THEOREM 2.3 (Shannon, 1956) Any Turing machine with m symbols and n states can be simulated by a Turing machine with just 2 states and $(4mn + m)$ symbols. In particular, there exists a 2-state universal Turing machine. [As a matter of fact, Shannon (1956) also shows that any UTM needs at least 2 states. The proof is a rather intricate analysis of the trace of a one-state TM computation which seems to foreshadow the later crossing sequence idea.]

Proof. The proof is by construction of the simulating 2-state TM together with an induction proof; we shall just show how the simulator works. Suppose A has m symbols $\{a_1, \ldots, a_m\}$ and n states $\{s_1, \ldots, s_n\}$. The simulator TM B has two states, say α and β, and the following $(4mn + m)$ symbols:

(i) $b_1, \ldots, b_m$ corresponding the symbols of A

(ii) symbols $b_{(i, j, x, y)}$ where $1 \leqslant i \leqslant m, 1 \leqslant j \leqslant n$,

$$x \text{ is either } + \text{ or } -,$$
$$y \text{ is R or L}$$

Given a representation of A as a table of quintuples of the form:

$$(a_i, s_j, a_k, s_l, d)$$

where $a_k = \text{mfn}(a_i, s_j)$, $s_l = \text{sfn}(a_i, s_j)$, and $d = \text{dfn}(a_i, s_j)$, the (less than $6mn + 6m$) quintuples of B can be *automatically* written down in two groups as follows.

The first group of quintuples for B are derived straightforwardly from the quintuples of A.

(i) To each 'no move' quintuple:

$$(a_i, s_j, a_k, s_l, N)$$

of A, give B the following two quintuples:

$$(b_{(i, j, -, R)}, \alpha, b_{(k, l, -, R)}, \alpha, N)$$

$$(b_{(i, j, -, L)}, \alpha, b_{(k, l, -, L)}, \alpha, N)$$

(ii) To each right-moving quintuple:

$$(a_i, s_j, a_k, s_l, R)$$

give B the following two quintuples (one each for $* = R$, $* = L$):

$$(b_{(i, j, -, *)}, \alpha, b_{(k, l, +, R)}, \beta, R)$$

(iii) Similarly, to each left-moving quintuple of A, B has the two quintuples:

$$(B_{(i, j, -, *)}, \alpha, b_{(k, l, +, L)}, \beta, L)$$

The second group of quintuples for B is essentially independent of the TM A being simulated:

$$(b_i, \alpha, b_{(i, 1, -, R)}, \alpha, R)$$

$$(b_i, \beta, b_{(i, 1, -, L)}, \alpha, L)$$

$(b_{(i, j, +, *)}, ?, b_{(i, (j-1), +, *)}, \beta, *)$ one each in case ? is α or β, $*$ is L or R

$$(b_{(i, j, -, *)}, \beta, b_{(i, (j+1), -, *)}, \alpha', *)$$

$$(b_{(i, 1, +, *)}, ?, b_i, \alpha, *)$$

At any given point of the computation of A, the tape will look something like:

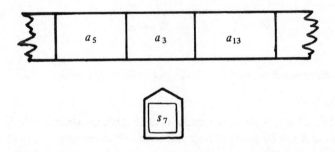

If A has the quintuple (a_3, s_7, a_8, s_4, R) the next tape configuration will be:

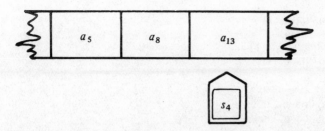

We now show how, in ten moves, B simulates this single move of A. At the start of the sequence of moves, B's tape will be configured as follows:

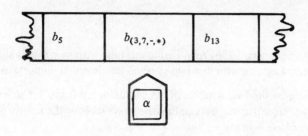

(whether $*$ is L or R depends on the previous move and is irrelevant). Here are ten snapshots of the squares corresponding to a_3, a_{13} in B.s moves.

1. (initial position)

$$b_{(3,\,7,\,-,\,*)}\ b_{13}$$
$$\alpha$$

2. [Effect the move by a quintuple of type (ii) in the first group]

$$b_{(8,\,4,\,+,\,R)}\ b_{13}$$
$$\beta$$

3. (We now have to get the fact that the state of A is s_4 into the new scanned square containing b_{13}. This is done by 'bouncing' between the squares in question).

$$b_{(8,\,4,\,+,\,R)}\ b_{(13,\,1,\,-,\,L)}$$
$$\alpha$$

4. $b_{(8,\,3,\,+,\,R)}\ b_{(13,\,1,\,-,\,L)}$
$$\beta$$

5. $b_{(8,\,3,\,+,\,R)}\ b_{(13,\,2,\,-,\,L)}$
$$\alpha$$

6. $b_{(8, 2, +, R)} b_{(13, 2, -, L)}$
   β

7. $b_{(8, 2, +, R)} b_{(13, 3, -, L)}$
   α

8. $b_{(8, 1, +, R)} b_{(13, 3, -, L)}$
   β

9. $b_{(8, 1, +, R)} b_{(13, 4, -, L)}$
   α

10. (Finally unload the information from the left square.)

$b_8 b_{(13, 4, -, L)}$
   α

THEOREM 2.4 (Shannon, 1956) Any Turing machine with m symbols and n states can be simulated by one with just two symbols and less than $8mn$ states.

Proof (outline). Suppose the two symbols of the simulator are 0 and 1. Our experience as computer scientists suggests coding the m symbols of the simulated machine as 1-bit numbers, where:

$$2^{l-1} < m \leqslant 2^l$$

and then working with sequences of length l in the simulator in much the same way as we suggested in Section 2.3. The reader is invited to complete the proof for himself.

CHECKPOINT 2.26 Show that any UTM needs at least 2 symbols.

At the end of his paper, Shannon poses the problem of finding the minimum state–symbol product for a UTM. The current smallest is Minsky's 4-symbol 7-state machine which is described by Minsky (1967, Section 14.8).

2.8 More computer-like abstract machines

Throughout this chapter we have emphasized the simplicity of TMs both as a model of computability and as a formalism in which to prove theorems of meta-computer science such as the unsolvability of the Halting problem (Section 3.1). But it is this very simplicity that makes TMs so useless either for communicating or constructing practical algorithms. Regarding the former, even with Minsky's elegant circle-and-arrow descriptions, it is virtually impossible to understand a TM with more than a very small number of states, say to the point of giving a terse description of its overall strategy as opposed to its detailed tactics. Regarding the latter, the control structure and memory medium, in which one has to leave a variety of punctuation marks to delineate areas of tape and set up uni-directional searches, is primitive in the extreme. It may be objected that I have argued throughout that the practical uselessness of TMs does not constitute an indictment, and that anybody wanting to do some practical computation should use a computer or programming language specifically designed for the purpose.

But there does seem to be room for a middle ground: an approach to computability based on abstract machines that more closely resemble actual computers yet are still sufficiently simple to make proofs of theorems feasible. Such an approach may well suggest results that would be difficult to discuss in terms of the TM model. This would appear to be Wang's (1957) belief: "Turing's theory of computable functions antedated but has not much influenced the extensive actual construction of digital computers. These two aspects of theory and practice have been developed almost entirely independently of each other. The main reason is undoubtedly that logicians are interested in questions radically different from those with which the applied mathematicians and electrical engineers are primarily concerned. It cannot, however, fail to strike one as rather strange that often the same concepts are expressed by very different terms in the two developments. One is even inclined to ask whether a rapprochement might not produce some good effect" (Wang, 1957, p. 63). (To a large extent, the approach taken in Chapters 3–5 is the author's attempt to answer this question affirmatively.)

In the remainder of this section we introduce three classes of abstract machines which, in varying degrees, are more like modern digital computers than TMs. The first, due to Wang (1957), separates out the device from its program (see the end of Section 2.5) but still has a sequential store. The second, due to Minsky (1967), has a random access store, but holds its program centrally instead of in the same store as the data. The final approach, that of Elgot and Robinson (1963), describes random-access stored program machines.* The interested reader should proceed to Scott (1967) for its references and its attempt to standardize some current ideas.

2.8.1 *B machines* (Wang, 1957)

Wang's machines consist of a central processor unit (CPU) which holds a program, and a reading head which scans a tape square in much the same way as a TM does. Unlike Turing's tape where the scanned character is erasable (as on magnetic tape), Wang's tape square may be punched with the single character '*' but not erased (as on paper tape).

A program is a sequence of commands of the form:

> label : instruction

(We have taken liberties with his syntax.) Labels are numbers as in FORTRAN except that consecutive commands have consecutive labels. Control enters the

---

* It should not be inferred that the author rates these approaches increasingly highly; they merely increasingly resemble current actual computers.

program at the command labelled '1'. The instruction part of a command is one of:

MOVEL   *move* the tape reading head one square to the *left*

MOVER   as MOVEL, but *right*

PUNCH   *punch* the symbol "*" into the scanned square; over-punching has no effect

IFMARKED *n*   *if* the scanned square is *marked* (i.e. punched), control continues at command labelled '*n*'; otherwise it continues at the next command

Notice that there is no explicit 'halt' command; the computation terminates if and when control passes out of range of the command labels (in particular by 'falling through the bottom' of the program text).

EXAMPLE 2.12 (Wang, 1957, p. 65) The following program searches to the right for the first unmarked square:

1: MOVER

2: IFMARKED 1

CHECKPOINT 2.27 Write a Wang program to decide if a given number is divisible by 2.

CHECKPOINT 2.28 Write a Wang program to decide whether two numbers m and n are equal. [Hint: a function $f(m,n)$ fo two arguments can be replaced by a function $f'(2^m 3^n)$ of one argument. What does the equality of m and n imply about $2^m 3^n$?]

Wang proves that his notion of computable is coextensive with Turing's, and then proceeds to consider other possible claimants to be basic operations. In particular he observes that, while all computable functions can be computed in terms of the operations given above, there are certain *tape operations*, for example erasing a mark, that cannot be achieved by a Wang program.

2.8.2 *Program machines* (Minsky, 1967, Chapter 11)

Minsky (1967, pp. 200ff) observes, as we did in Section 2.4, that, in order to develop a class of machines that are capable of computing all Turing-computable functions, one somehow has to lift the finiteness restriction of the FSM memory. He notes that a modern digital computer has a CPU and a random access store, which is a set of cells, and argues that the CPU is, and should be in any idealization, a FSM, since one could otherwise ignore the memory and just use the CPU. Thus, whereas ones first instinct is to relax the finiteness restriction by allowing an infinite set of cells, one must reject that solution since a random access store depends upon each cell being uniquely named. If the CPU is a FSM, these names must be finite strings of characters with length less than some *a priori* fixed maximum, which is impossible for an infinite number of cells! Accordingly he postulates an unspecified finite set $a, b, \ldots, z$ of storage cells each capable of holding an arbitrarily large number. But the requirement that the CPU be a FSM again intrudes, since one cannot allow it to deal directly with the contents of the store registers, for, being a FSM, it could not even find out what number is in a given register! His solution is to restrict the instructions that the CPU can interpret to the following set:

DZM   *a*   //*Deposit Zero in Memory* cell *a*

IMC   *a*   //*Increment Memory Cell a* by 1

HLT   //*Halt* the machine

SJZ   *a,n*   //*Subtract* 1 from the contents of *a* but *Jump* to *n* if *Zero*

(Again we have taken liberties with syntax, this time to make the instructions resemble those of a 2-address code computer.)

Thus a **program machine** consists of a CPU, into which a fixed program is loaded, and the finite set $a, \ldots, z$ of its memory cells:

Registers

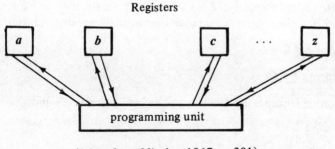

(taken from Minsky, 1967, p. 201)

Here is an example program for such a program machine; it computes the integer quotient $a \div 2$ in cell b.

1: DZM *b*

2: SJZ   *a*,7

3: SJZ   *a*,4

4: IMC *b*

5: DZM *z*

6: SJZ   *z*,2

7: HLT

Minsky (1967, p. 203) observes that the commands labelled '5' and '6' together have the effect of an unconditional jump. Thus one is led to the idea of a macro 'JUMP n' to replace them. Similarly one might define a subtract-if-possible-but-do-not-jump macro to make command labelled '3' clearer. Minsky moves on to introduce subroutines, compilers, iterative and recursive programs; his Section 11.7 in particular merits study, although it depends on the material we shall treat in Chapters 4 and 5.

2.8.3 *RASPs* (Elgot and Robinson, 1963)

Despite the mass of hieroglyphs, there is little conceptually difficult in Elgot and Robinson's paper, which introduces RASPs, i.e. *R*andom *A*ccess *S*tored *P*rogram machines. Basically,* their store is a set $L = \{l_0, l_1, \ldots\}$ of locations, with no comment on the size of L; presumably Minsky's (1967) considerations discussed in Section 2.8.2 did not trouble them. It is assumed that there is a set $V = \{v_0, \ldots\}$ of values, any one of which can be stored in any location in L. In essence then the contents of memory are specified by a function cont$: L \to V$; accordingly we shall denote $(L \to V)$ by C. They further postulated a program-counter, which records the location in which the currently-executed command is stored. Thus a *state* of a RASP is defined as a ⟨program counter, contents of memory pair⟩, i.e. as a member of $L \times C$. Given such a state, they define functions that say how the program counter and contents of memory will alter:

$$\text{next-pc} : L \times C \to L$$

$$\text{next-mem} : L \times C \to C$$

The computation sequence can (roughly) be defined in terms of a function:

$$\text{exec-cmd} : L \times C \to L \times C$$

where

$$\text{exec-cmd}(l,c) = (\text{next-pc}(l,c), \text{next-mem}(l,c))$$

Being a stored program computer, the instructions are a subset of the value set V, so control is defined by saying what is the next state when an instruction v in V is executed. In reality, Elgot and Robinson are interested in the semantics of programming languages. They define:

$$\text{meaning} : V \to (L \times C \to L \times C)$$

and discuss the compiler problem in terms of "richer" and "poorer" languages. They show that, in a certain precisely-defined sense, self-modifying (impure) programs are "more powerful" than non-self-modifying (pure) ones.

---

* Compare the discussion of self-application in Section 1.2.3. Presumably, this problem did not occur to them.

3 The Limitations of Computer Science

3.1 Introduction

In this chapter we investigate no less profound an issue than the limitations of computer science. It should be clearly understood that the word 'limitations' does not refer to the *practical* limitations which might be forced on any particular programming project but to *theoretical* limitations which apply to all such projects, not only now but in any possible future of computer science. Whereas the practicality of any project may be limited by the available hardware, software, and financial resources, not to mention the limited capabilities of the people engaged on the project, we shall demonstrate results such as the 'unsolvability of the halting problem for TMs', a result that implies that it is not, and never will be, possible to write a single program that will determine infallibly whether or not any program input to it will halt, or will loop infinitely. (Incredibly, the author is aware of a computer manufacturer who, in the past decade, attempted to build such a program despite the fact the the unsolvability result was proved in Turing's original 1936 paper!).

As we shall discuss more fully later in this section, the 'unsolvability' of the halting 'problem' corresponds to the existence of a certain non-computable function, say f_H, where by 'computable' we mean 'Turing-computable' as defined in Chapter 2. Consequently, the set of *computable* functions is a proper subset of the set of *all* functions of the form $(N^n \to N)$:

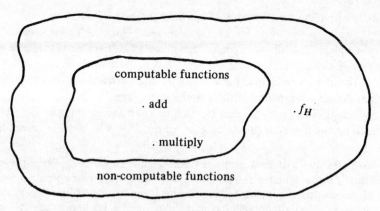

$\sim$ all functions of the form $(N^n \to N)$ $\sim$

The intention of this chapter is to give the reader an intuitive 'feel' for non-computable functions analogous to what we imagine to be his already extensive intuition regarding what *is* computable, programmable, algorithmic. We shall try to supply this intuition in two ways:

(a) In Section 3.4 we present a brief survey of some well-known non-computable functions. We shall particularly emphasize those that have emerged from recent work in two areas of the theory of computation, namely formal grammars and the program schema studies of Luckham, Park, and Paterson (1970).

(b) The majority of the non-computable functions discussed in Section 3.4. stem from the various systems attempting 'self-awareness' or 'introspection' in that they ask questions *within* the system *about* the system's capabilities. We shall consider several proofs of the existence of non-computable functions and will discover that two arguments continually reappear: Cantor's diagonalization argument and the Russell paradox argument; these arguments are presented more fully in Appendix A, and we observe that they are closely related.

The reader may have noticed the word 'problem' several times above. We now want to take a short detour and explain what is meant by 'problem' and what it means for a problem to be 'solvable' or 'unsolvable'. Strictly speaking, this detour is unnecessary since all mention of problems and solvability could be replaced appropriately by functions and computability. The reason for introducing the concepts is to connect the notion of 'computable' and the reader's intuition in yet another way. The point is that we *think* in terms of problems; only when a problem is fully formulated in the mind is it reasonable to model it as a mathematical conjecture about the computability of some function.

The sort of problems we discuss in this chapter consist of a set of instances or cases, each of which has a single correct answer. Here are some examples:

(1) The problem "Is $m * n = k$?" consists of an infinity of cases of which "Is $5 * 3 = 21$?" (correct answer "no") and "is $4 * 2 = 8$?" (correct answer: "yes") are but two

(2) The problem "is 29 a prime?" has only one case – itself.

(3) (The halting problem for Turing machines) "Does the Turing machine M halt when placed initially over a tape description t?". There is a separate case for each pair M and t.

(4) (The blank tape halting problem for Turing machines) "Does the Turing machine M halt when placed initially over a blank tape?".

(5) Fermat's last problem[*] asks for each trio of non-zero integers x, y, and z, and each integer n greater than 2, whether or not $x^n + y^n = z^n$. The answer in

---

[*] Named after the 17th century French mathematician Pierre de Fermat. Fermat habitually wrote remarks and theorems, without giving proofs, in the margins of his books. In his copy of *Arithmetica* by Diophantus he stated this problem as a theorem. To date nobody has supplied a proof other than in special cases of n.

each case is either "yes" or "no". To date, nobody knows of an instance in which the answer is "yes".

CHECKPOINT 3.1 There are several instances of the halting problem in Chapter 2 where the correct answer is "yes"; construct an instance where the answer is "no".

Notice that such a problem can be modelled by a function in a very natural way, namely the set of (case, correct answer) pairs. More precisely, if P is a problem, X is the set of instances of P, and Y is the set of correct answers of P, we can define the *associated function* $f_P : X \to Y$ of P by setting $f_P(x)$ to be the correct answer y to the instance x of P.

CHECKPOINT 3.2 Any function $g : A \to B$ 'suggests' an *associated problem* Q_g, namely "what is $g(a)$?", whose correct answer is some b in B. Show that the following duality relations hold:

$$f_{Q_g} = g, \quad Q_{f_P} = P$$

We suggest that we may reasonably consider that a problem is 'solvable' only if there is some uniform process that generates the correct answer given any instance of the problem. This amounts to defining that a problem P is *solvable* if the associated function f_p is computable (more precisely, Turing-computable). A problem that is not solvable, i.e. for which f_p is *not* computable, is called *unsolvable*; thus there is a one-one correspondence between unsolvable problems and non-computable functions. In Section 3.3 we shall introduce the additional notions of 'enumerable' and 'decidable' which are similarly defined in terms of computability and which provide a language in which we can discuss a rich variety of kinds of problem 'naturally'.

CHECKPOINT 3.3 (for class discussion) Do you think that the notions of 'problem' and 'solvability' introduced above accord with your normal everyday understanding of those terms? If not, how do you think they should be refined? If so, how would you encompass a high-school mathematics problem, or a chess problem, within the aegis of the definition?

There is sometimes confusion between whether a problem P is unsolvable or solvable, and whether P is solved or not solved. To illustrate the difference consider Fermat's problem. The associated function is clearly computable; hence Fermat's problem is *solvable*. But Fermat's problem is not *solved* since nobody knows whether or not there is an instance whose correct answer is "yes"; that is, it is not known whether the range of the associated (computable) function includes "yes".

3.2 A non-computable function

This short section is devoted to proving the following theorem, which asserts the existence of a non-computable function.

THEOREM 3.1 (Turing, 1936, p. 247) The halting problem for Turing machines is unsolvable.

Proof. The halting problem H was defined in the preceding section: recall that it asks, for each TM M and each tape t, whether M halts when initially placed on t. Let us denote the associated function f_H by $f: M \times T \to \{$true, false$\}$, where M is the set of TMs and T is the set of tapes. By definition:

$$f(M, t) = \text{true iff } M \text{ halts when placed initially over } t$$

We are to show that H is unsolvable, that is, that f is not computable. To do this, we shall suppose to the contrary that f *is* computable and then, in two steps, derive a contradiction.

Step 1: descriptions

In Section 2.6 we considered a method of coding a TM description as a number. In a very similar way we can code a Turing machine description onto a tape (see Sections 5.2 and 5.4 for further details of such a coding scheme). This amounts to asserting the existence of a computable coding functions:

$$\text{descn}: M \to T$$

Now f is presumed to solve the halting problem H for *all* machines M and *all* tapes t. In particular we can use it to solve the special instances of H in which the tape t is a machine description descn(M). That is to say, we can define:

$$e: M \to \{\text{true, false}\}$$

by

$$e(M) = f(M, \text{descn}(M))$$

so that

$$e(M) = \text{true iff } M \text{ halts when placed over the (machine description)} \\ \text{tape descn}(M)$$

Notice that e is defined solely in terms of f and descn. We know that descn is computable, and have assumed that f is computable; thus e is also computable.

Step 2: the Russell argument

We now define a function $d: M \to \{\text{true, false}\}$ as follows:

$$d(M) = (e(M) \to \textbf{valof } \$(\textbf{ let } x = 1$$

$$x := x \textbf{ repeat}$$

$$\textbf{resultis false}$$

$$\$),$$

$$\text{true})$$

Notice how we have arranged for the computation of $d(M)$ to terminate (with result "true") precisely in the case that the computation of $e(M)$ yields "false". Since e is computable, so too is d. By Turing's thesis, there is a TM, say D, that computes d. That is:

D halts over descn(M) iff the computation of $d(M)$ terminates
(with result "true")

$$\text{iff } e(M) = \text{false}$$
$$\text{iff } f(M, \text{descn}(M)) = \text{false}$$
$$\text{iff } M \text{ fails to halt over descn}(M)$$

Notice that this assertion has to hold true *for all* machines M, in particular in the special case $M = D$. But in that case we find:

D halts over descn(d) iff D fails to halt over descn(D)

This contradiction establishes the theorem.

The two-step argument we have just presented is very similar to Turing's original proof. However, where we used Russell's argument to get the final paradox, Turing used Cantor's diagonalization. The reader may like to peruse Minsky's (1967, pp. 146–149) proof, which is much closer to the above.

There are a large number of corollaries to Theorem 3.1, many of which are (in the author's opinion) rather contrived. We shall give just one, since it is typical of such results. For a number of similar results see Minsky (1967, pp. 150–151) and Arbib (1969, p. 150, exercises 8, 9, and 10).

COROLLARY 3.2 The blank tape halting problem is unsolvable.

Proof (Minsky, 1967, p. 150). The blank tape halting problem was defined in the preceeding section. In order to show that it is unsolvable, we demonstrate that (despite appearances) it is equivalent to the (non-blank) halting problem discussed in Theorem 3.1. More specifically we show that, to every instance (M,t) of the halting problem, there is an instance $N_{M,t}$ of the blank tape halting problem, that is, there is a TM $N_{M,t}$ such that:

$N_{M,t}$ halts over a blank tape iff M halts over t

The rest of the proof consists of showing how $N_{M,t}$ can be constructed out of M and t. Its logic is so designed that it writes a copy of t onto the blank tape, positions itself where M would, and then finally 'turns itself into' M. Suppose that when M starts over t the configuration is:

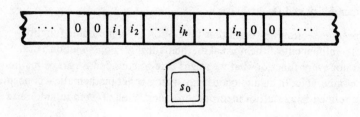

In the diagram, $i_1 i_2 \ldots i_n$ is the (finite) initial marked portion of t. The circle-and-arrow representation of $N_{M,t}$ is:

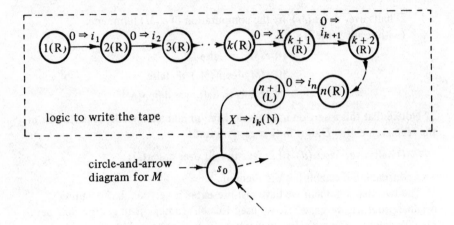

Notice that $N_{M,t}$ requires $(n + 1)$ states more than M, and thus depends crucially on the fact that t is finitely inscribed.

CHECKPOINT 3.4 The printing problem asks whether the TM M ever prints the symbol i when started over tape t. Prove that it is unsolvable.

CHECKPOINT 3.5 All of us have initiated (many!) non-terminating computations; usually, we recognize that we have by noticing that after some finite number of steps the program is looping, that is, repeatedly executing the same set of steps. We may feel that we should be able to define a general 'run time' function rt $: M \times T \to N$ such that if M has not halted over t after rt(M, t) steps then it never will. Show that no such runction rt can be computable.

A problem related to that discussed in Checkpoint 3.5 is the 'immortality problem'. This recognizes that some programs terminate for all data (i.e. tapes) while for others there are just some choices of data that cause non-terminating computations. It asks whether a TM M has *any* tape that causes such a non-terminating ('immortal'!) computation. It turns out that the immortality problem is unsolvable, although the proof is surprisingly difficult. The interested reader might like to study it for himself in Hooper (1966, p. 219).

3.3 Enumerability and Decidability

In the preceding section we found that the notion of 'computable function' represents a refinement of the normal mathematical idea of 'function', in the sense that not every function that we might care to consider as part of mathematics is computable. In an anologous way, many other mathematical concepts have been refined as a result of incorporating the notion of 'computable', and together they provide a rich language in terms of which many questions of interest in computer science can naturally be discussed. It suffices for our purposes to introduce just two such, 'enumerable' and 'decidable', which respectively refine the mathematical concepts of 'countable' and 'subset'. The reader who is motivated to explore further should consult Rogers (1967).

3.3.1 *Enumerability*

Recall (see Appendix A, p. 261) that a set S is *countable* if there is an onto function $f : N \rightarrow S$. In order for S to be *enumerable*,[*] we additionally insist that some such counting function f be computable.[†] By definition, any enumerable set is countable; we shall find that the reverse is false: there are countable non-enumerable sets.

   CHECKPOINT 3.6 How can the idea of a set being 'enumerable' be accommodated in the language of problems and solvability introduced in Section 3.1?

   In order to prove that a set S is enumerable, we have to show that a machine can be programmed to print successively the elements of S in such a way that any given element x of S is listed within a finite time of the start of the process. Accordingly, our proofs of enumerability usually consist of sketching a program to carry out the enumeration. This idea of a program as a constructive proof is in fact the main 'message' of the first part of the book, as we pointed out in the very first section of Chapter 1.

   We begin by proving a number of results about enumerability. The proofs demonstrate many of the 'programming techniques' that have been found useful in establishing such results.

   THEOREM 3.3 If R and S are enumerable sets, so is their union $R \cup S$.

Proof. Suppose that $f : N \rightarrow R$ and $g : N \rightarrow S$ are enumerations of R and S. We can define an enumeration h of $R \cup S$ by setting:

$$h(2n) = f(n), h(2n + 1) = g(n) \quad n \geqslant 0$$

In fact, we shall write h as a conditional expression to show how its program structure is similar to several other enumerations including the one in the following theorem. We need a predicate $even(n)$, which tests whether n is even or odd, and $n \div 2$, integer division by 2. The program for h is:

$$h(n) = (even(n) \rightarrow f(n \div 2), g(n \div 2))$$

Notice how h uses f and g alternately as part of a broad sweep through $R \cup S$;

---

[*] A frequently-used synonym for 'enumerable' is 'recursively enumerable'.

[†] By 'computable', we mean 'Turing-computable'. Consequently we should really talk about 'Turing-enumerable'. If the reader is worried on this account about the precision of any of the following arguments, we invite him to fill in the 'Turing-' prefixes appropriately.

this technique is highly reminiscent of Cantor's counting of $N \times N$ (which we shall revisit below).

THEOREM 3.4 If R and S are enumerable sets, so is their intersection $R \cap S$.

Proof (Arbib, 1969, p. 153). Suppose that f and g respectively enumerate R and S; we want to construct an enumeration $H : N \to R \cap S$. Any element x of $R \cap S$ also belongs to R, and so (since f is an enumeration of R) there must be a least number k such that $f(k) = x$. Similarly x belongs to S and so there is a least number l such that $g(l) = x$. If $k \leqslant l$ then $g(l)$, which is equal to x, belongs to the set $\{f(0), \ldots, f(k), \ldots, f(l)\}$ of elements of R, and conversely if $l \leqslant k$ then $f(k)$ belongs to $\{g(0), \ldots g(k)\}$. Thus we are assured of finding *all* the elements of $R \cap S$ if we test each $g(l)$ against the previous $f(i)$'s and each $f(k)$ against the previous $g(j)$'s. In the case that $g(l)$ or $f(k)$ are not in $R \cap S$ we choose to print some arbitrary element y of $R \cap S$.[*] Here is the program for h:

$$h(n) = (\text{even}(n) \to \textbf{valof } \$(\ \textbf{let } m = n \div 2$$

//check f against previous g's

for $i = 0$ **to** m **do**

if $g(i) = f(m)$ **then resultis** $f(m)$

resultis y

$),

valof \$(**let** $m = n \div 2$

//check g against previous f's

for $i = 0$ **to** m **do**

if $f(i) = g(m)$ **then resultis** $g(m)$

resultis y

$))

CHECKPOINT 3.7 Show how the proofs of Theorems 3.3 and 3.4 can be generalized to prove that if $R_1, \ldots, R_n$ are enumerable (where n is any finite number), so are $(R_1 \cup \ldots \cup R_n)$ and $(R_1 \cap \ldots \cap R_n)$.

THEOREM 3.5 The set $(N \times N)$ of pairs of numbers is enumerable.

Proof. The proof essentially consists of working out the details of Cantor's diagonal process for counting $N \times N$ (see Appendix A, p. 262) and showing that it is in fact an enumeration. Recall that Cantor suggested displaying the number

---

[*] We can do this so long as $R \cap S$ is non-empty. If the intersection is empty, it is trivially enumerable.

pairs $\langle x,y \rangle$ in the form of an infinite two-dimensional array and counting 'along the arrows'.

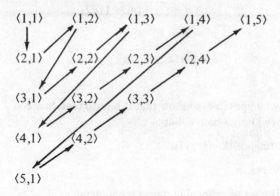

Notice how the majority of the steps in the counting process consist of working along diagonal 'slices'; in the mth such slice there are m elements $\langle m,1 \rangle$, $\langle m-1,2 \rangle$, . . . , $\langle 1,m \rangle$, each of which sums to $(m + 1)$. Consequently, the number pair $\langle x,y \rangle$ is in the $(x + y - 1)$st slice, and is the yth to be counted in that slice. Since $(x + y - 2)$ complete slices have been counted before starting on the slice containing $\langle x,y \rangle$, $\langle x,y \rangle$ is counted in the:

$$y + (1 + 2 + \ldots + (x + y - 2))$$

position. Thus we can define a function countingposition : $N \times N \rightarrow N$ such that countingposition$(\langle x,y \rangle)$ is the number of steps the counting process takes to reach $\langle x,y \rangle$. Simplifying gives:

$$\text{countingposition}(\langle x,y \rangle) = y + ((x + y - 2)*(x + y - 1))/2$$

Clearly countingposition is computable. To prove that $N \times N$ is enumerable, we show that the inverse of countingposition is computable, that is, we construct an enumeration function Cantorenum : $N \rightarrow (N \times N)$ so that Cantorenum(n) is the nth pair to be counted. To calculate Cantorenum(n) we first compute the slice m and then the pair $\langle x,y \rangle$ with in the mth slice. The reader can easily verify that:

$$y = n - (m*(m - 1))/2 \text{ and } x = m + 1 - y$$

Here is the program for Cantorenum:

```
Cantorenum(n) = valof $( let m = 1
                        let x,y = 0,0
                        //compute the slice
                        while (m*(m - 1))/2 < n do m := m + 1;
```

$$m := m - 1$$

//now compute x and y in slice m

$$y := n - (m * (m - 1))/2;$$

$$x := m + 1 - y;$$

resultis $\langle x, y \rangle$

$)

Cantorenum is clearly computable; to show that it is onto (and hence enumerates $N \times N$) we need only observe that:

Cantorenum(countingposition($\langle x, y \rangle$)) $= \langle x, y \rangle$

The details are left to the reader.

COROLLARY 3.6 The set of rational numbers is enumerable.

CHECKPOINT 3.8 Show that if R and S are enumerable so is $R \times S$.

CHECKPOINT 3.9 Prove that N^d is enumerable for any finite d.

CHECKPOINT 3.10 (mainly intended for joint mathematics/computer majors) The programming techniques of 3.3, 3.4, and 3.5 can be used to show the following: suppose that $\delta = \{S_\omega : \omega \varepsilon \Omega\}$ is a family of enumerable sets indexed by an enumerable set Ω. The intersection and union of δ are also enumerable (prove it). Show how these results and that of Checkpoint 3.7 can be used as the basis of a 'computable topology' analogous to the usual mathematical notion of topology. What do you think the computable analogues of compactness and connectedness would be? See Minsky and Papert (1969) for an interesting development along related lines.

We want to present one final programming technique that is useful for establishing enumerability. It is introduced in Theorem 3.7, where we prove that the set X^* of strings over some finite alphabet X is enumerable. Typical alphabets to which we may wish to apply Theorem 3.7 are the usual English alphabet $\{A, \ldots Z\}$, the binary digits $\{0, 1\}$, the ASCII character set, and the character set of a programming languages such as FORTRAN or ALGOL 60. As a matter of fact, as we discussed in Section 2.3 (see Example 2.8), X^* is even a regular set, and therefore is obviously enumerable; the point of Theorem 3.7 is to introduce the proof technique in a simple case so that it can be more readily understood in Theorem 3.8.

THEOREM 3.7 If $X = \{x_1, \ldots, x_k\}$ is a finite alphabet, the set X^* of (finite) strings over X is enumerable.

Proof. The idea of the proof is both simple and familiar; the details are a bit tiresome. Firstly we enumerate X^* 'shortest first', so that strings of length 1 precede strings of length 2, which precede strings of length 3, and so on. How are we then to order the k^l strings of some fixed length l? The answer comes from a consideration of the special case where X is the English alphabet $\{A, \ldots Z\}$, since we find strings of such letters in a dictionary. To apply dictionary order to strings of length l from a general set X, we first impose an order on the individual elements of X analogous to alphabetical ordering, say x_1 precedes x_2 (written $x_1 \ll x_2$) and:

$$x_1 \ll x_2 \ll \ldots \ll x_k.$$

Secondly, suppose that $i = x_{i_1}x_{i_2} \ldots x_{i_l}$ and $j = x_{j_1}x_{j_2} \ldots x_{j_l}$ are any two strings of length l from x; we put i before j (by extension we write $i \ll j$) if:

$$x_{i_1} \ll x_{j_1}$$

or

$$x_{i_1} = x_{j_1} \text{ and } x_{i_2} \ldots x_{i_l} \ll x_{j_2} \ldots x_{j_l}$$

It is now straightforward to define a program $\text{enum}_X : N \to X^*$ such that $\text{enum}_X(n)$ is the nth string in the ordering of strings just described.

CHECKPOINT 3.11 Complete the programming of enum_X.

CHECKPOINT 3.12 To what extent do you think that enum_X could serve as the basis for a table-lookup mechanism for identifiers in an implementation of a programming language?

THEOREM 3.8 The set of TMs is enumerable.

Proof. The proof is very similar to that used in Theorem 3.7; in what follows, we sketch the bare outline and invite the reader to fill in the details in Checkpoint 3.13. Suppose M_1 and M_2 are two TMs, say with M_1 having m_1 symbols and n_1 states, and M_2 having m_2 symbols and n_2 states. We first arrange for M_1 to precede M_2 if $m_1 < m_2$ or if $m_1 = m_2$ and $n_1 < n_2$. (This is analogous to the shortest-string-first part of Theorem 3.7.) We are left to consider the case $m_1 = m_2 (= m, \text{say}), n_1 = n_2 (= n, \text{say})$; the proof of Theorem 3.7 suggest that we should look for something akin to dictionary ordering. Recall from Section 2.5 that any TM can be represented by a table of quintuples of the form:

$$(s_v, i_w, i_x, s_y, d_z)$$

where $1 \leqslant v, y \leqslant n$, $1 \leqslant w, x \leqslant m$, and d_z is L, N, or R. The quintuples for a TM can be ordered by 'dictionary' order on (s_v, i_w). Now, if M_1 is different from M_2, there will be some first such quintuple in which they differ; M_1 precedes M_2 accordingly as the quintuple $(s_{v_1}, i_{w_1}, i_{x_1}, s_{y_1}, d_{z_1})$ of M_1 precedes that of M_2, namely $(s_{v_2}, i_{w_2}, i_{x_2}, s_{y_2}, d_{z_2})$ which are the first that differ.

CHECKPOINT 3.13 Construct an enumeration function tmenum : $N \to TM$ by filling in the details of the proof of Theorem 3.8.

COROLLARY 3.9 There are uncountable many non-computable functions!

Proof. Any computable function has the form $N^r \to N$ for some r. By Checkpoint

A16 of Appendix A there are uncountable many such functions. By Theorem 3.8, there are only countably many TMs, hence only countably many computable functions. Consequently, there are uncountably many non-computable functions. That is to say, the 'odds' on a random function of the form $(N^r \rightarrow N)$ being computable are vanishingly slight!

COROLLARY 3.10 If L is any programming language the legal (or well-formed) programs of L are enumerable.

Proof. Turing's thesis and Theorem 3.8.

We shall revisit Corollary 3.10 as Theorem 3.22 in Section 3.4.4 on formal languages.

CHECKPOINT 3.14 Corollary 3.10 is a somewhat non-constructive proof that ALGOL 60 programs (say) are enumerable. How would you set about giving a constructive enumeration of them?

CHECKPOINT 3.15 Do you think that the set of meaningful English sentences is enumerable?

COROLLARY 3.11 The set of enumerable sets is enumerable!

Proof. Suppose that tmenum $: N \rightarrow TM$ is an enumeration of Turing machines. Denote the Turing machine tmenum(n) by M_n. and suppose that M_n computes the function:

$$f_n : N^{r_n} \rightarrow N$$

Define the subset R_n of N to be the range of f_n, that is:

$$R_n = \{m | m = f_n(x_1, \ldots, x_{r_n}), \text{ each } x_i \in N\}$$

Since each f_n is computable and onto R_n, each R_n is by definition enumerable. Moreover, if S is an enumerable set, then there is a computable onto function $f : N \rightarrow S$. By Turing's thesis there is a TM M that computes f. Since tmenum is an enumeration of TM, for some k we have:

$$M = \text{tmenum}(k) = M_k$$

and so $S = R_k$. It follows that the function defined by:

$$\text{enumenum}(n) = R_n$$

enumerates the enumerable sets.

Up to now, our discussion of enumerability has largely consisted of a number of techinques for constructing enumerations. The reader may have noticed that many of the sets which typically would be used to exemplify countability turn out to be enumerable also. In fact, that is hardly surprising! For, as the name 'countable' suggests, we naturally try to demonstrate that a set is countable by exhibiting a *counting process*, that is to say, an enumeration. Indeed it may have occurred to the reader that enumerability and countability are the same concept, and that not only does enumerable imply countable but, conversely, countable implies enumerable. The following theorem shows that this conjecture is false (see Corollary 3.13); its proof is (yet again) by *reductio ad absurdum* and Cantor's diagonal argument.

THEOREM 3.12 The set C_{total} of total computable functions is *not* enumerable.

Proof. Recall that a function is total if it is defined for all arguments in it domain. We shall suppose, contrary to the statement of the theorem, that C_{total} *is* enumerable; that is, we suppose that there is a computable onto function:

$$enum : N \rightarrow C_{total}$$

For each number i, we denote enum (i) by f_i, to emphasize that f_i belongs to the set of total functions C_{total}. Now, inspired by Cantor's uncountability argument, we define a function:

$$nasty : N \rightarrow N$$

as follows:

$$nasty(i) = f_i(i) + 1$$

Since each f_i is total, $f_i(i)$ is defined for all i; hence nasty is a total function. Moreover, nasty is computable since computing any instance nasty (i) merely involves computing $f_i(i)$ and then adding 1, and each f_i is computable. Consequently nasty belongs to C_{total}. But, since enum is an *onto* function, there must be some j such that nasty = enum (j). To be equal, nasty and enum (j) must agree on all arguments; in particular they must agree on j. However:

$$
\begin{aligned}
nasty(j) &= f_j(j) + 1 &&//\text{defn of nasty} \\
&\neq f_j(j) \\
&= enum(j)(j) &&//\text{defn of } f_j
\end{aligned}
$$

This contradiction establishes the theorem.

COROLLARY 3.13 (a) C_{total} is a countable non-enumerable set. (b) If R is a subset of S, and S is enumerable, then it *does not follow* that R is enumerable (cf. Lemma A6 of Appendix A).

Proof. (a) Theorem 3.12 and Lemma A6 of Appendix A. (b) The case $R = C_{total}$, $S = C$ (the set of computable functions) provides a counter-example.

Part (b) of Corollary 3.13 provides the starting point for the discussion of decidability that follows below. We shall see in Theorem 3.16 that it is not enough to insist that R is a subset of S; rather we have to give a *process* that details the way in which R is a subset of S.

The proof of Theorem 3.12 does not have an entirely negative character, as the following corollary shows:

COROLLARY 3.14 Suppose that enum is any enumeration of some subset S of the total computable functions C_{total} (by Theorem 3.12, S cannot be the whole of C_{total}. Then there is an effective process for generating a total computable function that does not belong to S.

Proof. Define the function nasty as in the proof of Theorem 3.11 (except it would be more in the spirit of the corollary to call it "inventive"!).

The inventive or creative nature of proofs such as those of Theorem 3.12 and the unsolvability of the Halting problem (Theorem 3.1) form the basis of the study of productive sets. The interested reader should consult Arbib (1969, p. 158ff) and Rogers (1967 or 1959).

3.3.2 Decidability

In this sub-section we refine the notion of subset to that of decidable subset (often called recursive set) by incorporating computability; as a result we will be able to make precise questions such as "Is the set of legal ALGOL 60 programs a decidable subset of the set of strings of characters from the ALGOL 60 character set?". More generally, if S is a subset of T and t is an element of T, we ask if it is possible to decide mechanically (effectively) whether or not t is a member of S. In order to frame the definition of decidability, we need to look for a function f associated with S *qua* subset of T; given such an f we can define S to be decidable in the case that f is computable. Of course, there *is* such a function f, namely the characteristic function:

$$k_S : T \to \{0, 1\}$$

defined by:

$$k_S(t) = \begin{cases} 0 & t \notin S \\ 1 & t \in S \end{cases}$$

Accordingly, we say that S *is decidable relative to* T if the characteristic function k_S is computable.

CHECKPOINT 3.16 Decision processes are usually programmed as logical or boolean procedures. Design such decision processes in the case that T is N and S is: (a) the set of even numbers; (b) the set of odd numbers; (c) the set of prime numbers.

CHECKPOINT 3.17 Relate the notion of decidable to those of problem and solvability introduced in Section 3.1.

CHECKPOINT 3.18 Is the set of English words a decidable subset of the set of strings of English letters? (Hint: how do you *define* an English word?)

CHECKPOINT 3.19 Is the set of legal ALGOL 60 programs a decidable subset of the set of strings of ALGOL 60 characters? What role do such decision procedures play in computer science?

CHECKPOINT 3.20 Is the set C_{total} of total computable functions decidable relative to the set C of all computable functions?

CHECKPOINT 3.21 Do you think that the set of meaningful English sentences is decidable relative to the set of strings of English words?

CHECKPOINT 3.22 Is the set of integers decidable relative to the set of rationals?

Our first two theorems establish a relationship between enumerability and decidability.

THEOREM 3.15 Let S be a subset of T. If S and $(T - S)$ are enumerable, then S and $(T - S)$ are decidable relative to T.

Proof. Suppose that $f : N \to S$ enumerates S and $g : N \to (T - S)$ enumerates $(T - S)$. Consider the following program:

decide$(t) = $ **valof** \$(**let** $i = 0$

$\quad\quad\quad\quad\quad$ \$(R **if** $f(i) = t$ **then resultis** 1

$\quad\quad\quad\quad\quad\quad$ **if** $g(i) = t$ **then resultis** 0

$\quad\quad\quad\quad\quad\quad$ $i := i + 1$

$\quad\quad\quad\quad$ \$)R **repeat**

$\quad\quad$ \$)

We claim that decide computes the characteristic function of S and is therefore a decision procedure for S. To see this, observe that, if t is any element of T, then t either belongs to S or to $(T - S)$, but not both. If t belongs to S, then for some $k, f(k) = t$ [and for no l is it the case that $g(l) = t$]; conversely if t belongs to $(T - S)$ then for some $l, g(l) = t$. Hence after a finite number of steps the computation of decide(t) will terminate with the correct answer.

The proof of the decidability of $(T - S)$ is very similar; swap f and g.

CHECKPOINT 3.23 The program given in the proof of the above theorem works perfectly generally for any sets S and T. As a result it is often very inefficient in any individual case. To see this, consider the application of the theorem in the case $T = N, S = $ the even numbers (with f and g the 'natural' enumerations). Compare the resulting procedure with those you gave in Checkpoint 3.16.

The next theorem is a partial converse to the one just given; notice that we must insist additionally that T is enumerable.

THEOREM 3.16 Suppose S is a subset of T and that T is enumerable. If S is decidable relative to T then S and $(T - S)$ are enumerable.

Proof. Suppose that tenum $: N \rightarrow T$ enumerates T. In order to construct an enumeration senum $: N \rightarrow S$ of S, we merely list the elements of T, using tenum, successively ticking off those that (according to the computable function k_S) belong to S:

tenum:	t_0	t_1	t_2	t_3	t_4	t_5	$\cdots$
$k_S(t_i)$:	0	1	0	0	1	1	$\cdots$
senum:	$-$	s_0	$-$	$-$	s_1	s_2	$\cdots$

More precisely, we define:

senum(n) = **valof** \$(**let** tindex = 0

           let sindex = 0

           until sindex $> n$ **do**

               \$(U

                    if k_S(tenum(tindex)) = 1

                        then sindex := sindex + 1;

                    tindex := tindex + 1

               \$)U

           resultis tenum(tindex $-$ 1)

     \$)

CHECKPOINT 3.24 Show by counter-example that the condition that T be enumerable cannot be dropped.

COROLLARY 3.17 C_{total} is *not* decidable relative to the set C of all computable functions (which answers Checkpoint 3.20).

Proof. Theorems 3.12 and 3.16.

Suppose that S is a subset of T and that S is enumerable; say $f : N \rightarrow S$ enumerates S. Since it may well be the case that the complement $(T - S)$ of S in T is *not* enumerable, we cannot appeal to Theorems 3.15 and 3.16 and conclude that S is decidable in T. There is however a kind of 'half measure' for deciding S in T; consider the program:

$\text{semidec}(t) = \textbf{valof } \$(\textbf{ let } n = 0$

$\qquad\qquad \$(\textbf{ if } f(n) = t \textbf{ then resultis } 1$

$\qquad\qquad\quad n := n + 1$

$\qquad\qquad \$) \textbf{ repeat}$

$\qquad \$)$

This program will terminate precisely in the case that t is in fact a member of S. For this reason semidec is called a 'semi-decision' process and 'semi-decidable' is a frequently used synonym for 'enumerable'. We shall use the term semi-decidable in Section 3.4.3.

CHECKPOINT 3.25 Show that the Halting problem is semi-decidable.

We closed the preceding subsection with the theorem that asserted that enumerability was a stronger or more restrictive condition than countability. We close this subsection with an analogous result which asserts that decidability is genuinely stronger than enumerability. The proof is not easy to grasp; indeed it brings to bear most of the techniques we have assembled so far in the whole of this chapter. As a matter of fact, the result we about to present is an abstract form of one of the most celebrated (and misunderstood!) theorems of the whole of (meta)mathematics, Gödel's incompleteness theorem. We have decided that it would take too long and would be too tangential to the aims of a primer in the theory of computer science to detour at this point to prove Gödel's theorem. However, we do urge those readers whose imagination has in any way been caught by this material to study Arbib's (1969, pp. 156–160) superbly lucid account of the imcompleteness result and Myhill's *effective procedure* for overcoming the limitations that it alleges.

THEOREM 3.18 There is an enumerable, but undecidable, subset of N.

Proof. We begin by recalling Theorem 3.8 and Corollary 3.11. Theorem 3.8 proves that there is an enumeration, say tmenum : $N \to TM$, of Turing machines; let us denote tmenum(k) by M_k and suppose that M_k computes the function $f_k : N^{dk} \to N$. Corollary 3.11 uses the ranges of the functions f_k to define the (enumerable) sets R_k. Now, with a wary eye on the Russell argument (see Appendix A, p. 266, or the proof of Theorem 3.1), we define:

$$R = \{k \mid k \in R_k\}$$

We shall prove that R is undecidable relative to N but that R is enumerable.

(a) *R is undecidable relative to N*
Suppose, to the contrary, that R is decidable. Since N is enumerable, the conditions of Theorem 3.16 are satisfied, and so $(N - R)$ is enumerable. But we have an enumeration $R_0, R_1, \ldots$ of the enumerable sets, and so it must be the case that:

$$(N - R) = R_l$$

for some number l. Now l belongs either to R or to $(N - R)$, but not both. However:

$l \in R$ iff $l \in R_l$ //definition of R

iff $l \in (N - R)$ //since $(N - R) = R_l$

This contradiction establishes that R is undecidable relative to N.

(b) R is enumerable

We want to show how to construct a computable onto function enum : $N \to R$. By definition we have:

$$r \in R \text{ iff } r \in R_r \text{ iff for some } x, f_r(x) = r$$

$$\text{where } x \in N^{d_r}$$

The idea behind our construction of enum is simple; the details are very messy. Essentially we construct a 'subroutine' which explodes the argument n of enum into a pair (r, x), with x in N^{d_r}. Given such a subroutine we can define enum as follows:

enum$(n) = $ **valof** $\$($ **let** $\langle r, x \rangle = $ explode(n)

test $f_r(x) = r$ **then resultis** r

or resultis r_0

//r_0 is some fixed element of R

$\$)$

Apart from the details of explode, and its inverse, it is straightforward to show that for all n enum(n) belongs to R, and that for all r in R there is an n such that enum$(n) = r$.

To construct explode, we recall from Checkpoint 3.9 that the product set N^d is enumerable for any finite d; suppose that prod$_d : N \to N^d$ is an enumeration. We can now define:

explode$(n) = $ **valof** $\$($ **let** $\langle r, s \rangle = $ Cantorenum(n)

//see Theorem 3.5

resultis $\langle r, \text{prod}_{d_r}(s) \rangle$

$\$)$

CHECKPOINT 3.26 What set does explode enumerate? Show that there is a computable inverse (fizzle?) of explode in the same way that countingposition is inverse to Cantorenum in Theorem 3.5. Use this inverse to prove that, in the above example, enum is onto.

There is in fact an alternative development of Theorem 3.18 based on the existence of an enumerable set whose complement is 'productive'. For a gentle introduction to the method see Rogers (1959).

3.4 A survey of unsolvability results

In this section we survey some well-known solvability and unsolvability results, with particular emphasis on the recent work of Luckham, Park, and Paterson (1970) on program schmas (Section 3.4.3), and the study of formal languages (Section 3.4.4). We recall (see Section 3.1) that our primary reson for presenting such a survey is to give the reader an intuitive 'feel' for what is *not* computable, analogous to what we imagine to be his already extensive intuition regarding what is. Our secondary aims are to give the reader some indication of the scope of meta computer science and the richness of its connections with the rest of mathematics; thus in Section 3.4.1 we point the way into the literature of recursive function theory (which is what meta computer science is usually called) and in Section 3.4.2 we mention some results that answer problems, posed outside computer science, in mathematics and logic.

3.4.1 *Recursive function theory*

Recursive function theory is the branch of mathematics that has grown up around the notion of computability; it considers various attempts to frame definitions of computable, and attempts to build on the basic results of Sections 3.2 and 3.3. Despite its youth, it is already an extensive and beautiful theory whose long-term relevance for computer science is (the author believes) far greater than many of today's computer scientists seem prepared to admit.

Remember that the most compelling argument in support of Turing's thesis was based on a consensus view: there have been many approaches to defining computable; all of them turn out to be equivalent to Turing's formulation. The reader could profitably study any of these approaches, and consider its implications for computer science. For the moment we will briefly mention two such, both of which are mentioned again later in the book.

(a) Emil Post's point of departure was that mathematics could be viewed as a process of symbol manipulation; a theorem, notwithstanding any *interpretation* it may be given, is in the final analysis just a string of symbols. Accordingly he developed 'canonical systems' which allowed for the replacement, concatenation, and matching of strings of symbols. More precisely, a canonical system has an alphabet A, a set of 'axioms', which are just fixed strings made from the characters of A, and some 'rules of inference' or 'productions' which produce new strings out of old, starting from the axiom strings. The following example of a canonical system to produce palindromes* is from Minsky (1967, p. 228):

* Recall from Checkpoint 2.18 that the palindromes cannot be recognized by a
  FSM, but can be recognized by a TM [Checkpoint 2.19(b)].

The alphabet $A = \{a, b, c\}$

The axiom strings are a, b, c, aa, bb, cc

The productions are

$\$ \rightarrow a\$a$ //$\$$ is a variable

$\$ \rightarrow b\$b$ //which can be matched

$\$ \rightarrow c\$c$ //to any string of the set

Post's work laid the mathematical foundations for Chomsky's (1956) approach to natural language, as well as the extensive work within computer science on formal languages and their acceptor machines, for which see Section 3.4.4. His work foreshadowed many of the later developments to be found in string processing and pattern matching languages such as SNOBOL (Farber, Griswold, and Polonsky, 1964) and PLANNER (Hewitt, 1969). Sieckmann (1975) extensively explores pattern matching algorithms, as well as their limitations, which, largely, their inventors are seemingly unaware of.

Highly recommended reading: Minsky (1967, Chapters 12 and 13) is a 'must' for any computer science student.

(b) The earliest formulation of what we now accept as 'computable' was given by Alonzo Church (1936). He introduced the λ-calculus, a system that, as we shall explain in much greater detail in Chapter 6 and Section 8.2, provides a uniform way of naming computable functions. Since computer programs also name computable functions, it is no surprise to find several programming languages, notably LISP (McCarthy *et al.*, 1962), POP-2 (Burstall, Collins, and Popplestone, 1971), PAL (Evans, 1968), GEDANKEN (Reynolds, 1971), and ALGOL 68 (van Wijngaarden *et al.*, 1969), basing their approach to procedures on it. In the λ-calculus we write $\lambda x \cdot B$ for what in ALGOL 68 (say) might be written:[*]

proc fplist ; body

where fplist is the formal parameter (or dummy variable) list, and body is the procedure or routine body. Consequently one of the rules of the λ-calculus is that bound variable (as x is called) may be renamed, so long as no free occurrence within the body is thereby made a bound occurrence. That is:

$\lambda x \cdot x + y$ can be renamed $\lambda z \cdot z + y$

but not $\lambda y \cdot y + y$

The application of a procedure to an actual argument list consist of binding the actuals to the formals and then evaluating the body. Thus in the λ-calculus, an expression:

[*] For other correspondences between the λ-calculus and programming, see Chapter 8.

$\{\lambda x \cdot B\} A$

can be 'reduced' to B with A substituted for x. The alert reader will have noticed a problem: is the *value* of A or the *expression A* substituted for x in B? Both are allowed in ALGOL 60 under the headings 'call by value', 'call by name'. In fact, as a formal system, the value of a λ-expression is a piece of text, and equivalent λ-expression. Orders of evaluations roughly corresponding to call by value and call by name are described in Section 8.1. Some λ expressions such as $\lambda x \cdot x + 1$ cannot be reduced any further, and are said to be in *reduced* or *normal form*. λ-expressions such as $\{\lambda x \cdot x + y\}2$ are not in normal form but can be made so, in this case to give $y + 2$, by carrying out appropriate reductions. There are however some λ-expressions, such as $\{\lambda x \cdot x(x)\}\lambda x \cdot x(x)$ which are neither in normal form nor can be made so by renaming and reductions; we might think of such expressions as giving ruse to non-terminating computations. Not surprisingly, the set of λ-expressions that can be reduced to normal form is an undecidable subset of the set of all λ-expressions. The basic result of the λ-calculus is the Church–Rosser theorem (see Section 8.2) which states that all the normal forms (if any) of a λ-expression are equivalent up to renaming bound variables. The λ-calculus has been used as the basis for several approaches to the problem of providing a precise semantics for programming language constructs, see Chapter 8.

Recommended reading: Wegner (1968, Section 3.5).

In Sections 3.2 and 3.3 we presented several sovability and unsolvability results, and introduced the notions of enumerability and decidability. There is in fact a very extensive theory built upon the foundations of those two selections. The reader is highly recommended to read the survey by Hartley J. Rogers (1959), in particular his discussion of productive sets, recursive invariance, and isomorphism.

3.4.2 *Computability results in mathematics and logic*

We referred in Chapter 1 to Hilbert's lecture in 1900 in which he posed a number of mathematical and logical problems in terms of the possible existence of effective procedures. The notion of computability and the search for an algorithm has correspondingly appeared in many branches of mathematics; in this sub-section we briefly mention three instances.

(a) *Number theory*
One of Hilbert's problems, the tenth, asks whether it is possible to devise a program to decide whether or not an arbitrary polynomial in a finite number of variables with integer coefficients has integer roots. In 1971, Yuri Matyasevich showed that the tenth problem is unsolvable. (It is important not to confuse the notion of solvability here with that of finding the roots of equations, otherwise known as solving by radicals, in algebra.)

Recommended reading: Davis and Hersh (1973).

In view of the above, an obvious question to ask is which real numbers are computable, that is, generable by a program. There are various ways to refine the notion of real number by incorporating computability,[*] but perhaps the most straightforward for our purposes is the following: in Appendix A, p. 263, we observe that real numbers are (possibly infinite) decimals of the form:

$$r = n \cdot d_1 d_2 \dots$$

where n is some integer and the d_i's are digits in the range 0 to 9. Since we can compute any integer n, one way to compute r is to compute $0 \cdot d_1 d_2 \dots$ and then to add n. In this way we can reduce our definitional problem to considering real numbers in the range $[0, 1]$. Again, in Appendix A, we set up a bijection between such reals and functions of the form $(N \to N)$ whose values for any k lie in the range 0 to 9, namely:

$$r = 0 \cdot d_1 d_2 d_3 \dots \Leftrightarrow f_r : N \to N \text{ where}$$
$$f_r(k) = d_k$$

We now say that r is computable if f_r is computable. Since there are only countably many computable functions, there are only countably many computable reals; since each f_r is total on N (why is it?), the countable reals are not enumerable (Theorem 3.12). The rationals are computable; so are π, e, and all algebraic numbers. Naturally, if x and y are computable reals, so are $x + y$, $x * y$.

CHECKPOINT 3.27 Show that $\sin x$ and e^x are computable reals, where x is a computable real.

Recommended reading: Hartley J. Rogers (1967).

(b) *Algebra – groups*

Numbers have many aspects; one of the most important is that there are operations, such as addition, definable on them which enjoy properties such as associativity [that is, for all x, y, and z, $(x + y) + z = x + (y + z)$] and having an identity element 0 (so that $x + 0 = x$ for all x). Algebra essentially derives from abstracting some selection of these properties and applying the results thus obtained to other situations. For example, groups consist of a set G and a single associative binary operation, which we write as juxtaposition, such that:

(i) There is a group identity e. That is for all g in G:

$$ge = eg = g$$

(ii) Every element g in G has a unique inverse (written g^{-1}) such that:

$$gg^{-1} = e = g^{-1}g$$

---

[*] (See Sections 3.2) The usual way is to incorporate computability at each stage of the development of the reals from the rationals, which is normally done by Cauchy's method of sequences. See Hermes (1965, Chapter 7).

An element g is said to have exponent n if $g^n = e$ but for no m, $0 < m < n$, is it the case that $g^m = e$. Clearly if g has exponent n, $g^{n-1} = g^{-1}$. Group theory has been applied to nuclear physics, crystallography, permutations, and, via Galois theory, to the solvability by radicals of equations such as quintics. One way of presenting a group is by giving a set of generating elements for the group and by listing the additional relations which hold between the generations. Fro example:

$$G = \langle a, b | a^2 = b^3 = e \rangle$$

denotes a group whose generators a and b have exponents 2 and 3 respectively. The elements of G are strings such as:

$$g = abaababaabbaba$$

By applying the group relations, it can be seen that g is in fact collapsible to the group identity e. Thus we can define the set $E(G) = \{g \in G* | g$ is collapsible to $e\}$. The *word problem* for groups asks whether $E(G)$ is a decidable subset of $G*$ for all finitely-presented groups G; that is, it asks whether there is a general process (that works for all groups) that can decide whether an arbitrary string is just a circumlocutious way of writing e. In 1955, W.W. Boone and P.S. Novikov (independently) showed that the word problem is undecidable. There is a corresponding word problem in all algebraic systems such as semigroups and rings; it would take us too far afield to describe the state of the word problem in each.

Recommended reading: J.J. Rotman (1965)

(c) *Logic*

Logical systems specify a set of legal strings of symbols called well-formed formulae (wffs), which, when appropriately interpreted, become statements which are true or false. Some wffs are designated as *axioms* and serve with rules of inference as the basis for the discovery of *theorems*. Each theorem has a *Proof*, which is a sequence of axioms and theorems constituting the steps of the proof. In such a proof sequence each theorem is the result of applying a rule of inference to some previous elements of the sequence. Thus to any logical system there is a *decision problem*: is the set of theorems a decidable subset of the set of wffs? In the case that the decision problem for the logical system is solvable it is possible (in principle) to discover theorems by submitting wffs in turn to the deciding mechanism and letting it pronounce "yes" or "no".

There are many logical systems that variously attempt to formalize notions such as mathematical proof, or common sense reasoning about time or possibility. Three logics have been especially important in the development of mathematical logic: the propositional calculus, and the first-order and second-order predicate calculi. In each case, wffs are constructed out of symbols, some of which have a standard, or intended, interpretation: thus "$\wedge$" is to be interpreted as "and". "$\supset$" as "implies". We shall call such symbols 'fixed symbols'. The other wff symbols, typically variable names such as x, are to be *given* one of many possible interpretations (see also Section 3.4.3). Under any interpretation,

a given wff w may be a true or false assertion. If w yields a true assertion under
every allowable interpretation, it is said to be *valid*.

In each of the logical systems we consider, theorems are valid wffs; the *completeness problem* for the logic asks whether every valid wff is a theorem. That
is, it essentially asks whether every identically true statement that can be expressed *within* the system can also be *proved within* the system. This is clearly a
desirable property for any logical system to have! We shall now briefly detail the
propositional and predicate calculi, and consider their decision and completeness
problems.

The *propositional calculus*, the 'logic' referred to in computer hardware, only
allows wffs that (apart from the fixed symbols) have simple variable names, say,
p, q, and r. For example in the wff:

$$((p \wedge q) \vee r) \supset (p \vee r)$$

one might interpret p as "the voltage on wire one is ten volts". The decision
problem is solvable, by truth tables or Karnaugh maps. The propositional calculus is complete.

The *predicate calculus*, as its name suggests, allows one to name not only individuals but properties or predicates of variables. We denote simple variables by
lower-case letters, predicates by upper-case letters. Given a predicate $M(x)$ one
naturally wishes to ask whether it is true *for all* elements x or (at least) if *there
exists* some x for which it is true. Consequently the predicate calculus allows
quantification: fixed symbols $\forall$ and $\exists$, so that "$\forall x$" is intended to mean 'for
all x", and "$\exists x$" is intended to mean "there exists x".

The *first-order predicate calculus* restricts the application of quantifiers to
simple variables, so that:

$$(\forall x)(M(x) \supset H(x))$$

(which might be interpreted as meaning every *M*an is *H*uman) is a legal wff,
whereas the following statement of the principle of mathematical induction is
not:

$$(\forall P)((P(0) \wedge (\forall n)(P(n) \supset P(n + 1))) \supset (\forall n)P(n))$$

The latter wff is legal in the *second-order predicate calculus* which differs from
the first only in that quantification over predicate names is allowed.

It turns out that the first-order predicate calculus (and hence the second-order
also) is undecidable, a result first proved by Church (1936) in his original paper
on computability. The Entscheidungsproblem referred to in the title of Turing's
(1936) paper is essentially Hilbert's formulation of the decision problem for the
first-order predicate claculus.

The first-order predicate calculus is complete, a result first proved by Kurt
Gödel in 1930. Perhaps the most accessible proof of this result is by Leon
Henkin (reproduced in Hintikka, 1969). However, the second-order predicate

calculus is *incomplete*, a result also proved by Gödel (1931) (reproduced, in English, in von Heijenoort's 1967 anthology). This latter result has really fired the imaginations of mathematicians since it says that any sufficiently expressive formal logical system (such as the second-order predicate calculus) is either inconsistent, in the sense that both a statement *and* its negation can be proved as theorems, or else is incomplete, that is, permits the *expression* of valid expressions that cannot be proved with the system. Much has been written on the possible implications of this result regarding the existence of a theoretical limitation on the power of language as a means of communication between men (or between men and machines) and on the possibilities for an artificial or mechanized intelligence. In the latter connection, the great logician Georg Kreisel, for example, has argued in this way against artificial intelligence. Against him are ranged such notables as Turing (1950) and Minsky (1963). One such argument against Kreisel is that Gödel's result does not work against artificial intelligence so much as point up the weaknesses in the axiomatic approach to mathematics advocated so vehemently by David Hilbert (see van Heijenoort, 1967). It may be that there is a different formulation of language in which 'consistency' for example is not such a major issue. The essays in Schank and Colby (1973) seem to point to such computational formulations.

Recommended reading: E. Mendelson (1964); E. Nagel and J.R. Newman (1956); D.C Cooper (1966); B. Elspas *et al.* (1972).

3.4.3 *Program schemas: the work of Luckham, Park, and Paterson*

The basic problem to which Paterson (1968) and Luckham, Park, and Paterson (1970) (from now on collectively referred to as LPP) address themselves is the *equivalence problem*. Imagine that we have a program that, although it successfully solves some problem, does so unsatisfactorily. For example, it might need excessive time and/or storage or be poorly structured and difficult to follow or debug. In such circumstances we would like to replace the program by a more acceptable version that we could be certain did exactly the same job as the original. Further below, as part of a definition of equivalence, we shall make the phrase "did exactly the same job" more precise; for the moment however we continue with our general introduction.

Programs may be deemed unacceptable for a wide variety of reasons; the above list gives only a sample. Most such reasons derive from the fact that the underlying process leaves a lot to be desired, which in turn usually reflects the programmer's poor understanding of his problem or his machine. But there are also some general criticisms that can be levelled against a program fragment and that are essentially independent of the particular problem or indeed the particular programming language. For example, consider the following flowchart:

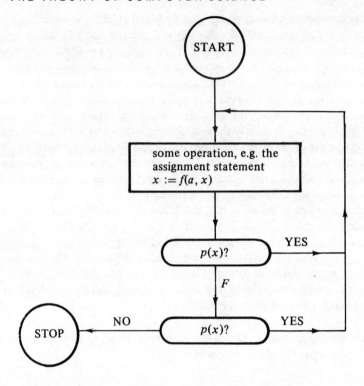

It should be obvious that, so long as successive evaluations of the test $p(x)$ always yield the same result [which may not be the case of course since $p(x)$ might be a logical procedure that side-effects some crucial variables], the second test can be completely cut-out, and the flow chart simplified to:

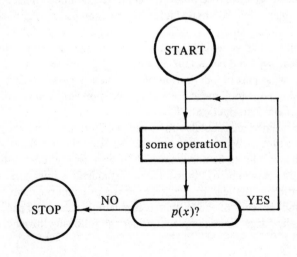

Observe that this improvement can be made without knowing precisely which p, x, or operation is involved; all we need to know are the rudiments of control at test boxes and the meaning of (say) assignment statements. To re-emphasize the point, specifying p, x and the operation determine one particular execution sequence; we are making a general statement about all of the execution sequences that the fragment might possibly give rise to. The information we have about the program is very similar to that which a compiler has; to emphasize the point, we do not call the objects of our study programs, rather we call them 'compile-time programs' or 'program schemas'. We will usually abbreviate this to 'schemas'.

LPP derived some general results about schemas and related them to other topics in computer science such as compiler optimization and (multi-head) automata. They observe that the equivalence problem is closely related to the problem of simplifying a schema; methods for demonstrating equivalence suggest ways of simplifying schemas and vice versa. Moreover, many of the steps in a proof of equivalence or similification are essentially algorithmic, so one might look for an exhaustive simplification process that would convert a general schema P into a standard (or canonical) 'simplest' equivalent form $P_{optimal}$. We shall discuss this further below; as an example, Paterson (1968) proves that the following schema P can be proved equivalent to, and therefore simplified to, schema Q (see diagram overleaf).

CHECKPOINT 3.28 (difficult) Construct an informal argument that P is equivalent to Q. (Hint: what happens if one of the tests takes on some value, say true, in one passage through a particular loop? Do any variables have the same value?)

LPP restricted themselves to considering schemas in which the operations are assignment statements of one of the forms:

$$L_i := c, L_i := L_j, L_i := f(L_{i_1}, \ldots, L_{i_n})$$

and tests are all of the form:

$$p(L_{i_1}, \ldots, L_{i_k})$$

in which the L_i are *program variables* or *locations*, and c is a constant. They further assumed that successive evaluations of the functions $f(L_{i_1}, \ldots, L_{i_n})$ and $p(L_{i_1}, \ldots, L_{i_k})$ with the same set of arguments always give the same result; that is, they assumed the referential transparency of mathematics and did not consider side-effects. It is possible to give a precise account of the syntax of schemas in the same way that programs can be syntactically correct or logical formulae can be well-formed. For example, one might define a schema to be a directed vertex-labelled graph with precisely one vertex of each of the forms:

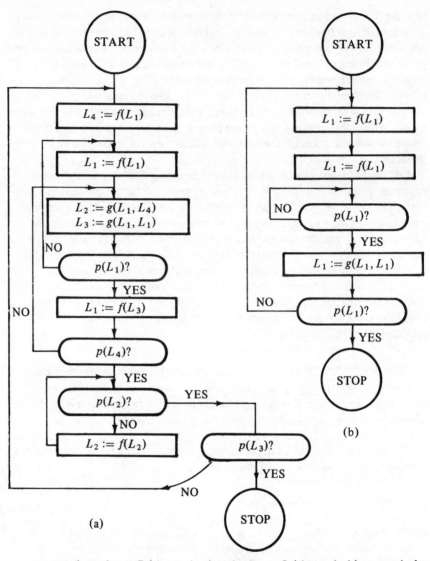

(a)

(b)

prove that schema P (shown in a) and schema Q (shown in b) are equivalent

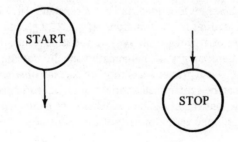

such that every other vertex has one of the forms:

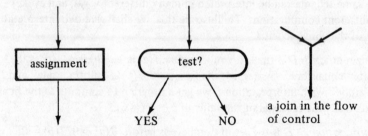

assignment test?

YES NO

a join in the flow of control

For example, the following graph is a schema:

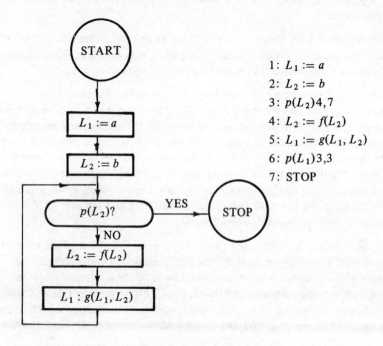

START

$L_1 := a$

$L_2 := b$

$p(L_2)?$ ——YES——→ STOP

NO

$L_2 := f(L_2)$

$L_1 : g(L_1, L_2)$

1: $L_1 := a$
2: $L_2 := b$
3: $p(L_2)4,7$
4: $L_2 := f(L_2)$
5: $L_1 := g(L_1, L_2)$
6: $p(L_1)3,3$
7: STOP

An alternative representation of schemas, based on viewing programs as pieces of text, each line of text being a labelled command, is given alongside. Notice that command 6 has the effect of an unconditional transfer of control, and is represented in the graph by the joining of two arrows.

If the symbols a, b, f, and p in the above schema are given a specific interpretation, the schema becomes a program with a fixed execution sequence. More precisely, an interpretation I of schema P is defined in terms of a set or domain D and has the following properties

(i) For all constants or location values $x, I(x) \in D$.
(ii) For all n-place function names $f, I(f) : D^n \to D$.
(iii) For all n-place test letters $p, I(p) : D^n \to \{\text{true, false}\}$.

If the domain D is finite, we say that I is a *finite interpretation*.

The same schema can be interpreted in many different ways, and evokes many different computations. To illustrate this, we shall give two interpretations I and J of the above schema.

Interpretation I D is the set N of numbers, $I(a)$ is $1, I(b)$ is $4, I(p)$ is the predicate "equals one". As regards the functions, $I(f)$ is "subtract one" and $I(g)$ is "multiply". With interpretation I, we get a program to compute as the final contents of L_1 the factorial of the value of $b - 1$ ($= 6$).

Interpretation J. D is the set of numbers as before, $J(a) = 0, J(b) = 0,$ $J(p) =$ "equals 10". This time $J(f) =$ "add one" and $J(g) =$ "add"; altogether we get a program to compute as the final contents of L_1 the sum of the first ten natural numbers.

CHECKPOINT 3.29   Devise a schema P and an interpretation I such that $I(P)$ computes the greatest common divisor of a pair m, n of numbers. Construct an interpretation J such that $J(P)$ computes a different function.

Given an interpretation I of a schema p, we can define the execution sequence seq(I) evoked by I, merely by making precise the notion of conditional execution. There are two possibilities: either seq(I) is finite because the execution reaches STOP, or seq(I) is infinite; the execution sequence gets stuck in an infinite loop and never reaches STOP. In the former case we say that p *terminates* under I, in the latter case we say it *diverges*. If p terminates under I we can define a value for the computation, namely the vector of values in the locations used by the program;[*] we will denote this by val(I, p), and say that val(I, p) is undefined in the case that P diverges under I.

CHECKPOINT 3.30   This is not necessarily a good definition of the value of the execution! For example, consider the interpretations I and J given above. The value of the program is more usually taken to be the contents of L_1; the value of L_2 is generally considered irrelevant for 'output' purposes. How would you modify the definition of val(I, P) to accommodate this criticism? (Hint: see Elspas *et al.*, 1972, pp. 102–103 or Section 7.4).

We can now define what it means for two schemas P_1 and P_2 to be equivalent. Actually, LPP consider several formulations; we shall consider three of them:

DEFINITION 3.1   A schema P_1 is *(strongly-)equivalent* to a schema P_2, written $P_1 \equiv P_2$, if under every interpretation I, *either* both val(I, P_1) and val(I, P_2) are undefined, *or* both val(I, P_1) and val(I, P_2) are defined and are equal.

---

[*] Referring back to Section 2.3, we can see that this notion of value is closely related to the idea of a final state of memory of an executing mechanism. However, we only refer to *some* memory locations, so it is a kind of 'small' state as opposed to the 'whole' state.

LPP also consider a notion of *weak-equivalence*, written $P_1 \simeq P_2$, which insists that val(I, P_1) be equal to val(I, P_2) when both are defined, but admits the possibility that one might be defined and one undefined. They also define *finite-equivalence*, written $P_1 \equiv {}_F P_2$, for the case of strong equivalence restricted to all *finite* interpretations.*

There are a couple of remarks that need to be made about these definitions. Firstly, the idea of defining equivalence in terms of the value computed would be rejected by some authors as too permissive. For example, Dijkstra (1972), in his influential article on structured programming, seems to argue that two processes may only be though of as equivalent if they are essentially structured in the same way, that is, if they *work* in essentially the same way. It seems to the author that 'equivalence', just like 'meaning' (see Chapter 8) can be defined differently at different levels to reflect different purposes; it is not reasonable to insist on a single definition of equivalence. There is clearly scope for a lot of research at this point, for example by relating equivalence to meaning. Scott (1971) seems to be a step in this direction.

Secondly, there is a potential mathematical snag with the definition of equivalence as we have framed it. By now, I hope that the reader has acquired a thorough distrust of definitions that speak in cavalier fashion of "all interpretations". In fact, this is a problem with interpretations in logic as well, and was solved in 1930 by Herbrand, who showed that it was sufficient to restrict discussion to "free interpretations" over the "Herbrand base". A more thorough discussion of this point is tangential to our immediate aims of presenting a survey; the interested reader should consult Elspas *et al.* (1972, pp. 103–104) or Cooper (1966).

Before stating the main results of LPP, we need to introduce a couple of special schemas (see diagram overleaf). D is the trivial schema which diverges under all interpretations, while Z is just a sequence of two assignment commands.

THEOREM 3.19 (Luckham, Park, and Paterson, 1970, p. 233) The following properties of schemas P *are not* semi-decidable (i.e. enumerable; see p. 67):

(a) P diverges under all interpretations

(b) P diverges under all finite interpretations

(c) $P \equiv D$

(d) $P \equiv {}_F D$

(e) P diverges under some interpretations

(f) P halts under all interpretations

---

* Actually LPP even go so far as to define the notion of a 'reasonable' concept of equivalence. An equivalence relation $\approx$ is *reasonable* if: (a) $P \equiv Q$ implies $P \approx Q$; and (b) $P \approx Q$ implies $P \simeq Q$. Thus $\simeq$ is the weakest and $\equiv$ the strongest reasonable notion of equivalence. It turns out that most of the results given below hold for all such reasonable notions!!

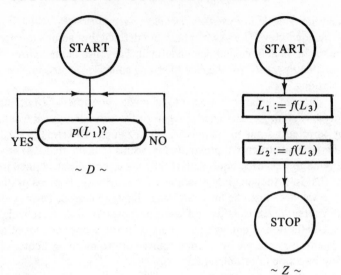

(g) $P \equiv {}_F Z$
(h) $P \not\equiv Z$
(i) $P \simeq Z$

CHECKPOINT 3.31   Relate parts (a)–(f) fof the above theorem to the Halting problem.

THEOREM 3.20 (Luckham, Park, and Paterson, 1970, p. 235)   Let Q be any schema that halts under all interpretations, and R be any schema. The following properties of schemas P are semi-decidable:
   (a) P halts under some interpretation
   (b) P halts under some finite interpretation
   (c) P halts under all interpretations
   (d) P diverges under some finite interpretation
   (e) $P \not\equiv D$
   (f) $P \not\equiv {}_F D$
   (g) $P \equiv Q$
   (h) $P \not\equiv {}_F R$
   (i) $P \not\simeq R$

We referred above to the connection between the equivalence between the equivalence problem and the simplification problem for schemas, and mentioned that LPP considered the possibility of an exhaustive simplification process for schemas: a program that would convert a general schema P into a standard "simplest" form $P_{optimal}$. More precisely, a *simplification process* is a program that, when given a schema P, generates a sequence $P_1, P_2, \ldots$ of (not necesarily distinct) schemas in which each P_i is a simplified equivalent form of P. A simplification process is *exhaustive* if for any pair P, Q of equivalent schemas the simplification process eventually generates the same simplified version of each, that is, for some $i, j, P_i = Q_j$. LPP effectively dampen all hopes of a general-purpose 'sausagemachine'' exhaustive simplification process by proving the following theorem (LPP, 1970, p. 241).

THEOREM 3.21 There is *no* exhaustive simplification process for the equivalence relations $\equiv$ and $\equiv_F$.

The theory of program schemas is by now very extensive; the interested reader should consult LPP or Elspas *et al.* (1972). We observe that the schemas discussed above relate to iterative processes, and do not cover recursive schemas such as:

$$f(x) = p(x) \rightarrow g(x), f(h(x-1))$$

We shall re-open our investigation of the equivalence problem in Chapter 6 where we discuss McCarthy's work on recursive schemas and proof by recursion induction.

3.4.4 *Formal language theory: the syntax of programming languages*

It is usual to trace the origins of formal language theory back to Post's work on canonical systems mentioned in Section 3.4.1, although as early as 1914 A. Thue was investigating rewrite rules or productions. We recall from Section 3.4.1 that Post's basic idea was that the legal constructs or theorems of a formal language are to be thought of as strings of symbols, and there are productions acting as rules of inference to enable the generation of new strings from old. In 1956, Noam Chomsky applied Post's idea to natural language with the idea of giving a more precise, mathematical account of at least a part of natural linguistics than had previously been the case. He introduced the idea of a phrase structure grammar and language and discussed the processes of generating and analysing (or parsing) sentences. In particular, he introduced a hierarchy of types of language by imposing increasingly severe restrictions on allowable productions. Chomsky's formal approach to natural linguistics excited the interest of computer linguists, especially compiler writers, since they too were concerned with precisely detailing what could be expressed and with algorithmically parsing programs as part of the compilation process.

This has led to a veritable explosion of work within computer science on formal languages, motivated by the hope of applying the results to computer languages. The first such application was to the International Algorithmic Language project, which eventually produced ALGOL 60. (We shall mention this again later.) It must be stressed that our aim in this sub-section is to introduce formal language theory only to the extent of presenting some unsolvability results and relating the work to the rest of Chapter 3; the reader who wishes to find out more about this fascinating topic should consult Hopcroft and Ullman (1969) or Gries (1971). In particular, we shall *not* discuss various important kinds of language [such as LR(k) grammars], the various ways of algorithmically parsing sentential forms, or the normal form theorems for context-free grammars.

Nowadays there is a tendency within computer science to play down the importance of formal language theory and to argue that it relates only to the syntax of programming languages, which itself is of interest in compiling techniques but not much else. Certainly, during the 1960's, when the theory was being developed, its importance was repeatedly exaggerated; but we should be careful not to over-compensate. Rather, we should recognize it for what it is, one of the very few areas in computer science in which the theory has been extensively worked out and applied to benefit practice.

Let us now work towards a definition of 'phrase structure grammar'. In programming languages and natural languages alike we can recognize two kinds of entity, namely *basic symbols* and *syntactic classes*. The syntactic classes derive from the recognition that a sentence or program has a grammatical structure, a structure that the parsing process aims to make explicit. Syntactic classes name substructures. Examples of syntactic classes in English are noun phrase and adverbial clause, whereas examples in ALGOL 60 are ⟨switch declaration⟩ and ⟨assignment statement⟩. There is one special syntactic class – the whole structure: sentence or ⟨program⟩. On the other hand, the whole point of a formal language as conceived by Post is that sentences or programs can be considered as strings of basic symbols. Examples of basic symbols in English are Fred, the, cat; whereas in ALGOL 60, **begin**, :=, *, and fred are basic symbols. The process of generating a sentence can be viewed as one of replacing the whole sentence structure by a particular configuration of substructures, replacing those substructures by other substructures, and so on, until eventually basic symbols are generated. Accordingly, alternative names for basic symbols and for syntactic classes are *terminal symbols* and *nonterminal symbols* respectively. We can now give our definition.

DEFINITION 3.2 A *(phrase structure) grammar* consists of a finite set V_T of terminal symbols, a finite set V_N of nonterminal symbols, a designated nonterminal symbol S (to represent "whole structure"), and a finite set of productions of the form:

$$v_1 ::= v_2$$

where v_1 and v_2 are strings (v_1 is non-empty, v_2 may be) in $V*$, where $V = V_T \cup V_N$ is called the vocabulary.

EXAMPLE 3.1 $V_T = \{a, b, c\}$, $V_N = \{S, X\}$. The productions are:

(i) $S ::= aX$;   (ii) $X ::= bX$;   (iii) $X ::= c$.

We note that productions (ii) and (iii) are usually presented in the shorthand form $X ::= bX|c$, where the vertical bar denotes alternation.

The idea of the production $v_1 ::= v_2$ is that, if v_1 is a substring of the sentential form produced thus far in the generation process, it can be replaced by v_2.

This leads to the idea of *derivability*, which (formally) is the reflexive and transitive closure of $::=$. That is, we can define the relation $::\Rightarrow$ as follows:

$v_1 ::\Rightarrow v_2$ if and only if either (a) v_1 is the same as v_2.

$$(b)\ v_1 ::= v_2,$$

or (c) there is some w with

$$v_1 ::= w \text{ and } w ::\Rightarrow v_2$$

Naturally, if G is a grammar, the sentences that it gives rise to are the strings of terminals that are derivable from the sentence symbol S. We denote the set of sentences by $L(G)$:

$$L(G) = \{v | v \in V_T^*, S ::\Rightarrow v\}$$

Notice that $L(G)$ is just a subset of V_T^*; this suggests the following definition of (phrase-structure) language.

DEFINITION 3.3 A *(phrase-structure) language* L in symbols X is a subset of $X*$ such that there is a (phrase-structure) grammar G with $V_T = X$ and $L(G)=L$.

CHECKPOINT 3.23 What is $L(G)$ for the grammar of Example 3.1?

CHECKPOINT 3.33 If $X = \{0, 1, \ldots, 9\}$, show that the set of natural numbers *qua* subset of $X*$, is a language.

The fact that a grammar has only a finite number of productions involving a finite vocabulary means that the generation process for sentences described above is essentially finitary; for example, at any stage in the generation of a sentence there are only finitely many choices available regarding how to continue generation. All of this is by way of motivating:

THEOREM 3.22 If G is a phrase structure grammar, $L(G)$ is enumerable.

Instead of giving a proof of Theorem 3.22, we invite the reader first to write a program to enumerate the sentences for the grammar of Example 3.1, and then to construct a proof himself.

CHECKPOINT 3.34 If the three occurrences of "finite" in the definition of phrase structure grammar G are relaxed to be "enumerable", is $L(G)$ still enumerable?

Surprisingly, with just the bare derinitions of grammar and language, we can use the concepts introduced in Section 3.2 to frame a number of questions with important practical implications:

QUESTION G1 If G is a grammar, is $L(G)$ decidable in V_T^*?

We hope that by this stage the reader is confidently predicting that the answer in general is "no", and that this undecidability result is yet another

formulation of the unsolvability of the Halting problem; on both counts he
would be right! A skeletal proof runs as follows: Grammars are equally powerful
as the apparently more general Post canonical systms, which are equally powerful as TMs. Consequently there is a one-one correspondence between languages
and the set of strings accepted as input sequences by TMs. That is, there is a one-
one correspondence between languages and the sets of inputs for which a TM
halts, which latter is undecidable by the unsolvability of the Halting problem.
We shall see in Theorem 3.23 below that in the special case that G is restricted to
be context-sensitive. Question G1 *is* decidable. Since many programming languages, especially ALGOL 60, have their syntax *in large part* specified by a
context-free (and hence context-sensitive) grammar (see below for a definition
of these terms), this implies that a parser for full ALGOL 60 can be constructed
(which fact no doubt reassures compiler writers enormously!).

QUESTION G2 Is it decidable whether $L(G)$ is empty, that is, whether G
generates *no* nontrivial sentences?

QUESTION G3 Is it decidable whether $L(G)$ is infinite?

QUESTION G4 If G_1 and G_2 are grammars, is it decidable whether $L(G_1) = L(G_2)$?

The answers to each of these questions are again, in general, "no"; for a list of
special cases see the table at the end of this section.

Consider now the grammar G of Example 3.1 and the string *abbc* in V_T^*. We
can show that *abbc* is in fact in $L(G)$ by exhibiting a derivation or parse of it
starting from S. We referred above to syntactic *structures* involving choice,
which suggests that the syntactic structure of *abbc*, and its parse, might best be
displayed in the form of a tree:

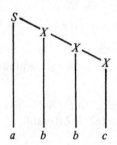

In fact, the notion of the *parse tree* has a central importance in fromal language
theory and many of the theorems of the theory are proved by considering parse
trees in some detail. Here is another grammar, allegedly generating a subclass of
arithmetical expressions:

EXAMPLE 3.2 $V_T = \{(,), *, +, a, b, c, \ldots\}$, $V_N = \{S, E, I\}$. The productions are:

$$S ::= E$$

$$E ::= E * E | E + E | (E) | I$$

$$I ::= a | b | c | \ldots$$

Consider the string $a + b * c$; it has the following two *distinct* parse trees, corresponding to different 'meanings' or 'values':

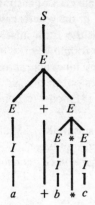 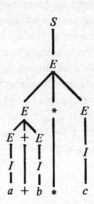

A grammar such as the one in Example 3.2 in which a single string has two different parse trees is said to be *ambiguous*. It is clearly highly undesirable for a grammar to be ambiguous since it means that the same program can be parsed in two different ways to give two different computations possibly yielding two different results! Indeed, the original ALGOL 60 grammar *was* ambiguous in several respects, notably the 'dangling **else**' in one- and two-armed conditional statements. This leads to our fifth question:

QUESTION G5 Is it decidable whether or not an arbitrary grammar G is ambiguous?

The answer in general is again "no". There is a possible way round this problem: for many ambiguous grammars G there is an unambiguous grammar G' such that $L(G) = L(G')$.

CHECKPOINT 3.35 Construct an unambiguous grammar G' generating the same strings as the grammar in Exercise 3.2. (Hint: read the relevant section of the ALGOL 60 report.)

It might be conjectured then that any language, or at any rate the important class of context-free languages, can be specified by an unambiguous grammar. The conjecture was shown by R.J. Parikh (1961) to be false by exhibiting "inherently ambiguous" context-free languages such as:

$$\{a^i b^i c^j : i, j \geq 1\} \cup \{a^i b^j c^j : i, j \geq 1\}$$

In the remainder of this subsection we introduce Chomsky's hierarchy of grammars, and describe their acceptors or recognizers. The general notion of grammar introduced in Definition 3.2 had finitely many productions of the form $v_1 ::= v_2$ where $v_i \in V*$, the only restriction being that v_1 had to be non-empty. Chomsky imposed three increasingly severe restrictions on the v_i's to define a hierarchy of languages called respectively type 1 or context sensitive, type 2 or context-free, type 3 or regular.

To each type of language there corresponds an appropriate class of abstract machines which recognize precisely languages of that type. In the general case, the abstract machine appropriate for the type-0 grammars is the Turing machine, a fact that restates Turing's thesis in the case of Chomsky's form of Post canonical systems. We shall show below that the abstract machines appropriate to languages of types 1 and 2 were not mysteriously plucked out of thin air but are related to the development of the FSM model into the TM model recounted in Chapter 2. We recall that this development had two aspects:

(i) By providing the FSM with a *separate* memory mechanism, the FSM did not have to waste its control states on remembering previous inputs.

(ii) In order to use the tape for *unlimited* memory, the tape was extended infinitely in both directions.

Type 1: Context-sensitive

A perfectly natural restriction on the v_i's (from the standpoint of linguistics) is that a production should provide for the elaboration of a syntactic class, or non-terminal symbol, in a given context. Thus productions take the form:

$$x\,A\,y ::= x\,a\,y$$

where x and y are (possibly empty) strings in $V*$, $A \in V_N$, and a is a non-empty string in $V*$. The production only allows A to be replaced by a in the context $\langle x, y \rangle$.

CHECKPOINT 3.36 Construct a grammar to prove that $\{a^n b^n c^n | n \geqslant 1\}$ is context-sensitive.

Clearly any context-sensitive grammar is also type-0 but the converse is not true, as the following theorem (and the discussion following Question G1) shows:

THEOREM 3.23 If G is context-sensitive, $L(G)$ is a decidable subset of V_T^*.

Proof (sketch) The easiest way to prove the theorem is via an alternative characterization of context-sensitive grammars. It turns out (see Arbib, 1969, p. 174) that a grammar is context-sensitive iff every production $v_1 ::= v_2$ has the property that $\text{length}(v_1) \leqslant \text{length}(v_2)$. Now suppose $v \in V_T^*$ is an arbitrary string, say of length l. Since each parsing step decreases the length of the resulting sentential form, there are only a finite number of such possible reductions applicable at each stage. Since l is finite, this reduction process can only be carried out finitely often. Thus in a finite number of steps it can be decided whether or not v can be reduced to S.

It turns out that the converse to Theorem 3.23 is false:

THEOREM 3.24   There are decidable subsets L of V_T^* which are *not* context-sensitive languages.

Proof. Let $G_1, G_2, \ldots$ be an enumeration of context-sensitive grammars, and let $x_1, x_2, \ldots$ be an enumeration of V_T^*. Define the subset L of V_T^* by:

$$x_i \in L \text{ Iff } x_i \notin L(G_i)$$

The reader should complete the proof for himself.

CHECKPOINT 3.37   Prove that L is decidable in V_T^* but that $L \neq L(G_i)$ for any i.

It is fairly obvious to see how to design a (not very efficient) recognizer for context-sensitive languages; using the characterization given in the proof of Theorem 3.23, the input string is the longest string that need be considered. Thus one might suspect that a TM restricted to work on the finite initially marked portion of tape would suffice; it does, and is called a *linear bounded automaton* (see Hopcroft and Ullman, 1969, Chapter 8).

Type 2: Context-free
As its name implies, a grammar is *context-free* if a syntactic class can be elaborated independent of the context. That is, productions have the form:

$$A ::= a$$

where $A \in V_N$ and a is a non-empty string in $V*$. Clearly any context-free grammar is also context-sensitive; but the converse is false: it can be shown that the context-sensitive language $\{a^n b^n c^n | n \geqslant 1\}$ given in Checkpoint 3.36 is *not* context-free.

CHECKPOINT 3.38   Show that the language $\{a^n b^n | n \geqslant 1\}$ is context-free.

Context-free languages are extremely attractive to computer linguistics; they have a very simple structure for describing the generation of programs, and since they are context-sensitive, Theorem 3.23 shows that they are decidable, that is, mechanically parse-able. However, context-free languages are a genuine subset of all type-0 languages, and by Turing's thesis the power to generate all languages is needed to name all computable functions. The solution adopted in practice is to give a context-free grammar supplemented with semantic rules, usually written in English. For example, as Floyd (1962) points out, the following *is* legal ALGOL 60:

begin integer x ; $x := 3$ **end**

while the following *is not*:

Begin integer x ; $y := 3$ **end**

despite the fact that they have the same grammatical structure. The point is that the grammar provides no mechanism for recognizing the use of the same name twice in different contexts within a program. See also Foster (1966, p. 93). Interestingly, the idea of supplementing the syntactic structures with semantic information has also been forced on Chomsky in his natural lingistics. A fuller discussion of this point is beyond the scope of this book; instead the reader is referred to Lyons (1970) or Schank and Colby (1973).

How are we to design a recognizer for context-free languages? Suppose that G is a context-free grammar and that $v = v_1 \ldots v_n \in V_T^*$ is an alleged sentence or program. We could parse v by reading in v_1 to v_i until a reducible substring $v_j \ldots v_i$ is encountered, say by the production $A ::= v_j \ldots v_i$. The sentential form $v_l \ldots v_{j-1} A v_{i+1} \ldots v_k$ would then be processed starting at v_{i+1}. Thus the part of the input v which has been consumed thus far grows until reducible sub-phrases are found and then collapses in a last-in-first-out way.[*] This is the motivation behind the *push-down automaton* (pda) which can be pictured as follows:

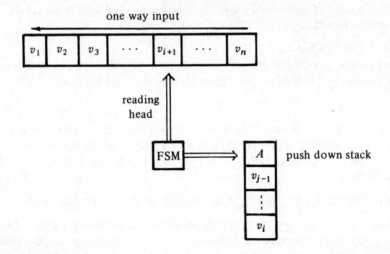

That is, a pda is a FSM augmented by a stack memory; at any point in the computation the state of the FSM, the symbol on top of the stack, and the input symbol together determine whether a new input is consumed or not, what the next state is, and whether information is popped off or pushed onto the stack. Pda's are more fully described in Hopcroft and Ullman (1969, Chapter 5) and are the devices that precisely recognize context-free languages.

---

[*] Readers familiar with compiling may recall Dijkstra's explanation of a parser for arithmetical expressions in terms of shunting. The siding is a stack as in the pda.

CHECKPOINT 3.39 Construct a formal definition of a pda.

Type 3: Regular
Productions are restricted to the forms:

$$A ::= a, B ::= aB$$

where $a \in V_T, A, B \in V_N$. Clearly any regular language is also context-free; the converse is false: it can be proved that the language $\{a^n b^n | n \geqslant 1\}$ discussed in Checkpoint 3.38 is *not* regular. The name "regular" may remind the reader of regular sets, discussed in connection with the acceptance of sequences of inputs by FSMs; they are in fact the same.

CHECKPOINT 3.40 Show that regular languages are precisely regular sets.

As Example 2.8 and Checkpoint 2.9 show, certain features of programming languages can be described by regular grammars; such features are often recognized and packed by the lexical analyser (or scanner) during the compilation process; see Gries (1971, Chapter 3). As we pointed out on p. 25, Kleene's theorem shows that the appropriate recognizer for regular languages is the FSM.

The existence of Chomsky's hierarchy suggests a number of other grammatical questions similar to Questions G1–G5:

QUESTION G6 If L_1 and L_2 are languages of (Chomsky) type t, is it decidable whether $L_1 \cap L_2$ is of the same type?

QUESTION G7 Analogously to Question G6, is $L_1 \cup L_2$ of the same type?

QUESTION G 8 If L is a language of type t, is it decidable whether $(V_T^* - L)$ is a language of the same type?

The status of Questions G2, G3, G4, G6, G7, and G8 is displayed in the following table (S means solvable, U means unsolvable, and ? mean not known).

Question	Type			
	0	1	2	3
G2	U	U	S	S
G3	U	U	S	S
G4	U	U	U	S
G6	S	S	U	S
G7	S	S	S	S
G8	U	?	U	S

CHECKPOINT 3.41 Is it decidable whether a context-sensitive grammar is in fact context-free?

4 The Functional or Programming Approach

4.1 Introduction

In Chapter 2 we introduced abstract machines, particularly Turing machines, as a way of approaching a solution to the basic problem of meta-computer science, namely giving a precise definition of 'computable'. Armed with the notion of Turing-computable, we explored in Chapter 3 the limits of computer science. In this chapter we return to the basic problem and, with particular reference to the *general recursive functions* of David Hilbert and Stephen Kleene, discuss a rather different approach, which we call the functional or programming approach, an approach that we argue stands in the same relation to abstract machines as programming languages do to (real) computing machines.

We shall exploit this relationship as follows: recall from Chapter 1 that a powerful argument in support of Turing's thesis is the consensus on definitions of 'computable'. What does this amount to in the case of the general recursive functions (GRF)? On the one hand we have a programming approach GRF, on the other an abstract machine approach TM. We are to prove that to each GRF there corresponds an equivalent TM, and conversely that every Turing-computable function is a GRF. In terms of our view that programs are constructive proofs, this clearly suggests developing a pair of programs: a 'compiler' from the GRF to TM and a TM 'simulator' in the GRF. The main features of such a compiler–simulator pair are sketched in Chapter 5; in particular we shall find that the approach points up certain shortcomings in a system (the GRF) intended to be a part of the theory of computation.

The functional approach entails specifying a set S of functions so that a function is defined to be computable precisely in the case that it is a member of S. Clearly any candidate for S has to be infinite; but, for reasons analogous to those advanced in the development of the basic, finite state, and Turing machine models in Chapter 2, S also has to be finitely specified. The problem is to devise an adequate finite specification of an infinite set of functions.

David Hilbert's (1925) suggestion derived from his advocacy of a formalist approach to mathematics. According to this view all of mathematics can be reduced to the development of theorems as well-formed formulae in formal logical languages; theorems ultimately derive from axioms by the application of rules of inference (see Section 3.2). Thus, for Hilbert, a computable function is to be regarded as a constructed object, that is, it has to be built. The force of this idea is that if a computable function f is to be regarded as *built* then the components, say $f_1, \ldots, f_m$ from which f is built surely also must be computable functions, combined together to form f according to one of a number of what we shall call *strategies*. Of course, it is normally the case that the components f_i themselves have to be built, and so on. If the components of f_i are $f_{i1}, \ldots, f_{in_i}, 1 \leqslant i \leqslant m$, we may illustrate a partial analysis of f as in Fig. 4.1.

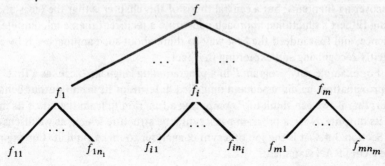

Fig. 4.1

It is important to realize that the branches in Fig. 4.1 *do not* refer to function (or subroutine) calls, but rather to explication. That is to say, f can be 'understood', to the extent of knowing how it can be applied to its arguments to yield its result, if the component functions f_i are 'understood' and the strategy by which the f_i are combined together to form f is 'understood'.

The finiteness restrictions that we referred to above regarding S amount to asserting that the building of a function may only take a finite time or effort. This means that the tree structure in Fig. 4.1 can only branch finitely at any point, according to one of a finite number of strategies, and can only be of finite depth. In particular, there must be some functions that are *not* decomposable; we call these *the base functions*, and suppose that they form a finite (or at least enumerable) set F. If we assume that the strategies form a finite (or again, enumerable) set C, we can denote the totality S of computable functions defined by this approach $C(F)$. [This notation is due to McCarthy (1963).] In terms of Hilbert's formalist program, the base functions F correspond to axioms, and the strategies C correspond to rules of inference.

In Section 4.2 we shall discuss the GRF be detailing the Hilbert–Kleene choice of C and F; in the remainder of this section we make a number of general observations about such functional approaches.

Firstly, we make the intuitive notion of 'strategy' more precise. Suppose C is the strategy that combines the component functions $f_1, \ldots, f_m$ to form the resultant function f. Essentially, C is a functional or higher-order function that takes a number of functions as arguments and produces a function as its result. Consider, for example, function composition (Appendix A, p. 260). If $f : S \rightarrow T$ and $g : T \rightarrow U$ are functions, we define the composition $f \circ g : S \rightarrow U$ of f and g by:

$$f_0g(s) = g(f(s)) \tag{4.1}$$

The composition strategy is itself a function:

compos : $f, g \rightarrow f_0g$

We will usually de-emphasize the functional aspect of strategies, and represent them by schemas such as (4.1).

We referred above to the formalist view of a *mathematician's* behaviour in discovering theorems; but a central thesis of this chapter is that the ideas underlying Hilbert's functional approach constitute a recurrent theme in computer science, and that indeed the best way to think about such approaches is by explicitly recognizing and exploiting that fact.

For example, any program P in a programming language L can, as a first approximation, be discussed and modelled in terms of its input–output behaviour; that is, we can think of P computing a function f_p from the set of its inputs to its outputs. Now, a program has a syntactic structure which, as we discussed in Section 3.4.4, it is the job of a syntax analyser to make explicit. For example the FORTRAN statement:

IF (X .EQ. 0) GOTO 20

results from applying the "logical if" strategy to the base statement GOTO 20 and the (structured) expression X .EQ. 0.

CHECKPOINT 4.1   Construct a complete explication tree (like Fig. 4.1) for the ALGOL 60 statement:

for $i := 1$ **step** 1 **until** a **do**

for $j := x$ **step** y **until** i **do**

if $(i + j) = 5$ **then** $i := 3$ **else goto** l;

This suggests that for any programming language L it may be possible to isolate a set F_L of base functions to express the meaning of, or function computed by, identifiers and primitive statements, and a set C_L of strategies to express the meaning of the linguistic structures and data structures of L. According to such a view, the meaning of programs in L would be computable functions in $C_L(F_L)$, a view that we might depict as follows:

meaning : $L \rightarrow C_L(F_L)$

It is important to distinguish L and $C_L(F_L)$: the objects in L are programs, the objects in $C_L(F_L)$ are mathematical functions; the equation states that the precise meaning of a program is a function. The idea that the meaning of a whole structure is related to the meaning of its components and the way they are put together was advanced by the German mathematician–philosopher Gottlob Frege in the late nineteenth century; it can be shown to have a profound influence on the meaning of programming languages (Laski and Brady, 1975). In fact, as we shall discuss further in Chapter 8, most approaches to giving a semantics for programming languages embody this view. However, there are some serious problems which we (deliberately) glossed over in the naive approach sketched above:

CHECKPOINT 4.2 How would you set about defining the meaning of *goto* statements or assignment statements as base functions? What implications do your answers have for the view of a program as meaning a function from inputs to outputs?

There is a converse to the idea that to any programming language L there is a functional approach $C_L(F_L)$. Suppose that $C(F)$ is a given functional approach; we can design a programming language L, indeed a whole family of such programming languages, such that $C_L = C$ and $F_L = F$. The first programming language to be explicitly designed this way was LISP (McCarthy *et al.*, 1962). More recently, PAL (Evans, 1968) and POP-2 (Burstall, Collins, and Popplestone, 1971) have been greatly influenced by the approach in general and LISP in particular. It is gratifying to see the theory of computation contributing so richly to computing experience.

The idea that a programming language L determines a functional approach $C_L(F_L)$ by taking account of a program's structure, suggests a link between functional approaches and structure programming (Dahl, Dijkstra, and Hoare, 1972). It would lead us far beyond the scope of this book to discuss the issue much here; in particular it would require us to be clear about what is in fact meant by the term "structured programming", since there seems to be a certain amount of confusion in the literature.* We believe that in essence structured programming is about problem solving. It argues firstly that a problem solution has an abstract structure that should be clearly reflected in the structure of any program to solve the problem. Secondly, it advocates the use of top-down problem solving. In Bornat and Brady (1976) we argue that it is important to separate these claims since the latter seems overly restrictive both in terms of problem solving and in terms of the virtual machines to which it leads.

Conversely, the construction of a computable function f in a functional approach $C(F)$, or, equivalently, a constructive proof that f is computable, suggests programming f. We have repeatedly argued that indeed a programming approach is both natural and insightful in computer science. We contend that an important component of understanding any theory (or metatheory) is a grasp of its proof techniques: what they are and when and how to use them. According to our approach, "proof techniques" can here be replaced by "programming techniques". In the following section, we will present the GRF as a system for programming in, although we should be mindful of the caveat issued in Chapter 1 that (being part of meta-computer science) it is unfair to overly criticize it because of its poor control structure.

Finally, the work in this chapter is even relevant to the study of the hardware of computer systems.(!) Hardware starts off with basic gates such as NAND, NOR, and inverters, and puts them together in various ways to form registers, adders, and whole computers. We can think of the basic gates as axioms, and

---

* A slightly more detailed discussion of structured programming appears in Section 7.2 in connection with program testing.

registers as theorems. In particular, wiring a pre-built adder becomes obvious when viewed as setting up the appropriate conditions to 'apply' the addition theorem.

CHECKPOINT 4.3 How can data structures be related to functional approaches? [Hint: see the notion of implicit data structure in Reynolds (1971).]

4.2 The general recursive functions

In the preceding section we saw how Hilbert's work in the foundations of mathematics led him to the $C(F)$ approach to defining 'computable'; in this section we present the Hilbert–Kleene *choice* of a set F of base functions and a set C of strategies. The choice of F directly reflected Hilbert's concern with numbers. Three of the base functions were inspired by Peano's (1889) axiomatization of the natural numbers:

(1) The *(constant) zero function* $c_0 : N \to N$, which always returns the result zero irrespective of its argument:

$$c_0(n) = 0$$

This function corresponds to Peano's axiom that there is a number called zero.

(2) The *successor function* succ $: N \to N$, which adds 1 to its argument:

$$\text{succ}(n) = n + 1$$

This function corresponds to Peano's rule of inference that any number has a unique successor.

(3) The *predecessor function* pred $: N \to N$, which undoes the work of succ. Since $0 - 1$ is not a natural number, we define pred(0) to be 0. That is:

$$\text{pred}(n) = n > 0 \to n - 1, 0$$

This function corresponds to Peano's rules that every number except zero has a unique predecessor and that zero is not the successor of any number. It will turn out that we could omit pred from the list of base functions since it can be programmed in terms of the other base functions and the strategies. It may even be argued that from a strictly reductionist point of view pred *ought* to be omitted. We include it as a base function for the simple practical reason that it makes programming in the early stages considerably easier.

So far, all of the base functions have taken a single argument. In order to be able eventually to build functions of more than one argument, such as add and product, we include in F an (infinite) family of *projector, or argument-selector, functions*:

$$p_{ni} : N^n \to N, \qquad 1 \leqslant i \leqslant n$$

defined by:

$$p_{ni}(x_1, \ldots, x_n) = x_i$$

Thus p_{ni} selects the ith argument out of a list of n. In the special case $n = 1$, the sole argument-selector function p_{11}, defined by:

$$p_{11}(x_1) = x_1$$

is the familiar *identity function*; in the sequel we shall call it "id" rather than p_{11}.

Hilbert (1925) claimed that two strategies would suffice for C, namely generalized composition and primitive recursion. We shall return to this claim shortly, but first we spend a little time discussing the strategies.

4.2.1 *Generalized composition*

Generalized composition provides a means of sequencing by function nesting, and is indeed the main form of sequencing used in 'pure' LISP (McCarthy, 1960). As its name implies, generalized composition derives from generalizing the simple notion of composition discussed in the preceding section in order to handle functions of several variables.

DEFINITION 4.1 If $h_1, \ldots, h_n$ are functions taking the same number m of arguments, and if g is a function taking n arguments, we can construct a function f out of g and the list $(h_1, \ldots, h_n)$ by *generalized composition* as follows:

$$f(x) = g(h_1(x), \ldots, h_n(x))$$

[x is an abbreviation for an arbitrary m-tuple $(x_1, \ldots, x_m) \in N^m$].

To see how generalized composition provides sequencing,[*] consider writing an interpreter to evaluate function applications such as $f(x)$ in Definition 4.1. Such an interpreter would probably involve the following procedure:

first   evaluate $h_1(x), \ldots, h_n(x)$ in some order (such as left-to-right) to yield values $t_1, \ldots, t_n$

second apply g to $(t_1, \ldots, t_n)$.

EXAMPLE 4.1 The constant one function $c_1 : N \to N$ can be defined by generalized composition out of succ and c_0:

---

[*] Strictly speaking, composition does *not* provide sequencing; a function is a set of ordered pairs, and it is not part of mathematics to discuss *how* a function application is to be evaluated. We shall consider this point in more detail in Section 6.1 and Chapter 8. The interpretation process describes the evaluation process that would be used by most mathematicians, since it is 'naturally suggested' by the form compos$(g, (h_1, \ldots, h_n))$.

$$c_1(n) = \mathrm{succ}(c_0(n))$$
$$= \mathrm{succ}(0)$$
$$= 1$$

EXAMPLE 4.2 The function $\mathrm{diffsq} : N^2 \to N$, defined by:

$$\mathrm{diffsq}(x, y) = x^2 - y^2$$

can be built by generalized composition out of the product, sum, and difference functions:

$$\mathrm{diffsq}(x, y) = \mathrm{product}(\mathrm{sum}(x, y), \mathrm{difference}(x, y))$$

since

$$\mathrm{product}(\mathrm{sum}(x, y), \mathrm{difference}(x, y)) = \mathrm{product}(x + y, x - y)$$
$$= x^2 - y^2.$$

In examples 4.1 and 4.2 we did not use f as the name for the functions being constructed; rather we chose the mnemonics c_1 and diffsq. The advantage of such mnemonics is that the *meaning* of the function is clear merely from inspection of the name; moreover, given any argument(s) one can predict the result without resorting to the definition. However, many functions do not have such obvious mnemonics, for example:

$$x, y \to (x + y + 1) * (x - y + 2).$$

Typically, as in Definition 4.1, we resort in such cases to using some spurious name such as f with the result that whenever we want to evaluate a call of f we have to ask to see its definition. Consequently, we introduce a *default or standard name* which has the advantages of a mnemonic name but which can be used even when there is no obvious mnemonic. There is a price to be paid of course; the default name is a rather long-winded composite structure:

$$\mathrm{compos}(g, (h_1, \ldots, h_n))$$

or, in the case $n = 1$:

$$\mathrm{compos}(g, h)$$

For example, the default names for the functions given in Examples 4.1 and 4.2 are:

$$c_1 = \mathrm{compos}(\mathrm{succ}, c_0)$$

$$\mathrm{diffsq} = \mathrm{compos}(\mathrm{product}, (\mathrm{sum}, \mathrm{difference}))$$

We will meet this idea of a composite default naming mechanism several times, particularly when discussing the λ-calculus (Section 8.2 and Chapter 6).

EXAMPLE 4.3 The function $x, y \to x + y + 1$ can be built by generalized composition out of succ and sum as follows:

compos(succ, sum)

Notice how the representation compos$(g, (h_1, \ldots, h_n))$ is a kind of flattened parse tree. For example, diffsq = compos(product, (sum, difference)) suggests the parsing:

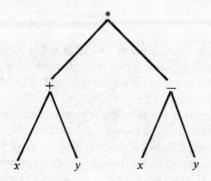

Our final example introduces a programming technique that we shall use repeatedly.

EXAMPLE 4.4 Generalized composition used in conjunction with the argument selector functions p_{ni} enables us to operate on one of a list of variables. For example, consider the function:

strangesq $: N^2 \to N$

defined by

strangesq$(x, y) = x^2$

which just 'ignores' its second argument y. We can 'program' strangesq as follows:

strangesq $=$ compos(ordinarysq, p_{21})

See what happens: strangesq *first* applies the argument selector p_{21} to (x, y) to select x, and *then* applies ordinarysq to return x^2 finally.

In a similar vein, the reader should check that the function $x, y \mapsto 2x$ can be programmed as follows:

compos (product, (compos$(c_2, p_{21}), p_{21})$)

This programming technique is called "explicit transformation" in the literature (see for example Arbib, 1969, p. 222).

CHECKPOINT 4.4 Program the following functions:

(i) $x, y \to x^2 + y^2$

(ii) $x, y \to 2 * (x + y)$

(iii) (assuming functions sqrt and sq)

$$a, b, c \to \frac{-b + \text{sqrt}(b^2 - 4ac)}{2a}$$

4.2.2 *Primitive recursion*

Hilbert's second strategy is called "primitive recursion", which is rather unfortunate given modern computing terminology, since, as we shall spell out more fully below, it really amounts to an iterative definition much more like FORTRAN's DO loop than the concept of recursion familiar from ALGOL 60 or LISP. Primitive recursion is based on the idea that the principle of mathematical induction can be used to construct *functions* as well as proofs. In view of our advocacy of viewing programs as proofs, this should come as no great surprise! Remember that (see Appendix A, p. 265), to prove that a property P holds for all numbers $n \geqslant 0$, the (common formulation of) the principle of mathematical induction suggests a two-step process:

(i) Prove that P holds for $n = 0$.

(ii) Assume that $P(n)$ is already proved true; on the basis of that assumption, prove $P(n + 1)$.

Now consider the following definition of the power function, where $\text{power}(x, y) = x^y$:

(i) $\text{power}(x, 0) = x^0 = 1$

(ii) $\text{power}(x, y + 1) = x^{y+1}$

$$= x * x^y$$

$$= x * \text{power}(x, y)$$

Thus power can be defined in terms of the auxiliary function c_1 and the product function '$*$' by a process that is highly reminiscent of proofs by mathematical induction.

Abstracting on this example leads to:

DEFINITION 4.2 If g and h are given functions with appropriate numbers of arguments, we can define a function f by *primitive recursion* from g and h as follows:

$$f(x, y) \; = \; y \; = \; 0 \to g(x), \qquad\qquad //\text{base of induction}$$

$$h(x, y, f(x, y - 1)) \qquad\qquad // \text{ inductive step}$$

It is worth checking the numbers of arguments for f, g, and h; if g has n, then f has $n + 1$ and h has $n + 2$.

A remark can be made about mnemonic names used in primitive recursion

analogous to that made above about generalized composition; the name we use is
$\text{recn}(g, h)$.

The idea of defining functions by a process akin to the principle of mathematical induction was advanced by Richard Dedekind as long ago as 1888;[*] it
was used by several authors and given its current formulation by Kurt Gödel
(1931). The name "primitive recursion" was introduced by David Hilbert and
Paul Bernays (1934). Somewhat more recently, the idea of relating different versions of the principle of mathematical induction to different iterative and recursive programming structures was explored by Zohar Manna and Richard
Waldinger (1971). See also Boyer and Moore's (1975) work on automatic programming.

The examples of construction by primitive recursion that follow lean heavily
on the programming technique introduced in Example 4.4, since in general the
$(n + 2)$ arguments x, y, and $f(x, y - 1)$ are not all needed for the inductive step
h.

EXAMPLE 4.5 The sum function can be constructed by primitive recursion
out of the base functions id and succ as follows:

$$\text{sum}(x, y) = y = 0 \to x,$$

$$1 + \text{sum}(x, y - 1)$$

Thus
$$\text{sum} = \text{recn}(\text{id}, h)$$

$$\textbf{where } h = \text{compos}(\text{succ}, p_{33})$$

In order to understand the 'where $h = \ldots$' notation, consider the parse tree
for sum:

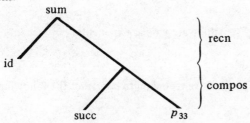

h names the subtree:

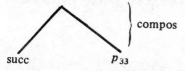

The **where**-notation originates from Peter Landin (1964)

[*] In his incredibly titled book *Was sind und was sollen die Zahlen?* publ. Bruns-
wick. ("What are the numbers, and what should they be?")

EXAMPLE 4.6 The product function can be constructed by primitive recursion out of c_0 and sum as follows:

$$\text{product}(x, y) = y = 0 \rightarrow 0,$$

$$x + \text{product}(x, y - 1).$$

Thus

$$\text{product} = \text{recn}(c_0, h)$$

$$\textbf{where } h = \text{compos}(\text{sum}, (p_{31}, p_{33}))$$

EXAMPLE 4.7 This example is intended to demonstrate that we really do have to be careful with the argument-selector functions p_{ni} in the **where** clauses. Consider the definition:

$$f = \text{recn}(c_0, h)$$

$$\textbf{where } h = \text{compos}(\text{sum}, (p_{32}, p_{33}))$$

in which the only change from the definition in Example 4.6 is p_{32} instead of p_{31} in the **where** clause. The reader should convince himself that f computes:

$$f(x, y) = 0 + 1 + \ldots + (y - 1)$$

Having thus demonstrated the importance of the argument selectors in constructions by primitive recursion, we will usually omit them from now on for the sake of clarity.

CHECKPOINT 4.5 Use primitive recursion to define the function superpower : $N^2 \rightarrow N$ where for $y > 0$:

$$\text{superpower}(x, y) = x^{x^{\cdot^{\cdot^{x}}}} \quad \text{(there are } y \text{ } x\text{'s as exponents)}$$

and superpower$(x, 0) = 1$.

CHECKPOINT 4.6 Use primitive recursion to construct the following functions:

(i) x logand y $(= 1$ if $x = y = 1$, otherwise 0)

(ii) $x \dotdiv y$ is the modified difference of x and y. It equals 0 if $x \leqslant y$, otherwise equals $x - y$

(iii) $x \div y$ integer division

EXAMPLE 4.8 This example introduces an important programming technique (trick?) that is often used in conjunction with primitive recursion. Notice that the way primitive recursion is defined, f has $n + 1$ arguments where n is the number of arguments for g. Since $n \geqslant 1$, any function constructed by primitive recursion must have at least 2 arguments. In particular, it is *not* possible to define the factorial function in the obvious way:

$$\text{fac}(y) = y = 0 \rightarrow 1,$$
$$y * \text{fac}(y - 1)$$

The trick is to introduce a spurious argument x, and then use the 'forgetting' technique outlined in Example 4.4. Here is a solution:

$$\text{facl}(x, y) = y = 0 \rightarrow x,$$
$$y * \text{facl}(x, y - 1)$$

(so that $\text{facl}(x, y) = x * \text{fac}(y)$)

$$\text{fac}(y) = \text{facl}(1, y)$$
$$= \text{compos}(\text{facl}, (c_1, \text{id}))$$

CHECKPOINT 4.7 Give primitive recursion constructions for the functions:

(i) $\text{iszero}(x) = x = 0 \rightarrow 1, 0$

(ii) $x \leqslant y$

We mentioned above that primitive recursion is more like iteration, as in a FORTRAN DO-loop, than the recursion of ALGOL 60 or LISP. We can demonstrate this by writing an interpreter to evaluate $f(x, y)$, where $f = \text{recn}(g, h)$, in much the same way as we did for $\text{compos}(g, (h_1, \ldots, h_n))$:

$$f(x, y) = \textbf{valof } \$(\textbf{ let } r = g(x)$$
$$\textbf{for } i = 1 \textbf{ to } r \textbf{ do}$$
$$r := h(x, i, r)$$
$$\textbf{resultis } r$$
$$\$)$$

We shall see later (in Chapter 6) that the primitive recursive definition of f is in fact in what John McCarthy (1963) calls "iterative form".

The functions that can be built out of the base functions F and the two strategies generalized composition and primitive recursion are called the *primitive recursive functions*. Hoare and Allison (1972, p. 175) have characterized the subset of ALGOL 60 programs computing primitive recursive functions as follows:

(a) The only **goto** statements that are allowed are forward jumps.
(b) No recursion is allowed.
(c) No **(for-)while** statements are allowed.
(d) In a **for**-statement such as:

$$\textbf{for } i := k \textbf{ step } l \textbf{ unitil } m \textbf{ do } S$$

the counting variable i, the step l, and the limit m must not be altered in the body of the loop S.

The examples of primitive recursive functions given above have been referred to as programming exercises. It should be noted however that, while constructing primitive recursive functions *is* very like programming it is also like programming in a language with (at best) poor control facilities, with the consequent need to resort to obscure tricks such as are familiar in machine code programming. To emphasize this point, we justify a claim made above (p. 96), namely that the predecessor function is (strictly speaking) redundant as a base function. The reader should convince himself that the following program for pred is correct:

$$\text{pred}(y) = y = 0 \rightarrow 0,$$

$$\text{notzero}(\text{pred}(y-1)) * \text{succ}(\text{pred}(y-1))$$

$$\textbf{where } \text{notzero}(y) = y = 1 \rightarrow 0,$$

Notice the repeated use of the techniques introduced in Examples 4.4 and 4.8. Observe also the use of multiplication by notzero to achieve the effect of the following more reasonable definition based on two 'boundary conditions' (which of course is not allowed in the primitive recursion schema):

$$\text{pred}(y) = y = 0 \rightarrow 0,$$

$$y = 0 \rightarrow 0, 1$$

$$\text{succ}(\text{pred}(y-1))$$

CHECKPOINT 4.8 Show how more useful conditional definitions such as:

$$f(x,y) = p_1(y) \rightarrow g_1(x),$$

$$p_2(y) \rightarrow g_2(x),$$

$$\vdots$$

$$p_m(y) \rightarrow g_m(x), h(x,y,f(x,y-1))$$

can be realized in the primitive recursive functions by an extension of the multiplication device.

CHECKPOINT 4.9 Show that, if f is primitive recursive, so are the functions g and h defined from f by 'limited addition' and 'limited multiplication':

$$g(x,y) = f(x,0) + f(x,1) + \ldots + f(x,y)$$

$$h(x,y) = f(x,0) * f(x,1) * \ldots * f(x,y)$$

4.2.3 *The GRF*

Hilbert (1925) asked whether there were any "obviously" computable functions that were *not* primitive recursive. He suspected that there were, but conjectured that they could still be defined using only the generalized composition and primitive recursion strategies, extended to have higher-order functions in the argument places of the schemas. Ackermann (1928) devised a counter-example consisting of an "obviously computable" function that did *not* need higher-order functions but that was not primitive recursive. This exposed the need to add further strategies to the primitive recursive functions in order to achieve an acceptable definition of computable; but it was far from obvious what such additional strategies might be. We shall discuss Ackermann's function more fully in the following section; for the moment, here is Hermes's (1965) version, which has the same recursion line as Ackermann's original but different termination conditions:

$$\text{Ack}(x, y) = x = 0 \to y + 1,$$
$$y = 0 \to \text{Ack}(x - 1, 1),$$
$$\text{Ack}(x - 1, \text{Ack}(x, y - 1)).$$

We can answer Hilbert's conjecture in another way, using only the tools assembled in Chapter 3. Consider (that is, do) the following checkpoints.

CHECKPOINT 4.10 Prove that every primitive recursive function is total.

CHECKPOINT 4.11 Prove that the set of primitive recursive functions is enumerable.

By Theorem 3.12 the total computable functions form a non-enumerable set; moreover, by Corollary 3.14, given any enumeration of a subset of the total computable functions such as the primitive recursive functions there is an effective diagonalization process for generating a total computable function that is *not* primitive recursive. It is however still far from clear how to devise strategies to 'plug the leak'. The real problem with the primitive recursive functions became apparent only when Turing's (1936) paper had appeared. Recall that a TM essentially executes:

valof $(**let** state = initialstate

        while state ≠ Halt **do** change state, position, etc.

        resultis state

  $)

The important point to grasp is that, as a result of the unsolvability of the Halting problem (Theorem 3.1), it is impossible to predict whether an arbitrary computation will halt; equivalently, it is impossible to determine *a priori* a bound on the run time of a TM computation. On the other hand, in terms of the interpreter definitions of recn and compos given above, it is always possible to predict that a computation of a primitive recursive function will halt, and it is always possible beforehand to bound its runtime. For example, with sum defined as in Example 4.5, one can predict that the evaluation of sum(79, 84) will take 85 steps.

CHECKPOINT 4.12 Sketch a proof of the theorem to the effect that, given any primitive recursive function f and any set x of arguments for f, the number of steps required to evaluate $f(x)$ can be specified in advance.

Kleene (1936) added a further schema, called the (unbounded) minimization operator, which we now know gets round this problem:

DEFINITION 4.3 If f is a function of $(n + 1)$ arguments and k is a number, we can construct a function g (of n arguments) by *minimization* out of f and k as follows:

$g(x)$ is the unique y such that

(i) $f(x, y) = k$

and (ii) for all $y' < y$, $f(x, y') \neq k$

The default name for a construction by minimization, analogous to compos and recn, is min(f, k). (min is called the μ-operator in the literature, from the first letter of the Greek word for small.)

We expect that it is not at all clear why min introduces partial functions that give rise to computations whose runtimes cannot be specified in advance! We also expect that it will be much clearer if we give an interpreter definition of Min(f, k) analogous to the ones for compos and recn:

Min$(f, k)(x) = $ **valof** $(**let** $y = 0$

$\qquad$ **while** $f(x, y) \neq k$ **do** $y := y + 1$

$\qquad$ **resultis** y

$\qquad$ $)

This little program bears a striking resemblance to that given above to describe a TM computation, a fact on which we shall capitalize in the next chapter. It may well be that the execution of the **while** statement never terminates – there may not be a y such that $f(x, y) = k$.

DEFINITION 4.4 The functions that can be constructed from the set $F = \{$succ, pred, $c_0, p_{ni}, 1 \leq i \leq n\}$ of base functions, together with the set $C = \{$compos, recn, min$\}$ of strategies, are called the *general recursive functions* (GRF).

EXAMPLE 4.9 Suppose factimes$(x, y) = x * y!$ (see Example 4.8), and we define $g = $ Min(factimes, 24). Then:

$\qquad g(4) = 3 \qquad$ //since $4 * 3! = 24$

but

$g(3)$ is undefined

since there is no number y such that $y! = 8$.

EXAMPLE 4.10 The least common multiple function lcm : $N^2 \to N$ can be constructed using minimization. Recall that:

$\text{lcm}(x_1, x_2) = $ the least y such that x_1 divides y and

$\qquad\qquad\qquad x_2$ divides y

CHECKPOINT 4.13 Show that the function exp can be constructed using minimization, where:

$$\exp(x, y) = n \text{ iff } x^n \leqslant y < x^{n+1}.$$

The interpreter 'definition' of Min based on the **while** statement may be more understandable by computer scientists than the logical Definition 4.3; but it is important to realize that the interpreter adds something not actually present in the logical definition. Specifically, both definitions require $\text{Min}(f, k)(x)$ to be the least y such that $f(x, y) = k$ (if such a y exists). Generally, y will have to be *searched* for in the set N of natural numbers. The interpreter definition completely specifies the search process by requiring the successive testing of $y = 0$, $y = 1, \ldots$, whereas the logical definition leaves the search process unspecified. There are two points to note:

(1) There may well be much cleverer ways to search N in particular cases than by exhaustive search. Pat Hayes (1974) has argued the same point in relating computation and deduction. He points out for example that the LISP interpreter eval uses depth first search in contrast to some of the sophisticated search processes used in computational logic.

(2) Consider the function:

$$f(x, y) = (y + x)/(y - x)$$

so that $\text{Min}(f, 2)(3) = $ the least y such that:

$$(y + 3)/(y - 3) = 2$$

The solution is $y = 9$ *but* the **while**-based interpreter encounters real problems in the test sequence $0, 1, \ldots, 9$ at $y = 3$.

We conclude this section by revisiting the relationship between Min and bounded runtime. Consider the functions factimes, lcm, and exp which were 'naturally' programmed in Examples 4.9 and 4.10 and Checkpoint 4.13 using minimization. It turns out that every one of them can be programmed without using Min; in fact they are all primitive recursive! The point is that in each case, the runtime can be bounded in advance, namely:

$\text{factimes}(x, y) = k \text{ implies } y \leqslant k \div x$

$\text{lcm}(x_1, x_2) = y \quad \text{implies } y \leqslant x_1 * x_2$

$\exp(x, y) = n \qquad \text{implies } n \leqslant y$

(the latter holding so long as $x > 1$). More precisely, we can define the bounded minimization operator as follows:

DEFINITION 4.5 If f is a function of $(n + 1)$ arguments and k is a number, we can construct a function g of $(n + 1)$ arguments by *bounded minimization* out of f and k as follows:

$g(x, l)$ is the unique least y such that

$f(x, y) = k$ and $0 \leqslant y \leqslant l$

or 0 if there is no such y

The standard name for g is $\text{Bdmin}(f, k)$.

To see that bounded minimization really does bound runtime, consider the following interpreter definition:

$\text{Bdmin}(f, k)(x, l) = $ **valof** $(

　　　　　for $y = 0$ **to** l **do**

　　　　　　　if $f(x, y) = k$ **then resultis** y

　　　　resultis 0

　　$)$

We can now prove the following theorem.

THEOREM 4.1 If f is primitive recursive, so is $\text{Bdmin}(f, k)$.

Proof. By program – of course. We could try to achieve the **for**-loop in the interpreter definition directly; but that is quite difficult (because of the need for a **resultis**-exit which is difficult to achieve with the poor control facilities of the GRF). Instead, we base our program on an alternative 'recursive' interpreter:

$\text{Bdmin}(f, k)(x, l) = l = 0 \to 0,$

　　　　$\text{Bdmin}(f, k)(x, l-1) = 0 \wedge f(x, 0) \neq k$

　　　　$\to (f(x, l) = k \to l, 0),$

　　　　$\text{Bdmin}(f, k)(x, l-1).$

We can now program:

$\text{Bdmin}(f, k)(x, l) = a_f(x, k, l)$

where　$a_f(x, k, l) = l = 0 \to 0$

　　　　　$b_f(x, k, l, a_f(x, k, l-1))$

where　$b_f(x, k, l, m) = m = 0 \to c_f(x, k, l), m$

　　where　$c_f(x, k, l) = l * (f(x, l) = k) * (f(x, 0) \neq k)$

CHECKPOINT 4.14 For reasons that will become clearer in Chapter 5, we define the coding function:

Gödelcode$(x, y) = 2^x * 3^y$

Composing Cantorenum (Section 3.2) with Gödelcode gives an enumeration $N \rightarrow N$. Prove that the composition is a GRF. Is it primitive recursive?

4.3 Ackermann's function and another look at complexity

We introduced Ackermann's function in the preceding section as an example of a function that is "obviously" computable but that we can prove is not primitive recursive. We begin this section by investigating Ackermann's function a shade more deeply, following Hermes (1965, para. 13). We shall describe the important process that leads to the construction of Ackermann's function as the single embodiment of an infinite sequence of primitive recursive functions, and we shall sketch the proof of a 'bounding' theorem that shows that the values of Ackermann's function grow more quickly than those of any primitive recursive function. We shall then show how substantially the same construction process and bounding theorem can be used to define the Grzegrocyck hierarchy, which gives a measure of the complexity of a primitive recursive function. The reader may well feel that the Grzegrocyck hierarchy is far too abstract to be relevant to a practical theory of complexity; to reassure him, we shall in conclusion present a brief account of the elegant work of Meyer and Ritchie on complexity which derived from a consideration of loop programs, and relate their work to the Grzegrocyck hierarchy.

4.3.1 *Ackermann's function*

Recall the following examples of primitive recursion from Section 4.2:

sum$(x, y) = y = 0 \rightarrow x,$

$\qquad\qquad$ succ(sum$(x, y-1))$

product$(x, y) = y = 0 \rightarrow 0,$

$\qquad\qquad$ sum$(x,$ product$(x, y-1))$

power$(x, y) = y = 0 \rightarrow 1,$

$\qquad\qquad$ product$(x,$ power$(x, y-1))$

superpower$(x, y) = y = 0 \rightarrow 1,$

$\qquad\qquad$ power$(x,$ superpower$(x, y-1))*$

$\qquad\qquad$ [this last example answers Checkpoint 4.5]

These examples suggest defining an infinite sequence $f_n, n \geqslant 0$, of functions such that $f_0 = \text{succ}$, $f_1 = \text{sum}$, $f_2 = \text{product}$, $f_3 = \text{power}$, $f_4 = \text{superpower}$, and, for $n \geqslant 1$:

$$f_n(x, y) = y = 0 \to g_n(x),$$
$$f_{n-1}(x, f_n(x, y-1)) \tag{4.2}$$

Moreover

$$f_1(x, y) < f_2(x, y) < f_3(x, y) < f_4(x, y) \tag{4.3}$$

Ackermann's idea was to replace the entire infinite sequence $\{f_n : n \geqslant 1\}$ by a single function f with n as an additional parameter:

$$f(n, x, y) = f_n(x, y)$$

In this way, f embodies all of each of the individual functions f_n. (Compare this construction with that used in the diagonalization process, for example in nasty, Theorem 3.12.) As a result, the recursion line (4.2) becomes:

$$f(n, x, y) = f(n-1, x, f(n, x, y-1)) \tag{4.4}$$

It can now be seen that x is irrelevant:

$$f(n, y) = f(n-1, f(n, y-1))$$

which is the recursion line in Ackermann's function. The result for $n = 0$ is obtained as follows:

$$f(0, y) = f_0(y) = \text{succ}(y) = y + 1$$

The result for $y = 0$ is chosen to facilitate the proof of the (bounding) Theorem 4.2 below. Renaming f to be Ack, we have the definition given in Section 4.2:[*]

$$\text{Ack}(n, y) = n = 0 \to y + 1,$$
$$y = 0 \to \text{Ack}(n-1, 1),$$
$$\text{Ack}(n-1, \text{Ack}(n, y-1))$$

---

[*] As a matter of fact, this is *not* Ackermann's original 1928 function but a simplification due to Hermes. Ackermann had the recursion line (4.4) but different boundary conditions:

$$\text{Ackorig}(n, x, y) = n = 0 \to x + y,$$
$$y = 0 \to a(x, n-1),$$
$$\text{Ackorig}(n-1, x, \text{Ackorig}(n, x, y-1))$$

Where $a(x, n) = n = 0 \to 0,$
$$n = 1 \to 1,$$
$$x$$

See van Heijenoort (1967, p. 493ff).

Given this definition of Ack, it is obvious that it is computable, but it is far from obvious that it is a GRF, particularly in view of the double recursion. In Section 5.2 we shall outline a GRF program to compute Ack; in anticipaction, the reader may care to evaluate $Ack(3, 1)$ and see if he can develop his own program.

The proof that Ack is not primitive recursive depends crucially on the following theorem which shows that Ack grows more quickly than any primitive recursive function. It is inspired by relation (4.3) above.

THEOREM 4.2 (Hermes, 1965, p. 84) For all primitive recursive functions $g : N^n \to N$ there is a number c (depending on g) such that for all $x = (x_1, \ldots, x_n)$:

$$g(x) < Ack(c, (x_1 + \ldots + x_n))$$

We shall return to the proof of this theorem in a moment, but first we prove:

THEOREM 4.3 Ackermann's function is not primitive recursive.

Proof. Suppose to the contrary that Ack is in fact primitive recursive. Now define $g(x) = Ack(x, x)$; g is obviously primitive recursive. By Theorem 4.2, there is a number c such that for all x:

$$g(x) < Ack(c, x)$$

But of course in the special case $x = c$ we have:

$$Ack(c, c) = g(c) < Ack(c, c)$$

The proof of Theorem 4.2 is by structural induction, after establishing a number of results about the way the value of $Ack(x, y)$ grows with x and y. In particular, it is possible to show:

$$y < Ack(x, y) \leqslant Ack(x, y + 1) \leqslant Ack(x, + 1, y) \tag{4.5}$$

CHECKPOINT 4.15 Prove Theorem 4.2 for the base primitive recursive functions c_0, succ, pred, p_{ni}.

CHECKPOINT 4.16 Assume that for all $c_1, \ldots, c_n$ there is a c such that:

$$Ack(c_1, x) + \ldots + Ack(c_n, x) \leqslant Ack(c, n)$$

Prove the composition part of the structural induction.

4.3.2 *Another look at complexity*

In Section 2.7 we described how Shannon based a complexity measure on the Turing machine model of computability. We now consider how a functional approach such as the GRF can lead to an analogous measure. We only consider the set *PR* of primitive recursive functions. Naively, a complexity measure for *PR* is a function:

complexity : $PR \to N$

which associates with any primitive recursive function f of a number complexity (f) which estimates the complexity of f. Suppose we have such a complexity function; then for all $n \geqslant 0$ we can define the subset S_n of PR consisting of all the functions of complexity at most n:

$$S_n = \{f | f \in PR \text{ and complexity}(f) \leqslant n\}$$

The sets $S_n, n \geqslant 0$ clearly have the following properties:

(i) $S_0 \subseteq S_1 \subseteq S_2 \subseteq \ldots \subseteq S_n \subseteq \ldots$

(ii) Any function g in PR belongs to some S_n, that is:

$$\bigcup_{n \geqslant 0} S_n = PR$$

The ascending chain $\{S_n | n \geqslant 0\}$ is called a *hierarchy*; what we have achieved is a 'reduction' of the problem of defining a complexity measure to the problem of defining a hierarchy. The Ackerman construction described above suggests defining a hierarchy in terms of an infinite family $\{f_n | n \geqslant 1\}$ of functions and a set C_1 of strategies such that:

$$S_n = C_1(\{f_i | i \leqslant n\})$$

In this way the problem of defining a hierarchy is itself 'reduced' to the problems of defining a suitable infinite family $\{f_n | n \geqslant 1\}$ of functions and a set C_1 of strategies.

Grzegrocyck (1953) defined such a family $\{f_n | n \geqslant 1\}$ and a set C_1 with the properties:

(i) For all $i \leqslant n, f_i \in S_n$ but $f_{n+1} \notin S_n$.

(ii) $f_{n+1}(x, x)$ increases more quickly than the values of any function in S_n.

(iii) If g is a primitive recursive function that can be given a Fig. 4.1-like tree explication of depth k, then g belongs to S_{k+3}.

(iv) *Any* enumerable set can be enumerated by a function in S_0.

These properties are rather difficult to prove, and depend crucially of course on the particular set $\{f_n | n \geqslant 1\}$ of functions. We shall be content merely to motivate the choice of the f_n's with reference to the development of Ackermann's function. The basic idea is to generalize Theorem 4.2. Recall from (4.5) that the proof of Theorem 4.2 depends on establishing monotonicity; consequently, we insist that the f_n's satisfy:

$$f_n(x, y) \leqslant f_n(x + 1, y)$$

$$f_n(x, y) \leqslant f_n(x, y + 1)$$

(4.6)

[These are Theorems 4.2 and 4.3 of Grzegrocyck (1953).] The choice of the f_n's can be deduced from insisting that if g is any primitive recursive function in S_n of (Fig. 4.1) tree depth m then the following generalization of Theorem 4.2 should hold:

$$g(x) < f_n(m, x)$$

(4.7)

Suppose now that $f = \text{compos}(g, h)$ and that (inductively) (4.7) has been proved for g and h in S_n which have tree depths k and l. Clearly, if $m = \max(k, l)$ then f has tree depth $(m + 1)$ and should belong to S_n. We choose the f_n's so that (4.7) holds for f also; that is:

$$f(x) < f_n(m + 1, x) \tag{4.8}$$

But

$$f(x) = g(h(x))$$

$$< f_n(k, h(x)) \qquad //(4.7) \text{ and induction on } g$$

$$< f_n(k, f_n(l, x)) \qquad //\text{monotonicity, (4.7) and induction on } h$$

$$\leqslant f_n(m, f_n(m, x) \qquad //\text{monotonicity (4.6)}$$

Thus we can guarantee (4.8) if we set:

$$f_n(m + 1, x) = f_n(m, f_n(m, x))$$

This is the "recursion line" in Grzegrocyck's definition of the f_n's:

$$f_0(x, y) = y + 1$$

$$f_1(x, y) = x + y$$

$$f_2(x, y) = (x + 1) * (y + 1)$$

$$f_n(0, y) = f_{n-1}(y - 1, y - 1), n > 2$$

$$f_n(x + 1, y) = f_n(x, f_n(x, y))$$

For further details, see Grzegrocyck (1953) or Arbib (1969).

The reader may well feel that the Grzegrocyck hierarchy is far too abstract to be of much interest in computer science; in case he does, we now discuss a rather different, more intuitively-appealing, approach to complexity due to Meyer and Ritchie (1967).

Meyer and Ritchie introduce "loop programs" which operate on an unlimited number of registers, each of which is capable of holding an arbitrarily large number. The program statements are either assignment statements of one of the restricted forms:

$$X = 0 \qquad\qquad //X \text{ and } Y$$

$$X = X + 1 \qquad\qquad // \text{ are}$$

$$X = Y \qquad\qquad //\text{registers}$$

or are "loop" statements of the form

LOOP X

P

END

in which the body P is itself a loop program. Loop statements are similar to FORTRAN DO loops, and have the following semantics:

(1) First evaluate the control variable X to get a value v.

(2) Then execute the loop body P v times irrespective of whether or not the control variable X is altered by assignment within P. In particular, if v equals zero, *do not* execute P. (Whether or not a loop statement is like an ALGOL 60 *for* loop depends on whether the *for* step and limit are 'called by value'.)

A consequence of (2) is that the effect of the loop statement:

> LOOP X
>
> $X = X + 1$
>
> END

is to double the value of X *not* to cause an infinite computation.

EXAMPLE 4.11

> ANS $= X$
>
> LOOP Y
>
>   ANS $=$ ANS $+ 1$
>
> END

computes the sum of X and Y.

CHECKPOINT 4.17 Construct a loop program to compute the product of X and Y.

EXAMPLE 4.12 The special case $v = 0$ in (2) above leads to a programming techinque that is commonly used in loop programming to overcome the lack of an explicit conditional statement. Consider the following program to compute the predicate $X \neq 0$:

> ANS $= 0$
>
> ANS $=$ ANS $+ 1$ //that is, initialize ANS $= 1$
>
> LOOP X
>
>   ANS $= 0$
>
> END

If $X = 0$ the loop body is not executed and the ANSwer is 1. If $X > 0$, the loop is executed and the ANSwer is 0.

CHECKPOINT 4.18 Use the same technique to compute the predicate $X \neq 1$.

EXAMPLE 4.13 There is no explicit subtraction allowed in loop programs; the effect of $X = X - 1$ can be achieved by the following program which is strikingly similar to the primitive recursive program for pred given on p. 104.

ANS $= X$

$X = 0$

LOOP ANS

  ANS $= X$

  $X = X + 1$

END

CHECKPOINT 4.19 Write an interpreter for loop programs in any programming language you like.

CHECKPOINT 4.20 Write an interpreter for the primitive recursive functions in the loop language.

THEOREM 4.4 All primitive recursive functions are computable by loop program.

Proof. By structural induction; equivalently, by the interpreter given in answer to Checkpoint 4.20.

We denote by L_n the set of loop programs in which LOOP statements are nested to a depth of at most n, and denote by C_n the functions computed by programs in L_n. Meyer and Ritchie (1967) define the runtime of a loop program to be the number of assignment statements executed, that is to say, the length of the trace. If P is a loop program, denote the runtime of P by t_p.

CHECKPOINT 4.21 Compute t_p for the loop programs given in Examples 4.11–4.13 and Checkpoints 4.17 and 4.18.

THEOREM 4.5 If P is in L_n, t_p is defined by a function belonging to C_n. Consequently, if f is computable by a loop program, it is total and computable.

Proof. Modify P as follows. Place the statement RUNTIME $= 0$ before the first statement of P, and include the statement:

RUNTIME $=$ RUNTIME $+ 1$

after every statement of P. It is assumed that the variable RUNTIME does not otherwise appear in P.

Meyer and Ritchie define the bounding functions f_n, $n \geqslant 1$, as follows:

$f_0(x) = x \leqslant 1 \to x + 1, x + 2$

$f_{n+1}(x) = f_n^x(1)$

and then prove the following bounding theorem.

THEOREM 4.6 (Meyer and Ritchie, 1967, p. 467) If P is a loop program in

L_n, the runtime t_p of P is bounded by the function f_n^k, where k is the number of statements in P.

Meyer and Ritchie show that f_n belongs to C_n but not to C_{n-1}, and they prove that for $n \geqslant 3$ it is undecidable whether an arbitrary program P in L_n is in fact bounded by f_{n-1}^k for some k. Finally, the converse to Theorem 4.4 holds: the functions computed by loop programs are precisely the primitive recursive functions. This suggests that there may be a relationship between the Grzegrocyck hierarchy $\{S_n | n \geqslant 0\}$ and the sets $\{C_n | n \geqslant 0\}$. In fact, for $n \geqslant 2$:

$$S_{n+1} = C_n$$

5 Evidence in Support of Turing's Thesis

5.1 Introduction

In the introduction to Chapter 4 we observed that the GRF are related to Turing machines in much the same way that programming languages are related to computers. We argued that one could develop a compiler from the GRF to TM and a TM simulator in the GRF as consensus evidence in support of Turing's thesis. Accordingly, in Section 5.2 we sketch the main features of such a simulator, and we will discover some apparent linguistic inadequacies of the GRF which make the programming (and proof) annoyingly complex. The approach in this section first appeared in Brady (1976). The programming techniques developed in building the simulator are then applied to prove that Ackermann's function is a GRF. In Section 5.3 we sketch the construction of a GRF to TM compiler and show how the conceptual simplicity is obscured by the poor addressing structure of TMs. An idea that is heavily used in Section 5.2 is that of interpreting a single number as a complex data structure; we consider this in more detail in Section 5.4.

5.2 A GRF simulator for Turing machines

Our aim in this section is to construct a program to compute the function:

    simulate : TM → GRF

so that if M is a Turing machine, simulate(M) is the GRF that simulates M. We should be clear what is meant by "simulate" [a precise definition can be found in Milner (1974)]: the crucial idea is that, if $x_1, \ldots, x_n$ is a set of arguments for M, then the *evaluation* of the expression:

    simulate$(M)(x_1, \ldots, x_n)$

should as far as possible follow step-by-step the *execution* of the Turing machine M when it is initially placed on the argument strip:

A good place to start programming simulate then is by recalling a 'top level' description of the execution of a TM such as is given on p. 39:

$(initialize$(x_1, \ldots, x_n)$;

while state $\neq$ halt do state $:=$ next(M, state);

extractresult( )

£)

This description shows the execution to be a sequence of three processes: *initialize* loads the argument strip onto the Turing machine's tape, positions the reading head and initializes the state. The *main loop* consists of a sequence of execution cycles (change state, scanned square, and reading head position) which terminates (if and) when the halt state is reached. Finally, according to Definition 2.5, if the main loop terminates, the reading head will be positioned over the rightmost '1' of the answer; the job of *extractresult* is simply to cycle leftwards keeping a count of the number of 1's before a ';'. A moment's thought should convince the reader that the initialize and extractresult processes are essentially independent of the particular Turing machine M.

Our first step (in accordance with the strictures of structured programming) in the programming of simulate(M) is to assume we have programmed the functions initialize, mainloop, and extractresult, and arrange for them to be called in the correct sequence. Remembering that sequencing in the GRF is acheived by function composition, we get:

$$\text{simulate}(M)(x_1, \ldots, x_n) =$$
$$\text{extractresult}(\text{mainloop}(\text{tm}, \text{initialize}(x_1, \ldots, x_n)))$$

(5.1)

The only novelty in (5.1) is the appearance of tm instead of the expected M in mainloop. The point is that mainloop, like all GRF, is constrained to have *numbers* as arguments while M is a *Turing machine*. For the rest of this section we assume that it is possible to *represent* M by a number tm $=$ tmcode(M) according to some coding mechanism:

tmcode : $TM \to N$

a point to which we shall return in Sections 5.2.1 and 5.4 (In fact, it should be no surprise in view of Checkpoint 2.25.) In the three subsections that follow we complete the programming of initialize, mainloop, and extractresult in turn.

5.2.1 *Initialize*

The job of initialize is to set up initial values for the various pieces of information needed in the execution of the mainloop: the scanned symbol, the state, and the TM tape loaded with the argument strip $x_1, \ldots, x_n$. However, just as we needed to postulate a coding system tmcode to represent a Turing machine M as a single number tm, so we need to postulate a similar coding mechanism for the information set up by initialize. We present the details of one possible coding mechanism in Section 5.4; for the remainder of this section however we need only assume that we have devised a coding system that initialize can use to pass all relevant information, coded as a single number and called an *information packet*, to mainloop. In these terms, the job of mainloop is to transform the information packet initialize$(x_1, \ldots, x_n)$ representing the TM configuration at the start of the computation into an information packet representing the configuration representing the end of the computation. We shall suppose that our interface to the coding system is via a set of *selector functions* sel-state, sel-scanned-char, etc., which allow us to access (decode) the component state and scanned character etc., from the current information packet, and an *updater function* next, which changes the information packet to mirror a particular TM cycle. [Cf. the treatment of records in POP-2 (Burstall, Popplestone, and Collins, 1971.] It will transpire in Section 5.4 that initialize is in fact primitive recursive.

5.2.2 *Mainloop*

The evaluation of mainloop(tm, infpack) is to simulate the execution of tm starting on the information packet infpack.[*] Slightly expanding the description of a TM execution given above, we get:

mainloop(tm, infpack) = **valof** \$(

> **while** sel-state(infpack) $\neq$ halt **do**
>
> > infpack := next(tm, infpack)
>
> **resultis** infpack

\$)

in which next(tm, infpack) is the information packet resulting from one execution cycle of tm starting at infpack. This little program has the same basic format, namely a **while** statement, as that given on p. 106 in the interpreter definition of the minimization strategy of the GRF, namely:

Min$(f, k)(x)$ = \$(**let** $y = 0$

> **while** $f(x, y) \neq k$ **do**
>
> > $y := y + 1$;
>
> **resultis** y

\$)

---

[*] To be more accurate, this sentence should read: "The evaluation of mainloop(tm, infpack) is to simulate the execution of the Turing machine whose representation is tm starting on the configuration that is represented by the information packet infpack". To aid readability we shall suppress mention representation.

Thus it seems reasonable to suppose that a simple application of the minimization strategy will complete the programming of mainloop. Unfortunately this is *not* the case, since closer inspection of the **while** statement in the Min strategy reveals that it takes a very restricted form, which only allows one to increment the control variable y by 1 at each step; in mainloop, on the other hand, we want to perform a quite complex operation, namely:

infpack := next(tm, infpack)

corresponding to an execution cycle of tm. However, we know from the unsolvability of the Halting problem that we are going to have to involve Min somehow in the programming of mainloop, because we cannot in general predict how many execution cycles tm will perform before halting (see Section 4.2). Consequently we have to use Min with a control variable, say l, which is incremented by 1 for each execution cycle. *Such a control variable l clearly counts the number of execution cycles of tm, that is, computes the runtime.* The top level of the programming solution to mainloop is:

(1) Use Min to program a function timesround that computes the runtime of tm on $x_1, \ldots, x_n$. (Clearly the computation of runtime may not terminate.)

(2) Use this *computed* or *a priori given* runtime in another function transform that computes the infpack change of mainloop but can be programmed without using Min. That is, transform is primitive recursive.

Again we have a sequence of two processes to perform, and we turn to composition:

mainloop(tm, infpack) = transform(tm, infpack, timesround(tm, infpack))

where transform(tm, infpack, runtime) = ... //programmed without

//using Min

and timesround(tm, infpack) = ...   //programmed using Min

The crucial points to note are the following:

(a) The linguistic inadequacy of the Min strategy, in particular the restricted form of the embodied **while**-statement, presented us with a programming problem, which led to an intricate but readily understandable programming solution.

(b) The solution adopted makes algorithmic nonsense! The computation is carried out in evaluating timesround, but we are restricted (again by the Min strategy) to returning as a result the runtime, and are unable to access the final infpack. Consequently, the entire computation has to be carried out again just to access the final infpack! Whereas it is fairly easy to see why this is necessary in programming terms, it is not so in most mathematical proofs (for example, Hermes, 1965, para. 18, or Minsky, 1967, Chapter 10.)

(c) It is obvious (from a programming point of view) how to design a more general minimization strategy that leads to a straightforward program (and proof), namely:

Genmin$(f, k, g, y\text{init})(x) =$

   valof \$(**let** $y = y\text{init}$

      while $f(x, y) \neq k$ **do**

         $y := g(x, y)$

      resultis y

   \$)

With this definition, it is clear that:

   mainloop$(\text{tm}, \text{infpack}) = $ Genmin$(\text{sel-state}, \text{halt}, \text{next}, \text{infpack})(\text{tm})$

We shall use Genmin in Section 5.2.4 to give a simple GRF program for Ackermann's function. At the end of this section we make a formal statement about the Genmin programming technique; first we want to complete the programming of simulate.

   CHECKPOINT 5.1   How could one give a 'logical' definition of Genmin analogous to Definition 4.3?

   We are left to program transform and timesround. Transform$(\text{tm}, \text{infpack}, \text{runtime})$ is the information packet resulting from executing runtime cycles of tm starting from infpack. We know that transform is primitive recursive, and so we naturally program transform in a recn-like way:

   transform$(\text{tm}, \text{infpack}, \text{runtime}) = \text{runtime} = 0 \to \text{infpack},$

      transform$(\text{tm}, \text{next}(\text{tm}, \text{infpack}), \text{runtime} - 1)$

   Closer inspection of the recn strategy shows up yet another programming problem; fortunately, Minsky (1967, Section 10.3.2) has devised the following programming solution.

   THEOREM 5.1   If g and h are GRF, and f is defined by:

$$f(x, y, l) = l = 0 \to g(x, y),$$
$$f(x, h(x, y), l - 1)$$

then f is also a GRF.

Proof. Consider the (traces of the evaluation of the) following applications of f:

$$f(x, y, 0) = g(x, y)$$
$$f(x, y, 1) = f(x, h(x, y), 0) = g(x, h(x, y))$$
$$f(x, y, 2) = f(x, h(x, y), 1) = g(x, h(x, h(x, y)))$$

and generally for $l \geqslant 0$:

$$f(x, y, l) = g(x, h(x, h(x, \ldots, h(x, y) \ldots)$$

there being l h's. If we define:

$$H(x, y, l) = l = 0 \rightarrow y,$$

$$h(x, H(x, y, l-1))$$

then H is clearly a GRF and:

$$H(x, y, l) = h(x, h(x, \ldots h(x, y) \ldots))$$

with l h's. Finally:

$$f(x, y, l) = g(x, H(x, y, l))$$

Theorem 5.1 shows how to program transform, which leaves only timesround. The program for timesround is surprisingly easy and re-emphasizes point (b) above.

Timesround(tm, infpack) is the least runtime such that the state of the tm after runtime execution cycles is halt. That is:

timesround(tm, infpack) = Min(getstate, halt)(tm, infpack)

where getstate(tm, infpack, runtime) =

sel-state(transform(tm, infpack, runtime))

5.2.3 *Extractresult*

According to Definition 2.5, if the tm computation halts, it does so with the tape configured as follows:

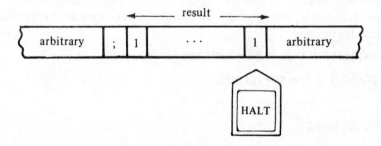

The 'obvious' way to program extractresult is by a **while** loop (Min strategy) moving left until a semicolon is reached. The detailed programming clearly depends on the particular coding scheme chosen for information packets. It turns out that in *any* such coding system it is possible to bound *a priori* the computational length of the leftwards plod. Consequently it is possible to program extractresult using the bounded minimization operator Bdmin (see page 108) although this will usually be an obscure and inefficient thing to do. In particular, extractresult is primitive recursive. Gathering together all our programming effort we have proved:

THEOREM 5.2 (Kleene normal form theorem) Any general recursive function f can be computed by a function of the form:

   compos(extractresult, compos(mainloop, initialize))

   where mainloop = compos(transform, timesround)

      where timesround = Min(getstate, halt)

in which extractresult, initialize, transform, and getstate are primitive recursive.

COROLLARY* 5.3 Any ALGOL 60 program (for example) can be written with a single **for-while** or backwards **goto** statement or a single recursive subroutine definition.

The reader is urged not to take Corollary 5.3 too much to heart!

We conclude the programming of simulate with a more precise description of Genmin.

THEOREM 5.4 If f and g are GRF, and k and $y$init are numbers, then Genmin(f, k, g, yinit) is a GRF.

Proof. Straightforward from the programming of mainloop:

   Genmin(f, k, g, yinit)(x) =

      transform(x, yinit, timesround(x, yinit))

   where transform(x, y, l) = $l = 0 \rightarrow y$,

                  transform($x, g(x, y), l - 1$)

                                             //now use Theorem 5.1

   and timesround = Min(transformandtest, k)

      where transformandtest(x, y, l) = $f(x,$ transform(x, y, l))

5.2.4 *Ackermann's function is a GRF*

We can apply the programming techniques developed in the programming of simulate, particularly Genmin, to prove that Ackermann's function Ack is a GRF. Recall from Sections 4.2 and 4.3 that Ack is defined by:

   Ack(x, y) = $x = 0 \rightarrow y + 1$,

         $y = 0 \rightarrow$ Ack($x - 1, 1$),

         Ack($x - 1$, Ack($x, y - 1$))

---

* This is not really a formal statement. We call it a corollary because it follows from Theorem 5.2. It would in fact be very difficult to prove.

We follow Minsky (see Theorem 5.1 above) and base our analysis of Ack on the 'trace' of a sample evaluation, for example $\text{Ack}(2, 2)$. We have:

$$\text{Ack}(2, 2)$$
$$= \text{Ack}(1, \text{Ack}(2, 1))$$
$$= \text{Ack}(1, \text{Ack}(1, \text{Ack}(2, 0)))$$
$$= \text{Ack}(1, \text{Ack}(1, \text{Ack}(1, 1)))$$
$$= \text{Ack}(1, \text{Ack}(1, \text{Ack}(0, \text{Ack}(1, 0))))$$
$$= \text{Ack}(1, \text{Ack}(1, \text{Ack}(0, \text{Ack}(0, 1))))$$
$$= \text{Ack}(1, \text{Ack}(1, \text{Ack}(0, 2)))$$
$$= \text{Ack}(1, \text{Ack}(1, 3))$$
$$= \text{Ack}(1, \text{Ack}(0, \text{Ack}(1, 2)))$$
$$= \text{Ack}(1, \text{Ack}(0, \text{Ack}(0, \text{Ack}(1, 1))))$$
$$= \text{Ack}(1, \text{Ack}(0, \text{Ack}(0, \text{Ack}(0, \text{Ack}(1, 0)))))$$
$$= \text{Ack}(1, \text{Ack}(0, \text{Ack}(0, \text{Ack}(0, \text{Ack}(0, 1)))))$$
$$= \text{Ack}(1, \text{Ack}(0, \text{Ack}(0, \text{Ack}(0, 2))))$$
$$= \text{Ack}(1, \text{Ack}(0, \text{Ack}(0, 3)))$$
$$= \text{Ack}(1, \text{Ack}(0, 4))$$
$$= \text{Ack}(1, 5)$$
$$= \text{Ack}(0, \text{Ack}(1, 4))$$
$$= \text{Ack}(0, \text{Ack}(0, \text{Ack}(1, 3)))$$
$$= \text{Ack}(0, \text{Ack}(0, \text{Ack}(0, \text{Ack}(1, 2))))$$
$$= \text{Ack}(0, \text{Ack}(0, \text{Ack}(0, \text{Ack}(0, \text{Ack}(1, 1)))))$$
$$= \text{Ack}(0, \text{Ack}(0, \text{Ack}(0, \text{Ack}(0, \text{Ack}(0, \text{Ack}(1, 0))))))$$
$$= \text{Ack}(0, \text{Ack}(0, \text{Ack}(0, \text{Ack}(0, \text{Ack}(0, \text{Ack}(0, 1))))))$$
$$= \text{Ack}(0, \text{Ack}(0, \text{Ack}(0, \text{Ack}(0, \text{Ack}(0, 2)))))$$
$$= \text{Ack}(0, \text{Ack}(0, \text{Ack}(0, \text{Ack}(0, 3))))$$
$$= \text{Ack}(0, \text{Ack}(0, \text{Ack}(0, 4)))$$
$$= \text{Ack}(0, \text{Ack}(0, 5))$$
$$= \text{Ack}(0, 6)$$
$$= 7$$

We presume that the reader is familiar with a situation in computer science where the depth of function or subroutine nesting increases and decreases in the same way as in the above interpretation of $Ack(x, y)$: the ALGOL 60 run-time stack processing of procedure calls, especially of recursive procedure calls (such as Ack). Based on our experience of programming simulate, we suppose that we can code such a stack as number, and program a GRF version grfack of Ack as a stack-transforming function:

$$grfack(x, y) = pop(transform(initializestack(x, y)))$$

where $initialize(x, y) = push(y, push(x, emptystack))$ initializes the stack, pop removes the top of stack, and:

transform(stackinit) = **valof** \$(**let** stack = stackinit

while stacklength(stack) $\neq 1$

do stack := processstack(stack)

resultis stack

\$)

actually interprets Ack. The functions push, pop, and stacklength are determined by the particular coding system for stacks represented as numbers; Ackermann's function determines the function processstack so that, for example:

$$processstack([1120]) = [1111]$$

since $Ack(2, 0) = Ack(1, 1)$. Clearly:

transform(stackinit) =

Genmin(stacklength, 1, processstack, stackinit)(stackinit)

CHECKPOINT 5.2 Complete the programming of grfack.

5.3 A TM compiler for the GRF

Our aim in this section is to indicate briefly how to build a compiler for the general recursive functions:

compiler : **GRF** → **TM**

Our approach is to build Turing machines to compute the base GRF succ, pred, c_0, and the p_{ni}, and then to show how to handle the strategies compos, recn, and Min. By "handling the strategies" we mean in the sense of structural induction; suppose for example that:

$$f = compos(g, (h_1, \ldots, h_n))$$

then we assume (inductively) that we already have compiled Turing machines

$M_1, \ldots, M_n, M_g$ to compute $h_1, \ldots, h_n, g$ respectively, and show how to put them together to realize M_f to compute f. In machine terms, we think of M_f as having $M_1, \ldots, M_n$ and M_g wired-in; in programming terms we think of $M_1, \ldots, M_n$ and M_g as subroutines. Thsi approach is strikingly similar to the way many compilers operate on the linguistic structures (which as we pointed out in Section 4.1 are rather similar to the strategies) of ALGOL 60 say. Consider the statement:

if boolexp **then** stat$_1$ **else** stat$_2$

which is constructed by the (two-armed) conditional linguistic structure out of the boolean expression boolexp and the statements stat$_1$ and state$_2$ (which themselves might be quite complex). Typically, the machine code that would be planted by a compiler for the conditional statement would look like:

compiled code to evaluate boolexp
Jump if false to L_1
compiled code to execute stat$_1$
Jump to L_2
L_1: compiled code to execute stat$_2$
L_2:

Handling the strategies raises the problem of putting together a number of circle-and-arrow diagrams to effect subrouting linkage. Suppose we want to call

M_1 to compute $h_1(x)$. Clearly we do not want M_1 to enter its halt state! Rather, we want to deflect arrows within M_1 which lead to the halt state and lead them instead to appropriate resumption points. We might indicate this as follows:

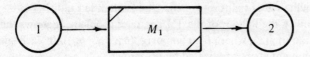

The idea is that the arrow from state 1 leads to the start state of M_1; the arrows leading to the halt state of M_1 are led instead to state 2. We presume of course that no confusion results between using 1 and 2 as state names outside and inside the circle-and-arrow diagram for M_1. This is of course precisely the problem of clash of variable names, particularly label names, inside and outside a subroutine. There are two ways to handle it for TMs:

(a) Make sure the problem never occurs by naming each new state with a name supplied by a unique-name generator.

(b) By detailing a scope system as in ALGOL 60.

The fact that the strategies compos, recn, and Min require us to wire together machines that themselves in general have machines wired-in means that we must obey certain programming disciplines. Continuing with our example, we first apply $M_1, \ldots, M_n$ in turn to the argument strip x to get $h_1(x), \ldots, h_n(x)$ and then finally set up $h_1(x), \ldots, h_n(x)$ as an argument strip for M_g. We clearly need to:

(1) Ensure that such workspace as is needed by M_2 say does not cause information such as $g_1(x)$ or x, which will be needed later on, to be overwritten.

(2) Know where temporary results such as $g_1(x)$ are stored on the tape so that they can later be retrieved and passed to M_g.

Rules such as (1) and (2) are familiar to computer scientists in the guise of the run-time stack of block-structured languages such as ALGOL. We take our cue from this, and impose the following restriction on compiled TMs over and above those listed in Definition 2.5.

(a) Only the half tape to the right of the rightmost ';' is to be used as work space.

(b) The half tape to the left of the right-hand ';' is to be the same at the end of the computation as at the beginning. (One step to take in this direction is to try not to visit any squares to the left of the left-hand ';'.)

It is interesting to note that mathematicians have reached the same conclusions; indeed they have dignified the extra conditions with a name: "standard" Turing-computable (Hermes, 1965, para. 15).

CHECKPOINT 5.3   Design Turing machines to compute the base GRF in accordance with rules (a) and (b) above.

The handling of the strategies compos, recn, and Min seems inescapably

messy and profligate in terms of use of space. The main reason for this appears
to be the lack of pointer words by which subroutines and parameters may be
linked, and the fact that arguments occupy whole regions of tape delimited by
punctuation rather than single computer words whose contents can easily be
accessed. The following set of snapshots of the tape is intended to bring out
these points and convey the flavour of the TM compiler problem. It shows the
trace of the execution of $f(x)$, where $f = \text{compos}(g, (h_1, \ldots, h_n))$. In each snap-
shot the current argument strip is indicated by up-arrows.

$$; x ;$$

$$; x ; h_1(x)$$

$$; x ; h_1(x) ; x ; h_2(x)$$

$$\vdots$$

$$; x ; h_1(x) ; x ; h_2(x) ; \ldots ; x ; h_n(x)$$

$$; x ; h_1(x) ; x ; h_2(x) ; \ldots ; x ; h_n(x) ; h_1(x), \ldots, h_n(x)$$

$$; x ; h_1(x) ; x ; h_2(x) ; \ldots ; x ; h_n(x) ; h_1(x), \ldots, h_n(x) ; f(x)$$

CHECKPOINT 5.4 Fill in the details of the construction of M_f.

The way to compile $\text{recn}(g, h)$ and $\text{Min}(f, k)$ can similarly be deduced from
the traces of their interpreter Definitions 4.2 and 4.3; we shall be content to
develop $\text{recn}(g, h)$ a little further and leave $\text{Min}(f, k)$ as an exercise. Recall that if
$f = \text{recn}(g, h)$ then:

$$f(x, y) = \text{valof } \$(\ r := g(x)$$

$$\text{for } i = 1 \text{ to } y \text{ do}$$

$$r := h(x, i, r)$$

$$\text{resultis } r$$

$$\$)$$

The majority of the processing is in the **for**-loop which requires us at each stage
to set up the argument strip:

$$; x, i, f(x, i - 1);$$

and call M_h. Thus we get skeletal traces:

$$; x, 1, f(x, 0) ; f(x, 1)$$

$$; x, 1, f(x, 0) ; f(x, 1) ; x, 2, f(x, 1) ; f(x, 2)$$

and so on. Only two problems remain, namely starting the **for**-loop going and stopping the **for**-loop after y cycles. The initial argument strip is:

$; x, y ;$

If y is zero (comma adjacent to semicolon), just copy x, execute M_g, and halt. Otherwise, copy x, execute M_g to write $g(x)$, which equals $f(x, 0)$, onto the tape and then set up the argument strip:

$; x, 1, f(x, 0) ;$

in readiness for the processing of the **for**-loop. To stop the **for**-loop simply copy y, reduced by 1 at each step, and test for zero. Here is a sequence of snapshots describing the computation of $f(x, 2)$; notice the use of '*' to mark the position of information that is to be picked up later:

$; x, 2 ;$
$\uparrow \quad \uparrow$

$; x, 2 ; x ; g(x)$
$\qquad \uparrow \ \uparrow$

$; x, 2 * x, g(x) ; x, 1, g(x)$
$\uparrow \qquad\qquad\qquad \uparrow$

$; x, 2 * x, g(x) ; x, 1, g(x) ; f(x, 1)$
$\qquad\qquad \uparrow \qquad\qquad \uparrow$

$; x, 2 ; x, g(x) * x, 1, g(x), f(x, 1) ; 2 - 1 ; 2 - 1 \neq 0$
$\qquad\qquad\qquad\qquad\qquad\qquad \uparrow \qquad \uparrow$

$; x, 2 ; x, g(x) ; x, 1, g(x), f(x, 1), 2 - 1 * 2 - 1 \neq 0 ; x, 2, f(x, 1)$
$\qquad\qquad \uparrow \qquad\qquad\qquad\qquad\qquad\qquad\qquad\qquad \uparrow$

$; x, 2 ; x, g(x) ; x, 1, g(x), f(x, 1), 1 * 2 - 1 \neq 0 ; x, 2, f(x, 1) ; f(x, 2)$
$\qquad\qquad\qquad\qquad\qquad\qquad\qquad\qquad\qquad \uparrow \qquad\qquad \uparrow$

$; x, 2 ; x, g(x) ; x, 1, g(x), f(x, 1), 1, 1 \neq 0 * x, 2,$

$\qquad f(x, 1), f(x, 2) ; 1 - 1 ; 0 = 0$
$\qquad\qquad\qquad\qquad\qquad \uparrow \qquad \uparrow$

$; x, 2 ; x, g(x) ; x, 1, g(x), f(x, 1), 1, 1 \neq 0 ; x, 2,$

$\qquad f(x, 1), f(x, 2) ; 0, 0 = 0 ; f(x, 2)$
$\qquad\qquad\qquad\qquad\qquad\qquad\qquad \uparrow$

CHECKPOINT 5.5 Perform an analysis of $\text{Min}(f, k)$ similar to the above analysis of $\text{recn}(g, h)$.

5.4 Numbers as data structures

In Section 5.2 we assumed that it is possible to treat a single number as a data structure; in particular, we assumed the existence of functions which:

(1) Constructed such data structures

tmcode(M)

initialize$(x_1, \ldots, x_n)$

(2) Selected components of such data structures

sel-state(infpack)

pop(stack)

lookup(tm, state, char)

(3) Updated components of such data structures

next(tm, infpack)

processstack(stack)

We now want to justify this assumption.

It may be objected that hardly any justification is necessary, since it is normal computing practice to treat certain numbers as data structures. If D is a data structure, then D will normally be stored in an area of memory and the components of D will be obtained from the origin point of D by executing an appropriate traversal process. If n is the origin point of D, the traversal algorithm decides whether to interpret n as a datum or an address specifier. In the former case n is returned or altered as appropriate. In the latter case, a contents function is applied to part of n to given another number contents component (n), and the process repeated.

This objection is perfectly reasonable, except that we are really not programming but doing mathematics, in which case the preceding paragraph may be interpreted as a first attempt to develop a mathematical semantics of data structures. [For a more highly developed attempt, see C.A.R. Hoare (1973).] In fact, the concept of address is unknown in traditional mathematics (see Strachey, 1967) and it is possible to implement data structures as numbers without introducing the idea. Such implementations have been known since Gödel (1931) showed how logical expressions could be coded as numbers (see Example 5.2). In order to focus discussion, we consider the problem of coding a Turing machine as a number, posed as Checkpoint 2.25. Suppose that the TM has m states $s_1, \ldots, s_m$ and n characters $i_1, \ldots, i_n$ and is defined by the following table of quintuples:

$$
\begin{array}{ccccc}
s_{11} & i_{11} & i_{12} & s_{12} & d_1 \\
s_{21} & i_{21} & i_{22} & s_{22} & d_2 \\
& & \vdots & & \\
s_{k1} & i_{k1} & i_{k2} & s_{k2} & d_k
\end{array}
$$

where $s_{uv} \in \{s_1, \ldots, s_m\}$, $i_{uv} \in \{i_1, \ldots, i_n\}$, and $d_u \in \{L, R, N\}$.

EXAMPLE 5.1 (Binary plus punctuation) The states s_u, inputs i_u, and directions L, N, and R are represented appropriately by binary numbers, the digits 2 to 9 being used for punctuation. The above TM might be presented as a single (long) number as follows:

4	k	3	s_{11}	2	i_{11}	2	i_{12}	2	s_{12}	2	d_1	3	s_{21}	$\cdots$	4

It may be objected that such a scheme is ridiculous; all but the simplest Turing machines generate enormous numbers which are very difficult to update, traverse, or select components from. It should be remembered however that we are giving *constructive existence* proofs as part of meta computer science, not trying to devise an efficient or non-redundancy coding scheme for which one would (naturally) use a high-level programming language.

EXAMPLE 5.2 (Gödel numbering) An entirely different approach, deriving from Gödel (1931), is based on the unique factorization theorem from number theory. According to this theorem, any number can be expressed uniquely as a product of powers of prime numbers; for example:

$$360 = 2^3 * 3^2 * 5$$

Thus the TM quintuple:

$$s_{u1} \quad i_{u1} \quad i_{u2} \quad s_{u2} \quad d_u$$

can be represented by the number:

$$n_u = 2^{s_{u1}} * 3^{i_{u1}} * 5^{i_{u2}} * 7^{s_{u2}} * 11^{d_u}$$

And the entire TM by the number:

$$2^k * 3^{n_1} * 5^{n_2} * \ldots$$

CHECKPOINT 5.6 Why is it important that the factorization into a product of prime powers be unique?

CHECKPOINT 5.7 Show how a coding mechanism could be based on the Cantor enumeration (Theorem 3.5).

EXAMPLE 5.3 The 'information packets' used in programming simulate in Section 5.2 required us to be able to code a TM tape as a single number. The following solution derives from Minsky (attributing Wang, 1957) (1967, p. 170). Consider the tape configuration:

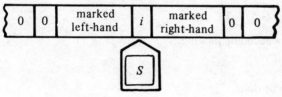

The tape is naturally divided into a right half and a left half about the scanned square. The information packet can be represented using Gödel numbering as follows:

$$\text{infpack} = 2^s * 3^i * 5^{rh} * 7^{lh}$$

where rh and lh are numbers representing the left and right halves of the tape. Consider rh:

Since the tape is only ever finitely inscribed, k is finite and rh can be represented by the finite number:

$$rh = a_0 + 2 * a_1 + 2^2 * a_2 + \ldots + 2^k * a_k$$

The advantage of this representation is that the selector and updater functions are particularly simple since a TM can only ever move one square left or right at a time.

CHECKPOINT 5.8 Use the representation outlined in the preceding Example to implement the functions initialize, sel-stat, next, and extractresult used in programming simulate.

We conclude this section with a brief discussion of the notion of coding. The basic idea is very simple: we have a set S of objects that we wish to process in some way. The point is that it is usually more convenient or efficient to deal with a particular representation of the elements of S for reasons dictated by the kinds of process involved. For example, it is usual in computer science or telephony to deal with bit-string representations of symbolic information since the processors involved are constructed from bistable (that is, 2-state) devices. More precisely, if T is the set of objects chosen as representations of S, we have a function:

$$\text{code} : S \to T$$

We clearly need to be able to decode coded representations of elements of S, otherwise any information coded into T would be lost forever. To make this precise, define:

$$T_1 = \{\text{code}(s) | s \in S\} \subseteq T$$

and suppose we have a decoding function:

$$\text{decode} : T_1 \to S$$

We clearly want to insist that:

all s in S, $\text{decode}(\text{code}(s)) = s$

all t in T_1, $\text{code}(\text{decode}(t)) = t$

$$(5.2)$$

In fact, these requirements severely restrict the possible choices for code and decode:

LEMMA 5.5 Both code and decode must be 1-1.

Proof. We only give the proof for code; that for decode is exactly similar. We are to show that for all s_1, s_2 in S:

$$\text{code}(s_1) = \text{code}(s_2) \text{ implies } s_1 = s_2$$

The proof is trivial. By (5.2):

$s_1 = \text{decode}(\text{code}(s_1))$

$\quad = \text{decode}(\text{code}(s_2)$ //by assumption

$\quad = s_2$ //by (5.2)

It is however not sufficient merely to insist that code and decode be mutually inverse and hence 1-1. Clearly the incorporation of coding mechanisms such as are described in the above examples into programs such as simulate or Ack suggests that code and decode at least must be computable. Furthermore, the introduction of the subset T_1 of T should suggest that in general code will not be onto: that is, T_1 will be a proper subset of T. Certainly this is true of Gödel numbering where it will usually be quite a complex task to show that a given number n (element of T) is in fact a Gödel number (element of T_1). As a result we insist that T_1 be decidable in T. Gathering all of these ideas together we can finally define:

DEFINITION 5.1 A pair of functions code $: S \rightarrow T$ and decode $: T_1 \rightarrow S$, where $T_1 = \{\text{code}(s) | s \in S\}$, is a *coder–decoder pair* in the case that:
  (i) code and decode are computable;
  (11) code and decode are mutual inverses, and hence are both (1-1);
  (iii) T_1 is decidable relative to T.

CHECKPOINT 5.9 Prove that the Gödel numbering of Turing machines defines a coding mechanism according to Definition 5.1.

PART TWO

Towards a Theory of Computer Science

6 McCarthy's Pioneering Studies

6.1 Introduction

In Section 1.2 we introduced John McCarthy as the outstanding pioneer worker in the theory of computation, and argued that two of his major contributions were the formulation of a list of problems with which the emergent theory should concern itself, and the development of a set of methods and a formalism in his initial analyses of those problems. His work contributed to many areas of computer science, and suggests rich inter-relationships between them. It is indeed notable that most prominent computer scientists have contributed to many facets of the subject. This can be contrasted with the typical situation in older sciences such as mathematics or physics, in which the vast majority of workers only contribute to a single highly specialized area of the subject. The following list of McCarthy's early technical achievements outlines the structure of the chapter.

(a) *The development of a* (mathematical) *formalism in which to express the results and concepts of the theory of computation*
The extent to which appropriate languages or formalisms are an important part of the development of a science is an issue that we cannot reasonable take up here. The reader is referred to the impact of logical languages, set theory, and vector notation on the practice of mathematics. We introduce McCarthy's formalism in Section 6.2, and hope to demonstrate its value in the rest of the chapter.

(b) *A preliminary theory of a class of (non-numerical) symbolic expressions called S-expressions*
Traditional mathematics has largely been concerned with properties of numbers, or with essentially unstructured data spaces such as sets, which are abstracted from numbers. Even algebra and topology, which attempt to generalize about certain kinds of relational and spatial structure, essentially only support the use of numerical computations to elicit their substructures.

Computers on the other hand should more properly be called 'information processing machines', since their early application to computing the numerical parameters of missile trajectories distracted attention from their more profound use as machines able to process symbolic data capable of representing a wide variety of kinds of information so that the conceptual structure of that data was manifest. McCarthy (1963) argued that numbers were far too restrictive to express adequately the various kinds of information that the theory of computation needed to handle, and introduced for this purpose a class of symbolic expressions called S-expressions. His aim was essentially to develop a calculus of S-expressions analogous to number theory. S-expressions are introduced in Section 6.3.

(c) *Application of the formalism: the equivalence of programs*

In the early 1960's, recursion was a new and highly controversial feature of programming languages such as ALGOL 60. The overwhelming majority of programs were iterative; in particular they were directly representable by flow charts, which were widely used programming aids. Since McCarthy's formalism necessitated the use of recursion for nontrivial programs, he investigated the extent to which recursive programs and iterative programs were interchangeable or equivalent. He also developed the technique of 'recursion induction' for proving pairs of recursive programs such as the 91-function (p. 14) equivalent. This technique, and others like it, was expected to play an important role in developing the calculus of symbolic expressions alluded to above. We discuss this application of the formalism in Section 6.4.

(d) *Application of the formalism: the semantics of programming languages*

We discussed in Section 1.2 the circumstances leading to the development of BNF notation as a means of precisely specifying the syntax of programming languages. Moreover, we mentioned how the problems raised by use of English in the ALGOL 60 report to specify the semantics of each syntactic construct led to the problem of giving a precise specification for semantics also. In Section 6.5 we describe McCarthy's application of his formalism to the semantic problem, based on the idea that the meaning of a program can be expressed in terms of the change it effects in the state vector of an idealized interpreter.

(e) *Application of the formalism: proof checking*

McCarthy (1962b), muses on the potential impact on mathematics and engineering of a program capable of checking alleged mathematical proofs. The notion of 'proof' is generalized to mean any information that, when supplied to a verification process, is sufficient to enable that process to prove that the alleged theorem is indeed a theorem. More particularly, proofs are to be regarded as programs for generating relevant applications of rules of inference. There were few developments of proof checking systems following McCarthy (1962b) until Milner (1972) described a sophisticated interactive implementation of a proof checker for Dana Scott's logic for computable functions (LCF). Work on the LCF system continues, while McCarthy's own most recent work has been with Weyrauch and others on a proof checking system FOL (Weyrauch and Thomas, 1974) based on first-order predicate logic rather than on LCF. This work is considered to be too recent for inclusion in this introductory text.

6.2 McCarthy's formalism

We begin this section by arguing the need for a *new* formalism for the theory of computer science different from those presented in Part 1 of the book: finite state machines (FSM), Turing machines (TM), and general recursive functions (GRF). There is no suggestion that the formalism that we shall describe below is the 'final solution'; rather we may expect that the development of computer science will always proceed hand in hand with the development of increasingly richer formalisms and programming systems, as important ideas and results are crystallized into notation.

The first point to notice is that, if it is to help at all with the problems outlined in Section 1.2, any formalism for the theory of computer science must be capable of representing all programs and algorithms. That is to say, by Turing's thesis, any suitable formalism must have the expressive power of TM or GRF. We observed in Section 2.4 that this rules out the use of FSMs as 'suitable' in general, although it should be recalled that we also made the point (it is made more fully in Chapter 1) that FSMs are suitable for a particular class of problems that typically involve a small number of states (so that arguments based on the necessary repetition of some state are reasonable to use).

Now we can ask why we need a *new* formalism as opposed to using the older, established formalisms TM, GRF, and so on presented in Part 1. We have repeatedly made the point that those formalisms were expressly designed for use in *meta*-computer science; their simplicity makes them ideal for proving the kind of results *about* computer science introduced in Chapter 3. But this very simplicity also makes them hard to use *within* computer science to 'program', or prove computable, non-trivial functions. We showed in Chapters 2, 4, and 5 how primitive the control structure for TM and GRF 'programs' is, mainly because it is based on integer calculations. 'Programming' in the TM or GRF is rather like using a primitive machine code; continuing that analogy, we need a formalism that is more like a high-level programming language in that it enables the succinct description of a wide range of interesting computable functions.

CHECKPOINT 6.1 Why not directly base a formalism for computer science on a high level programming language such as ALGOL 60, FORTRAN, or PL/1? (Hint: What is the relationship between a programming language and a formalism for computer science?)

McCarthy's suggested formalism, which we now describe, is based on an idea similar to that underlying the GRF: there is a set F of base or primitive functions, and a set C of functionals or strategies for building new functions out of old, the claim being that the closure $C(F)$ comprises all computable functions. Actually, McCarthy just suggested a set C_{MC} of strategies, leaving the user to define a base set F appropriate to his data structures. For numerical computation, F might be the primitive functions of the GRF, which, as we saw in Section 4.2, were based on Peano's axiomatization of arithmetic. In the following section we define S-expressions, and a corresponding set F_{LISP} of functions. C_{MC} consists of generalized composition, conditional expressions, and recursion. We have met generalized composition already (Section 4.2), in the guise of the composition operator of the GRF. Recall how compos generalizes function nesting and provides a form of sequencing. The other two strategies are new and are discussed briefly in turn.

Conditional expressions
McCarthy (1963, p. 36) observed that it is common in mathematics to define functions *by cases*. This usually involves a schema such as in the following definition of the function abs, which gives the absolute value of its argument:

$$\text{abs}(x) = \begin{cases} x & x \geqslant 0 \\ -x & \text{otherwise} \end{cases}$$

His idea was to make the dependence of the value abs(x) on the boolean quantity $x \geqslant 0$ more explicit, while at the same time linearizing the definitional schema:

$$\text{abs}(x) = (x \geqslant 0 \to x, \text{true} \to -x)$$

More generally, a conditional expression takes the form:

$$(p_1 \to e_1, \ldots, p_n \to e_n)$$

and corresponds to the ALGOL 60 expression:

if p_1 **then** e_1

else if p_2 **then** e_2

.

.

.

else if p_n **then** e_n

(Actually, ALGOL 60 syntax insists on a final **else** clause, but that is irrelevant for our explanatory purpose.)

Of course this is all very familiar, as most programming languages have included conditional expressions since McCarthy (1959b) suggested their incorporation into ALGOL 60.

The flow diagram on the next page embodies a process for the valuation of the above conditional expression:

EXAMPLE 6.1
   (i) $(1 < 2 \to 4, 1 \geqslant 2 \to 3) = 4$
   (ii) $(2 < 1 \to 3/0, 2 > 1 \to 4) = 4$
   (iii) $(2 < 1 \to 1, 3/0 = 7 \to 5)$ is undefined

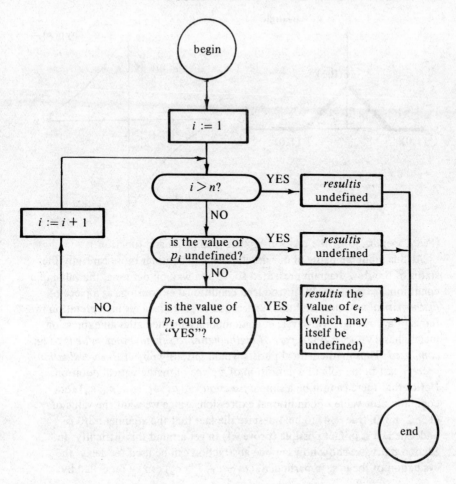

CHECKPOINT 6.2 What is the value of each of the following conditional expressions?

(i) $(1 < 2 \to 5, 1 < 2 \to 6)$

(ii) $(2 < 1 \to 5, 3 < 1 \to 6)$

(iii) $(1 < 2 \to 3/0, 1 = 2 \to 4)$

CHECKPOINT 6.3 What is the value of the conditional expression $(79 \to 4, 1 < 2 \to 3)$? If, as a result, you are dissatisfied with the above flow-chart, say how it might be modified.

CHECKPOINT 6.4 Use conditional expressions to define the functions triangle and hyp, whose graphs are as follows:

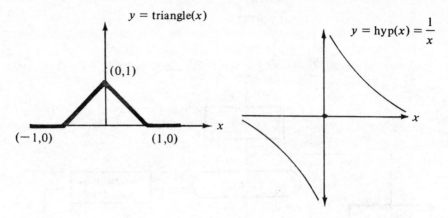

(See Appendix A for the relationship between graph and function.)

At this point we pause in our development to consider more carefully the status of the flow diagram presented above as a way of 'defining' the value of a conditional expression. We introduced conditional expressions as a piece of *mathematical* notation, and then proceeded to give a *process* interpretation in terms of a flowchart. However, in contemporary mathematics an expression merely has a value; *it is not part of mathematics to say how that value is to be computed*. Thus mathematical purists would seriously object to an *evaluation process* cast in the role of a definition of a piece of mathematical notation. Notice that there cannot be a simple *function* $\text{val}(p_1, e_1, \ldots, p_n, e_n)$ for computing the value of conditional expressions, since we want the value of $(1 > 2 \rightarrow 3/0, \text{true} \rightarrow 4)$ to be 4 despite the fact that the argument $3/0$ is undefined. It is in fact possible (prove it!) to get around this difficulty. In Section 8.3.1, we show how lambda abstraction can be used to 'delay' the evaluation of the e_i's. In particular, $(p_1 \rightarrow e_1, T \rightarrow e_2)$ can be modelled by:

$$[\text{ifasfn}(p_1)(\lambda(\ ).e_1, \lambda(\ ).e_2)](\ )$$

where ifasfn is a function that returns a second-argument-selector function when applied to false and a first-argument-selector function when applied to true. This model will probably be easier to understand when we discuss it again in Section 8.3. It is the author's opinion that the understanding of conditional expressions *fundamentally* involves understanding a process, and we take the above problem as suggestion of an inadequacy of modern mathematics rather than as indicative of the inappropriateness of conditional expressions as a part of a mathematical formalism. We recall that a similar problem was raised by our interpreter definition of the Min operator (p. 106) and its generalization Genmin (p. 120). It is the author's belief that modern mathematics is too rigidly based on the static 19th century notions of set theory and logic, and that it needs changing to incorporate the idea of process. Similar remarks apply to the interpretation process for recursive function definitions given below; but we will let this discussion suffice.

CHECKPOINT 6.5 The flowchart definition uses conditional execution to define conditional expression evaluation, and is thus circular! The flowchart merely reinforces your understanding of the process of conditional execution irrespective of whether it is correct. How could you change the flowchart to avoid this problem? [This is quite difficult: see Reynolds (1972, Section 4) for a solution if you cannot derive one.]

We recall that a *predicate* is a function, such as less : $N \times N \to$ {true, false}, whose value set is {true, false}. Of course we usually prefer to write $x < y$ rather than less(x, y). All of the propositional connectives such as **and** are predicates and can be defined by conditional expressions, for example:

$$p \text{ and } q = (p \to q, \text{true} \to \text{false})$$

CHECKPOINT 6.6 Use conditional expressions to define p **or** q, **not** p, p **implies** q and p **notboth** q.

CHECKPOINT 6.7 Give example values to p and q to show that when **and** and **or** are defined in this way they are not commutative: that is p **and** $q \neq q$ **and** p. Do you think **and** and **or** should be commutative? If so, say how you would define them; if not, say why not.

Recursion

The idea of recursion is familiar to anybody who has programmed in LISP, ALGOL 60, or the majority of more recent programming languages. Basically, a procedure is recursive if its evaluation with one set of arguments ever requires the evaluation of a subexpression consisting of an application of the procedure to another set of arguments. Thus, to quote the time-honoured example, the factorial function can be defined recursively by:

$$\text{fac}(x) = (x = 0 \to 1, x * \text{fac}(x - 1))$$

in which the evaluation of fac(3) necessitates the evaluation of fac(2). A good introduction to the subject of recursion in programming is given by Barron (1969). The value of recursive procedure definitions as a programming language feature was a very vexed question throughout the 1960's but (probably) no longer is; Barron (1969) gives a considered account of most of the issues involved.

The recursion strategy in McCarthy's formalism allows one to give recursive definitions such as fac above.

EXAMPLE 6.2 The function power(x, y) computing x^y can be defined in McCarthy's formalism as follows:

$$\text{power}(x, y) = (y = 0 \to 1, \text{true} \to x * \text{power}(x, y - 1))$$

CHECKPOINT 6.8 (i) Give a recursive definition of the function gcd computing the greatest common divisor. (ii) Give a recursive definition of $x + y$ in terms of the successor function. In both cases compare your definitions with GRF definitions of the same functions.

Up to now, the discussion of recursion has been very intuitive; we have not, for example, given an interpreter definition analogous to the above flowchart interpretation for conditional expressions. (We shall see why in Section 6.4.) We shall partly correct this omission below with a pair of English rules specifying the evaluation of applications of recursively defined functions; the reader is invited to give a more precise account in Checkpoint 6.10. To motivate the rules, consider the evaluation of 3^2 relative to the above definition of power:

$$\text{power}(3, 2) = (2 = 0 \rightarrow 1, \text{true} \rightarrow 3 * \text{power}(3, 1))$$

$$= 3 * \text{power}(3, 1) \quad //\text{evaluation of conditional expression}$$

To complete the evaluation, we need to consider power$(3, 1)$:

$$\text{power}(3, 1) = (1 = 0 \rightarrow 1, \text{true} \rightarrow 3 * \text{power}(3, 0))$$

$$= 3 * \text{power}(3, 0)$$

By a similar process(!):

$$\text{power}(3, 0) = 1$$

so that finally:

$$\text{power}(3, 2) = 3 * 3 * 1 = 9$$

The two rules are: (1) evaluate conditional expressions as before; (2) if a sub-expression $f(b)$ occurs, replace it by the right-hand side of the definition of $f(x)$ with b substituted for x throughout.

Notice that we have implicitly suggested that the general form of a recursive definition is:

$$f(x) = \epsilon(x, f)$$

where $\epsilon(x, f)$ is a (usually conditional) expression of the formalism involving the variable(s) x and f. We can more generally define a whole set $f_1, \ldots, f_n$ of functions simultaneously or 'mutually' by recursion. Barron (1969, Section 2.2) gives examples of mutual recursion naturally arising in compiling techniques.

EXAMPLE 6.3 We define mutually recursive functions f and g as follows:

$$f(x) = (x = 0 \rightarrow 1, \text{true} \rightarrow f(x-1) * g(x))$$

$$g(x) = (x \leqslant 1 \rightarrow 2, \text{true} \rightarrow f(x-2) * g(x-1))$$

CHECKPOINT 6.9 Extend the evaluation rules given above to evaluate $f(2)$. Do the evaluations of $f(a)$ and $g(a)$ terminate for all integers a? How would you prove that they do?

CHECKPOINT 6.10 Give a BNF syntax for the legal expressions of McCarthy's formalism. Write an interpreter program to evaluate those legal expressions.

A postscript on naming functions[*]

So far in this section we have been 'fortunate' that all the functions we have considered have had obvious mnemonics such as abs. Such mnemonics not only provide a name but also convey *by that name* the meaning of the function. Sadly, not every function has an obvious mnemonic. Consider, for example, a function of two arguments x and y which squares the first and adds the second to produce $x^2 + y$. Of course, we could call it 'addsecondtosquareoffirst' or some such thing, but that would be an unfortunate precedent. Alternatively, we could invent a totally spurious name such as 'fred'; but then the name no longer conveys the meaning. Fortunately, Church (1941) invented a technique called λ-*notation* of giving a standard or *default name* to any function we either cannot or do not want to name by a mnemonic, with the property that the name conveys the meaning. For example, the problematical function just discussed would be named:

$$\lambda(x,y) \cdot x^2 + y$$

The (x,y) part of this name is called the *bound-variable part* and the $(x^2 + y)$ part is called the *body*. Notice the close resemblance between such a name and a procedure declaration in ALGOL 60 (say): the bound variable part is analogous to the formal parameter part, and the body to the procedure body. In fact, the treatment of procedures in many programming languages has been consciously based on the λ-notation. (See Section 8.2 for details.)

The λ-*notation* should not be confused with the λ-*calculus*, but almost invariably is. The λ-notation is just a way of giving a systematically complicated default name to any function. The λ-*calculus* refers to a set of conversion rules invented by Church (1941) which allows one λ-name to be converted or changed into another. The conversion rules variously reflect the operations of renaming bound variables, applying a function to a set of arguments, and so on. Church (1941) argued that the λ-calculus embodied a precise definition of 'computable'; his sytem has the same power as Turing machines (see Section 1.1). The λ-calculus is discussed in more detail in Section 8.2.

Consider a definition involving a mnemonic such as:

$$abs(x) = (x \geqslant 0 \to x, \text{true} \to -x).$$

There is a simple process called λ-*abstraction* which can be applied to this definition to give the default name:

$$abs = \lambda x \cdot (x \geqslant 0 \to x, \text{true} \to -x)$$

CHECKPOINT 6.11 Use λ-abstraction on your solutions to Checkpoints 6.4 and 6.6 to generate default names.

[*] The reader may recall that the following discussion was foreshadowed in Chapter 4 in the introduction of compos, recn, and min as default or standard names, and in Section 3.4.1 in discussions of unsolvability.

There is a problem in applying λ-abstraction to recursive definitions such as fac:

$$\text{fac} = \lambda x \cdot (x = 0 \to 1, x * \text{fac}(x - 1))$$

which does not work since the default name still involves 'fac'. It is very tempting to conclude that the λ-notation is incapable of naming recursively defined functions; surprisingly, this is not so, as we now demonstrate. Consider the general form:

$$f(x) = \epsilon(x, f)$$

By λ-abstraction we have:

$$f = \lambda x \cdot \epsilon(x, f)$$

where there may be several occurrences of f in a variety of positions on the right-hand side. We achieve just one occurrence of f in a standard position as follows:

$$f = \{\lambda g \cdot \lambda x \cdot \epsilon(x, g)\}(f)$$

since the application of the λ-name in curly brackets to f merely substitutes f for g throughout $\epsilon(x, g)$. Now $\lambda g \cdot \lambda x \cdot \epsilon(x, g)$ is a functional, say F, which takes f as an argument. We have:

$$f = F(f)$$

so that f is a *fixed point* of F, just as 0,1 are the fixed points of square (that is, $\lambda x \cdot x^2$) and $-2,3$ are the fixed points of $\lambda x \cdot x^2 - 6$. What we do now is show that there is a function Y, which has a rather complex λ-name (but a λ-name nonetheless), and which, when applied to F, yields one of its fixed points f. That is:

$$Y(F) = f$$

so that we can take:

$$Y(\lambda g \cdot \lambda x \cdot \epsilon(x, g))$$

as the λ-name for f. The development of Y is based on the following (amazing trick!): we want to find f so that $F(f) = f$. This is solved by:

$$f = \text{selfapply}(h) \text{ where } h = \lambda y \cdot F(y(y))$$

since

$$
\begin{aligned}
f &= h(h) && \text{//definition of selfapply} \\
&= \{\lambda y \cdot F(y(y))\}(h) && \text{//definition of } h \\
&= F(h(h)) && \text{//substitute } h \text{ for } y \text{ in the body} \\
&= F(f) && \text{//since } f = h(h)
\end{aligned}
$$

Now we can derive a λ-name for Y. Selfapply has λ-name $\lambda g \cdot g(g)$, so the full λ-name for f is:

$$\{\lambda g \cdot g(g)\}(\lambda y \cdot F(y(y)))$$

Now we have:

$$Y(F) = f$$

so that finally:

$$Y = \lambda G \cdot \{\lambda g \cdot g(g)\}(\lambda y \cdot G(y(y)))$$

Y was invented by Curry and Feys (1958) and is called the *paradoxical combinator* because, as we saw in Chapter 1, selfapply generates a number of paradoxes. The development of Y has a number of interesting theoretical consequences (see Chapter 8); it is not suggested as a *practical* mechanism for evaluating recursively defined function applications!

CHECKPOINT 6.12 How could the above derivation of Y be extended to handle a set of mutually recursive function definitions. [This is rather difficult; see Scott and Strachey (1971) if desperate.]

6.3 S-expressions

The symbolic data structures called S-expressions analysed by McCarthy (1960) (McCarthy *et al.*, 1962) are essentially binary trees with identifiers called 'atoms' for their leaves. Such data structures were not chosen arbitrarily but because of their intended application to an ambitious Artificial Intelligence project known as the Advice Taker, preliminary considerations for which were outlined by McCarthy (1959). The Advice Taker was to be capable of solving a wide range of problems; clearly, in order to solve some externally posed problem an intelligent program must first be capable of having it described to it. Such problem descriptions are naturally symbolic as opposed to numerical. Consequently the overwhelming majority of Artificial Intelligence studies have been concerned with the processing of symbolic data.

There are a number of problems associated with the efficient processing of symbolic data on a computer with a conventional (von Neumann) store organized as a vector of sequentially numbered cells. These are problems that imply that setting aside a predetermined amount of contiguous storage, which is the implementation technique normally used to support efficient numerical computation, is inappropriate for computing with symbolic structures. In particular:

(1) It is a pragmatic fact that programs that process symbolic data tend to require data structures that grow unpredictably large. As a result, storage must be allocated incrementally if it is to be used sparingly and efficiently.

(2) Symbolic information processing tends to call for the replacement of a substructure, say of size l, by one of size m, where l and m vary unpredictably. This subsumes the cases of insertion ($l = 0$) and deletion ($m = 0$). Since it is generally the case that $l \neq m$, it is inappropriate to store whole structures in contiguous memory blocks.

These problems had been faced as early as the mid-1950's by (amongst others) Newell, Shaw, and Simon, in connection with their Artificial Intelligence studies known as the Logic Theorist and General Problem Solver programs [see Newell, Shaw, and Simon (1956), Newell and Simon (1963)]. The result was a set of techniques known collectively as *list processing*.

A full account of list processing is somewhat tangential to our aims [see Knuth (1968b) or Foster (1967)]; however, the basic principle is easy enough to describe. Instead of working with large blocks of contiguous storage, one organizes memory into *nodes* consisting of two components, either of which may contain either information relevant to the problem or a pointer to another such node. For example, Fig. 6.1(a) shows four nodes $n1$ to $n4$; the components of $n2$ and $n4$ both contain information, both components of $n1$ contain pointers, while $n3$ has one of each sort. Fig. 6.1(b) illustrates one way in which the structure depicted in Fig. 6.1(a) might be stored in a conventional computer memory.

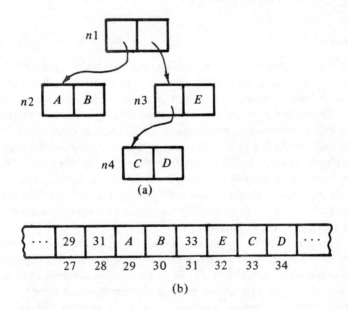

(a)

(b)

Fig. 6.1

New nodes are incrementally obtained from a central reservoir called the *free storage list* which initially contains a large proportion of the available storage linked together in the form of a list. Nodes can be inserted into, or deleted from, data structures, by simple routines that respectively take a node from, or return one to, the free storage list.

S-expressions are based on the observation that data structures such as the one illustrated in Fig. 6.1(a) have the form of binary trees with the useful information held at the leaves. McCarthy called the information at the leaves 'atoms', while S-expressions refer to a particular linear representation of binary trees. Fig. 6.2 shows the S-expression corresponding to the binary tree depicted in Fig. 6.1(a).

$$((A \cdot B) \cdot ((C \cdot D) \cdot E))$$

Fig. 6.2

The syntax of S-expressions can be specified by the following BNF productions:

⟨ S-expression ⟩ :: = ⟨ atom ⟩ | (⟨ S-expression ⟩ · ⟨ S-expression ⟩))
    | ⟨ list ⟩ | ⟨ list-structure ⟩

⟨ list ⟩ :: = ({⟨ atom ⟩}$_0^\infty$)

⟨ list-structure ⟩ :: = ({⟨ S-expression ⟩}$_0^\infty$)

S-expressions of the second alternative form are often called *dotted pairs*.

EXAMPLE 6.4
  (i) Dotted pairs: $(A \cdot B)$
                        $(F \cdot (A \cdot B))$
                        $((A \, B \, C) \cdot ((D) \cdot E))$
  (ii) Lists $(A \, 7 \, B)$
                        $(\ )$
  (iii) List structures: $((A \cdot B) \, C \, D)$
                        $((A \cdot B))$
                        $(A \, B \, C \, D)$

CHECKPOINT 6.13 Draw the binary trees corresponding to the following dotted pairs: $(A \cdot B)$, $(F \cdot (A \cdot (B \cdot C)))$, $(((A \cdot B) \cdot (C \cdot D)) \cdot (E \cdot F))$. Write a program to produce such drawings of S-expressions.

⟨ list ⟩s and ⟨ list-structure ⟩s are in fact a special case of dotted pairs, and were introduced as a convenient shorthand for the programmer when it was found in practice that one frequently wanted to *order* the atoms within a data structure. It is clearly more convenient to write $(A \, B \, C)$ than its equivalent longhand form $(A \cdot (B \cdot (C \cdot \text{NIL})))$. We shall give below a rule for translating lists and list structures into their longhand equivalent dotted pairs.

We now describe the set F_{LISP} of primitive functions defined on S-expressions, analogous to the primitive functions of the GRF. Together with the set C_{MC} of strategies of McCarthy's formalism presented in the preceding section, F_{LISP} generates the set $C_{\text{MC}}(F_{\text{LISP}})$ of computable functions of S-expressions. The name F_{LISP} reflects the implementation of the computable functions $C_{\text{MC}}(F_{\text{LISP}})$ as a programming language LISP, which will not be discussed here (see McCarthy *et al.*, 1962, or Weissman, 1967). The functions atom, eq, car, cdr, and cons in F_{LISP} clearly reflect our characterization of S-expressions as linearized binary trees:*

(1) The predicate *atom*: S-expression → {true, false} tests whether an S-expression has the form of an atom or is a non-degenerate tree. For example:

atom $[A]$ = true

atom $[(A \cdot B)]$ = false

atom $[(A\ B)]$ = false

(2) The predicate *eq*: S-expression × S-expression → {true, false} tests for equality or identity of atoms. It is not defined unless both of its arguments are atoms. For example:

eq$[A, A]$ = true

eq$[A, B]$ = false

eq$[A, (A \cdot B)]$ is undefined

eq$[(A \cdot B), (A \cdot B)]$ is undefined

(3) The selectors *car*, *cdr*: S-expression → S-expression compute the left and right subtree of their argument S-expression; naturally they are undefined in case their argument is an atom. For example:

car$[(A \cdot B)]$ = A

cdr$[(A \cdot B)]$ = B

car$[((A \cdot B) \cdot (C \cdot D))]$ = $(A \cdot B)$

cdr$[((A \cdot B) \cdot (C \cdot D))]$ = $(C \cdot D)$

car$[A]$ is undefined

The reader may well be wondering why the selectors are called 'car' and 'cdr' instead of more obvious mnemonics such as 'left' and 'right', or, anticipating our scheduled discussion of list notation, 'head' and 'tail'. The reason is rooted in history; LISP was originally developed for the IBM 704,709 series of computers; these had $32K$ ($= 2^{15}$) words of storage, each consisting of two 16 bit half words called the address register and decrement register. The least significant 15 bits of each half word could be used in list processing to specify an address, that is, to point to another node. For this reason (!), the two subtree selectors were called 'car' and 'cdr', which respectively were acronyms for '*c*ontents of *a*ddress *r*egister' and '*c*ontents of *d*ecrement *r*egister'. It was only after a good deal of

---

* We use square brackets to denote function application to avoid confusion with the circular brackets used in S-expressions.

thought that the author decided to perpetuate these ugly machine-oriented names; in the end, he did so to avoid confusing anybody wishing to deepen his understanding of this chapter by programming in LISP. We applaud systems such as POP-2 (Burstall, Collins, and Popplestone, 1971) which have ignored this tradition.

(4) The constructor function *cons*: S-expression × S-expression → S-expression builds a tree t out of its arguments lt, rt such that $car[t] = lt$, $cdr[t] = rt$. For example:

$$\text{cons}[A, B] = (A \cdot B)$$

$$\text{cons}[((A \cdot B) \cdot C), D] = (((A \cdot B) \cdot C) \cdot D)$$

CHECKPOINT 6.14 What are the values of the following expressions:

(i) $\text{cons}[(A \cdot B), (C \cdot D)]$

(ii) car and cdr applied to $(((A \cdot B) \cdot C) \cdot ((A \cdot B) \cdot D))$

(iii) $\text{car}[\text{cdr}[\text{cons}[(A \cdot B), ((C \cdot D) \cdot E)]]]$

It is easy to see that the following properties hold for the functions in F_{LISP}:

(a) $\text{car}[\text{cons}[a, b]] = a$

(b) $\text{cdr}[\text{cons}[a, b]] = b$

(c) $\text{cons}[\text{car}[l], \text{cdr}[l]] = l$, so long as l is not atomic.

We shall use these properties in the following section.

List notation
We observed above that a commonly occurring problem in symbolic information processing is the construction of a data structure that clearly reflects a conceptual ordering of the items of data in the data structure. The obvious solution is to list the items; the problem then arises of representing lists as S-expressions, that is to say, as binary trees. A list is a naturally sequential structure in which to access the $(n + 1)$st item one has successively to access the first through nth.

Since 'accessing' in the context of S-expressions means using car and cdr, we might depict a first attempt to represent the list L containing atoms A, B, C, and D (in that order) as in Fig. 6.3.

Observe that with this representation:

$$A = \text{car}[L]$$

$$B = \text{car}[\text{cdr}[L]]$$

$$C = \text{car}[\text{cdr}[\text{cdr}[L]]]$$

These relationships suggest accessing the $(n + 1)$st element of a list L by computing $\text{car}[\text{cdr}^n[L]]$. Unfortunately this fails for the last element D of L, since

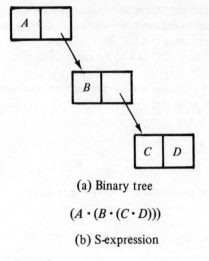

(a) Binary tree

$(A \cdot (B \cdot (C \cdot D)))$

(b) S-expression

Fig. 6.3

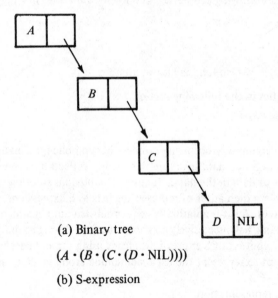

(a) Binary tree

$(A \cdot (B \cdot (C \cdot (D \cdot \text{NIL}))))$

(b) S-expression

Fig. 6.4

$$D \neq \text{car}[\text{cdr}[\text{cdr}[\text{cdr}[L]]]]$$

The idea behind list notation is to fix on a standard atom NIL (to represent the empty tree) so as to make the relationships generally applicable, even to the last element of a list. The modified representation is shown in Fig. 6.4.

The S-expression shown in Fig. 6.4(b) can be given in the shorthand form

$(A\ B\ C D)$. We can write a recursive function list-to-pair which describes a process for converting list notation into the corresponding longhand dotted pair as follows:

$$\text{list-to-pair}\,[(\epsilon_1 \ldots \epsilon_n)] \;=\; (n \;=\; 0 \rightarrow \text{NIL},$$

$$\text{true} \rightarrow (\epsilon_1 \cdot \text{list-to-pair}\,[(\epsilon_2 \ldots \epsilon_n)]))$$

EXAMPLE 6.5 The following examples illustrate applications of the function list-to-pair:

$(A) = (A \cdot \text{NIL})$
$(A\ B) = (A \cdot (B \cdot \text{NIL}))$
$(\ ) = \text{NIL}$

CHECKPOINT 6.15 Write down the longest longhand forms of the following list structures:

(i) $((A)\ B)$; (ii) $((A\ B)(C \cdot D))$; (iii) (NIL).

CHECKPOINT 6.16 By considering the longhand forms, *deduce* the effect of car, cdr, and cons on lists with reference to the following examples:

car$[(A\ B\ C)]$ cdr$[(A\ B\ C)]$

car$[((A)\ B)]$ cdr$[((A)\ B)]$

car$[(((A)))]$ cdr$[(((A)))]$

car$[\text{NIL}]$

CHECKPOINT 6.17 Prove that the cdr of a list structure is a list structure. Prove that cons$[S, L]$ is a list structure for any S-expression S and list structure L.

Computable functions of S-expressions
The computable functions of S-expressions comprise the set $C_{\text{MC}}(F_{\text{LISP}})$; we conclude this section with some examples.

EXAMPLE 6.6 We have seen that the atom NIL plays a special role with regard to list notation. We can define a predicate null that tests to see if its argument is NIL:

$$\text{null}\,[l] \;=\; (\text{atom}\,[l] \rightarrow eq\,[l, \text{NIL}], T \rightarrow F)$$

For our application in the following section, we need to add a fourth relationship to the three given on p. 151:

(d) null$[\text{cons}\,[a, b]] = \text{false}$

Notice that in null we first have to test that l is atomic since eq is otherwise not defined. This particular problem is solved by the following checkpoint.

CHECKPOINT 6.18 Write a function equal that tests for equality of two arbitrary S-expressions (trees).

EXAMPLE 6.7 We define a predicate member that tests whether an atom x occurs in a list l:

$$\text{member}[x, l] \; = \; (\text{null}[l] \to \text{false}, \, eq\,[x, \text{car}[l]] \to \text{true},$$
$$\text{true} \to \text{member}[x, \text{cdr}[l]])$$

This kind of function, which successively works its way through a list by applying cdr, is called a *cdr-loop*, since (as we shall see below) it embodies an essentially iterative process despite its recursive definition.

CHECKPOINT 6.19 Write a function length that computes the number of atoms in a list.

EXAMPLE 6.8 The function append takes two lists as arguments and glues them together, so that for example:

$$\text{append}[(A\,B\,C), (D\,E)] \; = \; (A\,B\,C\,D\,E)$$
$$\text{append}[k, l] \; = \; (\text{null}[k] \to l,$$
$$\text{true} \to \text{cons}[\text{car}[k], \text{append}[\text{cdr}[k], l]])$$

In the following section, we shall use the technique of recursion induction to show that:

$$\text{length}[\text{append}[k, l]] \; = \; \text{length}[k] + \text{length}[l]$$

CHECKPOINT 6.20 Define the following functions in $C_{\text{MC}}(F_{\text{LISP}})$. You should use null, append, and so on, without re-definition.
  (i) *reverse* applied to a list reverses it.
  (ii) *interleave*, applied to $(A\,B\,C)$ and $(D\,E\,F)$, produces $(A\,D\,B\,E\,C\,F)$.
  (iii) *union* merges two lists to produce their set-theoretic union; for example,
        union $[(A\,B\,C\,D), (D\,E\,B)] = (A\,B\,C\,D\,E)$.
  (iv) *powerset* of a list, for example $(A\,B\,C)$, produces a list structure representation of its power set:

$$((A\,B\,C)\,(A\,B)\,(A\,C)\,(B\,C)\,(A)\,(B)\,(C)\,\text{NIL})$$

6.4 Application of the formalism: equivalence of programs

One of the goals of the theory of computation listed in Section 1.2 was the development of techniques for proving the equivalence of programs. This section presents McCarthy's influential early skirmishes with the problem (1962a, 1963).

As a hopefully simple first case, he considered loop-free schemas such as that depicted in Fig. 6.5. (See Section 3.4.3, p. 75 for the idea of a schema.)

He observed that loop-free schemas can be represented directly and succinctly

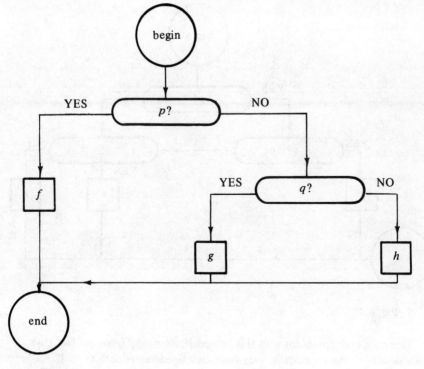

Fig. 6.5

by conditional expressions; in the case of Fig. 6.5, the expression is $(p \to f, q \to g, h)$. [In this section we use $(p \to a, b)$ as an abbreviation for $(p \to a, \text{true} \to b)$.] There are four possible truth value combinations for p and q, potentially leading to three different computations; Fig. 6.6 summarizes them.

p	q	Effect of computation
T	T	f
T	F	f
F	T	g
F	F	h

Fig. 6.6

Fig. 6.6 is reminiscent of a truth table, and indeed suggests using a modified form of truth tables to prove equivalence.

CHECKPOINT 6.21 Give the conditional expression and 'truth table' representing the schema shown in Fig. 6.7.

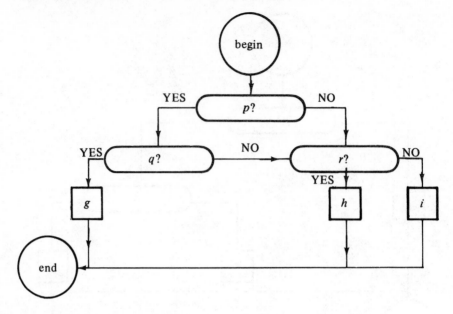

Fig. 6.7

There is a slight problem with this approach, stemming from the fact that tests in conditional expressions may have undefined values such as "3/0 = 1". If p is such a test, then the value of $(p \rightarrow f, g)$ is undefined. In particular, our naive expectation that $(p \rightarrow f, f)$ is equivalent to f turns out to be wrong. The solution is to extend the normal two-valued logic in which propositional variables may only assume the values true and false to a three-valued logic in which they may also assume the value undefined. The 'truth table' for $(p \rightarrow f, g)$ in this three-valued logic is:

p	Effect of computation
true	f
false	g
undefined	undefined

Pairs of schemas that give the same 'truth table' in the three-valued logic are called *strongly-equivalent* (written $=_s$); if they give the same 'truth table' in the two-valued logic they are called *weakly-equivalent* (written $=_w$). Clearly strong equivalence implies weak equivalence. From our discussion above, $(p \rightarrow f, f)$ is weakly, but not strongly, equivalent to f. Fig. 6.8 shows a pair of strongly equivalent schemas.

In order to prove mathematical relationships (for example equivalence) the usual mathematical practice for the past century or so has been to devise logical systems in which theorems can be established, starting from appropriate rules of inference and accepted truths called axioms. The axioms of a logic of equivalent

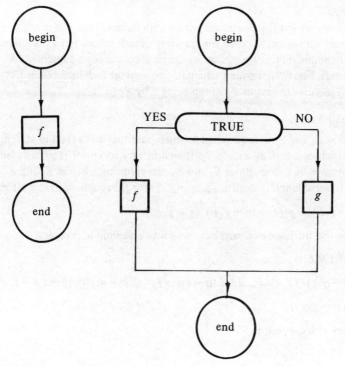

Fig. 6.8

loop-free schemas (or conditional expressions) correspond to pairs of 'obviously' equivalent schemas such as those shown in Fig. 6.8. McCarthy (1963, p. 55) suggested the following eight axioms:

(E1) $(p \to f, f) =_w f$
(E2) $(\text{true} \to f, g) =_s f$
(E3) $(\text{false} \to f, g) =_s g$
(E4) $(p \to \text{true}, \text{false}) =_s p$
(E5) $(p \to (p \to f, g), h) =_s (p \to f, h)^*$
(E6) $(p \to f, (p \to g, h)) =_s (p \to f, h)^*$
(E7) $((p \to q, r) \to f, g) =_s (p \to (q \to f, g), (r \to f, g))$
(E8) $(p \to (q \to f, g), (q \to h, i)) =_s (q \to (p \to f, h), (p \to g, i))$

CHECKPOINT 6.22 Draw the pairs of equivalent schemas corresponding to axioms (E3)–(E8).

Having specified the axioms of the logic of equivalence, we now have to give the rules of inference; there are two: substitution and replacement.

---

* Compare this with the discussion of redundant tests in schemas on p. 76.

Replacement

If S is a subexpression (or subschema) of an expression T, and if S is replaced by an equivalent expression S_1, then the resulting overall expression T_1 is equivalent to T. For example, Fig. 6.9(a) shows a schema T containing a subschema S (broken lines), Fig. 6.9(b) gives a schema S_1 equivalent to S (use axiom E1), and Fig. 6.9(c) pictures the result T_1 of replacing S by S_1 in T.

Substitution

Suppose that S_1 and S_2 are equivalent schemas, and that x is a (test or statement) variable which occurs in S_1 and/or S_2. If an arbitrary schema T is substituted for each occurrence of x throughout S_1 and S_2, the resulting schemas S_1' and S_2' are equivalent. For example, substituting $(q \to g, h)$ for f throughout axiom E1 gives:

$$(q \to g, h) =_w (p \to (q \to g, h), (q \to g, h))$$

We now use the logic of equivalence to prove an example theorem.

THEOREM 6.1

$$((p \to q, r) \to f, g) =_w (r \to (q \to (p \to f, f), (p \to g, f)), (q \to (p \to f, g),$$
$$(p \to g, g)))$$

Proof (McCarthy, 1963, p. 55ff)

By E7:

$$((p \to q, r) \to f, g) =_s (p \to (q \to f, g), (r \to f, g))$$

By E1 and substitution, we get:

$$(p \to (r \to (q \to f, g), (q \to f, g)), (r \to f, g))$$

We now use E8 to change the order of p and r:

$$(r \to (p \to (q \to f, g), f), (p \to (q \to f, g), g))$$

By E1 and two simple substitutions, we get:

$$(r \to (p \to (q \to f, g), (q \to f, f)), p \to (q \to f, g), (q \to f, g)))$$

We finally use E8 (twice) to change the order of p and q:

$$(r \to (q \to (p \to f, f), (p \to g, f)), (q \to (p \to f, g), (p \to g, g)))$$

which is the right-hand side.

CHECKPOINT 6.23 Prove that $(p \to (q \to a, b), (q \to c, d)) =_s (q \to (p \to (p \to a, b), c), (p \to b, (p \to a, d)))$.

In the proof of Theorem 6.1, we used axiom E8 whenever we wanted to change the order of tests; by a similar process we can replace any conditional expression by an equivalent 'canonical' form in which the tests are performed in a predetermined order. Clearly, two expressions are equivalent if and only if their canonical forms are equivalent. McCarthy (1963, p. 56ff) shows how the equivalence problem can be automated by a program that generates such canonical forms.

With a slight modification, the above technique of translating a loop-free schema into a conditional expression can be extended to translate a general schema into a set of recursive function definitions in McCarthy's formalism. It is obvious that an execution instance of a schema with loops can only terminate if the values of some of the variables, which are tested to determine the flow of control, are altered in the loop bodies. As in Section 3.4.3, we are straightaway led to the idea of program variables (see p. 80) or a *state vector x* consisting of an association of the variables manipulated by the program and their values. We shall attempt to define the transformation $A(x)$ effected on the state vector x

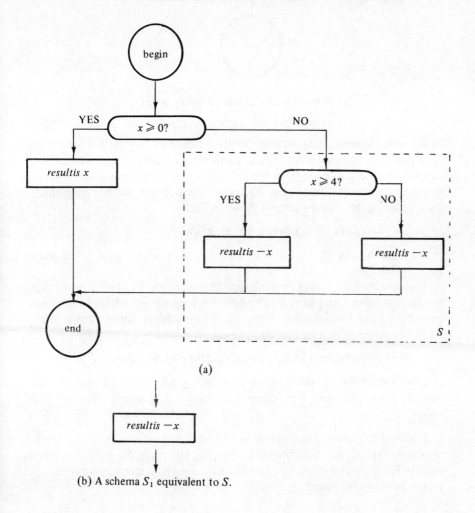

(a)

(b) A schema S_1 equivalent to S.

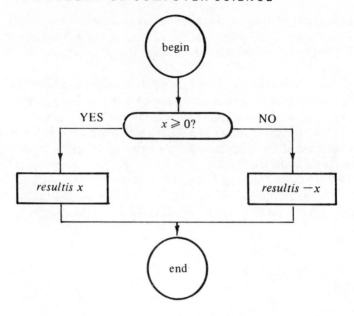

(c) The result of replacing S by S_1 in (a).

by the whole schema in terms of the predicates and functions within the schema. (This implicitly entails a point of view about the semantics of programs and schemas that we shall consider in more detail in the following section.) This makes no significant difference in the case of the loop-free schemas considered above; for example, for the schema shown in Fig. 6.5:

$$A(x) = (p(x) \rightarrow f(x), (q(x) \rightarrow g(x), h(x)))$$

Fig. 6.10 shows a schema involving a loop that is a modification of the one in Fig. 6.5.

The only change to $A(x)$ occurs in case both $p(x)$ and $q(x)$ are false, so that $h(x)$ is computed. After $h(x)$ is computed, the program loops back to the point just before $p(x)$ is tested, which is the start of the schema. Remembering that function nesting provides sequencing, we get:

$$A(x) = (p(x) \rightarrow f(x), (q(x) \rightarrow g(x), A(h(x))))$$

CHECKPOINT 6.24 Modify the schema in Fig. 6.7 so that the i-computation leads back into the p-test. Write down the corresponding recursive function definition.

It should be clear that in this way any iterative process can be directly translated into a set of recursive function definitions. Moreover, any iterative process leads to function definitions in which the recursive applications assume the particular restricted form:

$$A(x) = \ldots \rightarrow A(x')$$

Not surprisingly, McCarthy (1962a, p. 25) called such function definitions 'iterative'. The predicate 'member' defined in Example 6.7 is in iterative form, whereas the traditional definition of the factorial function given on p. 143 is not. The reader may care to try to design an iterative schema that directly translates into the definition of factorial. We should be clear that, although it is obviously possible (either by Turing's thesis or inspection of an iterative interpreter for a language having recursion) to find an iterative program P_1 equivalent to any given recursive program P_2, the translation from P_2 to P_1 is by no means direct, and generally involves simulating a stack evaluator.

For this reason, in order to prove recursively defined functions equivalent, it is clearly better to develop techniques that work directly with the recursive definitions than via some translation into iterative schemas. McCarthy's contribution was a technique that he called 'recursion induction'.

Suppose that we have recursively defined functions g and h which we want to prove equivalent.* *The principle of recursion induction* asserts that we may conclude that g is equivalent to h if we can find an equation:

$$f(x) = \epsilon(x, f)$$

that we can prove: (1) defines a function f; and (2) is satisfied by both g and h.

Recursion induction is intended for use in proving the equivalence of computable functions of symbolic S-expressions. However, to introduce the method, we prove a couple of simple theorems about numbers. Denoting the successor and predecessor of x by x^+ and x^- respectively, we can define addition as follows:

$$x + y = (x = 0 \rightarrow y, x^- + y^+)$$

THEOREM 6.2 $(x + y)^+ = x + (y^+)$

Proof (McCarthy, 1963, p. 59ff) The equation:

$$f(x, y) = (x = 0 \rightarrow y^+, f(x^-, y^+)) \tag{6.1}$$

clearly (actually, a simple induction proof is needed) specifies a function which is defined for all x, y greater than zero. We want to show that the functions $g(x, y) = (x + y)^+$ and $h(x, y) = x + (y^+)$ satisfy Equation (6.1). First g:

---

* Actually, this is not quite right. A function is a set of ordered pairs, and so two functions can be *equal* (as such sets) but not equivalent. Equivalence refers to programs. The distinction between a program (say in LISP) and the associated computable function of S-expressions is blurred throughout McCarthy's treatment of recursion induction. Recursion induction is really used for proving the equality of two computable functions (in McCarthy's formalism) that have different specifications. In line with other published work, we shall continue to use the word 'equivalent'.

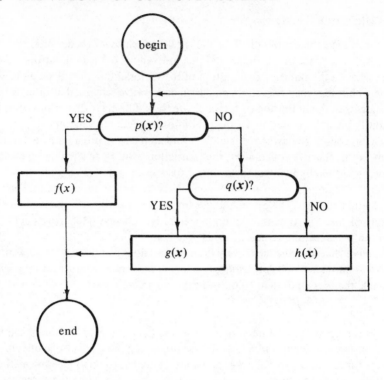

Fig. 6.10

$$g(x,y) = (x+y)^+ \qquad\qquad //\text{definition of } g$$
$$= (x = 0 \to y, x^- + y^+)^+ \qquad //\text{definition of addition}$$
$$= (x = 0 \to y^+, (x^- + y^+)^+) \quad //\text{property of conditional}^*$$
$$= (x = 0 \to y^+, g(x^-, y^+)) \qquad //\text{definition of } g$$

so that g does indeed satisfy Equation (6.1). Finally h:

$$h(x,y) = x + (y^+) \qquad\qquad //\text{definition of } h$$
$$= (x = 0 \to y^+, x^- + (y^+)^+) \quad //\text{definition of addition}$$
$$= (x = 0 \to y^+, h(x^-, y^+)) \qquad //\text{definition of } h$$

so that h also satisfies (6.1). By the principle of recursion induction we conclude that g is equivalent to h.

CHECKPOINT 6.25   Use the principle of recursion induction to prove that $(x+y)^+ = (x^+) + y$. (Hint: use an alternative definition of addition which counts down on y.)

---

* Compare the BCPL expressions $f(p \to a, b)$ and $p \to f(a), f(b)$.

COROLLARY 6.3 $(x+y)+z = x+(y+z)$.

Proof. We use the equation:

$$f(x,y,z) = (x = 0 \to (y+z), f(x^-,y,z)^+) \qquad (6.2)$$

An easy application of Theorem 6.2 shows that $h(x,y,z) = x + (y+z)$ satisfies Equation (6.2). On the other hand:

$$
\begin{aligned}
(x+y)+z &= (x = 0 \to y, x^- + y^+) + z &&\text{//definition of addition} \\
&= (x = 0 \to y+z, (x^- + y^+) + z) &&\text{//property of conditional} \\
&= (x = 0 \to y+z, (x^- + y)^+ + z) &&\text{//Theorem 6.2} \\
&= (x = 0 \to y+z, ((x^- + y) + z)^+) &&\text{//Checkpoint 6.25}
\end{aligned}
$$

so that the left-hand side also satisfies (6.2).

In the remainder of the section we apply the principle of recursion induction to computable functions of S-expressions. We shall use the functions append (Example 6.8), length (Checkpoint 6.19), and reverse (Checkpoint 6.20(i)); for convenience we reproduce them here:

$$\text{append}[x,y] = (\text{null}[x] \to y, \text{cons}[\text{car}[x], \text{append}[\text{cdr}[x],y]])$$

$$\text{length}[x] = (\text{null}[x] \to 0, \text{length}[\text{cdr}[x]]^+)$$

$$\text{reverse}[x] = (\text{null}[x] \to \text{NIL}, \text{append}[\text{reverse}[\text{cdr}[x]],$$

$$\text{cons}[\text{car}[x], \text{NIL}]])$$

We shall also need the following properties of S-expressions (pp. 151 and 153):

(S1) $\text{car}[\text{cons}[a,b]] = a$
(S2) $\text{cdr}[\text{cons}[a,b]] = b$
(S3) $\text{cons}[\text{car}[a], \text{cdr}[a]] = a$, if a is not atomic
(S4) $\text{null}[\text{cons}[a,b]] = \text{false}$

THEOREM 6.4 $\text{length}[\text{append}[x,y]] = \text{length}[x] + \text{length}[y]$

The practical significance (for LISP programs) of Theorem 6.4 is a considerable saving of space and time. We need the following Lemma:

LEMMA 6.5

(i) $\text{length}[\text{cons}[x,y]] = \text{length}[y]^+$

(ii) $\text{length}[x] = 0$ iff $\text{null}[x]$

(iii) $\text{length}[\text{cdr}[x]] = \text{length}[x]^-$

Proof. (i) By definition of length:

$$\text{length}[\text{cons}[x,y]] = (\text{null}[\text{cons}[x,y]] \to 0, \text{length}[\text{cdr}[\text{cons}[x,y]]]^+)$$

The proof follows from properties S4 and S2 of S-expressions and axiom E3 of conditionals (p. 157).

(ii) If $\text{null}[x] = \text{true}$, $\text{length}[x] = 0$ from axiom E2 of conditionals. If $\text{null}[x] = \text{false}$, then by property S3 of S-expressions and axiom E3, $\text{length}[x] = \text{length}[\text{cdr}[x]]^+$, which is not zero, by definition of the successor function.

(iii) Use (i) and (ii).

We can now prove Theorem 6.4 by recursion induction. We shall use the following equation:

$$f[x, y] = (\text{null}[x] \rightarrow \text{length}[y], f[\text{cdr}[x], y]^+) \tag{6.3}$$

As in the proof of Theorem 6.2, we merely observe that Equation (6.3) clearly defines a function. If $g[x, y] = \text{length}[\text{append}[x, y]]$:

$$g[x, y] = \text{length}[\text{append}[x, y]]$$

$$= \text{length}[(\text{null}[x] \rightarrow y, \text{cons}[\text{car}[x], \text{append}[\text{cdr}[x], y]])]$$

//definition of append

$$= (\text{null}[x] \rightarrow \text{length}[y], \text{length}[\text{cons}[\text{car}[x],$$
$$\text{append}[\text{cdr}[x], y]]])$$

//property of conditional

$$= (\text{null}[x] \rightarrow \text{length}[y], \text{length}[\text{append}[\text{cdr}[x], y]]^+)$$

//Lemma 6.5(i)

$$= (\text{null}[x] \rightarrow \text{length}[y], g[\text{cdr}[x], y]^+)$$

//definition of g

So that g satisfies (6.3). Now define $h[x, y] = \text{length}[x] + \text{length}[y]$; then:

$$h[x, y] = \text{length}[x] + \text{length}[y]$$

$$= (\text{length}[x] = 0 \rightarrow \text{length}[y], \text{length}[x]^- + \text{length}[y]^+)$$

//definition of addition

$$= (\text{null}[x] \rightarrow \text{length}[y], (\text{length}[\text{cdr}[x]] + \text{length}[y]^+))$$

//Lemma 6.5

$$= (\text{null}[x] \rightarrow \text{length}[y], (\text{length}[\text{cdr}[x]] + \text{length}[y])^+)$$

//Theorem 6.2

So that h also satisfies (6.3).

Theorem 6.4 and Lemma 6.5 suggest an analogy between the successor, predecessor, and addition functions on numbers and the cons, cdr, and append operations on S-expressions. We now invite the reader (in Checkpoint 6.26) to exploit this analogy by generalizing the proof of Corollary 6.3 to prove the associativity of append. This analogy, and the fact that the proof of Theorem 6.2 generalizes to a non-numerical data structure, provides compelling evidence in support of our claim in Section 6.1 that it is possible to develop a calculus of S-expressions, analogous to number theory, which is certain to be of value in the practice of computing.

CHECKPOINT 6.26

(i) Prove that $\text{append}[x, \text{NIL}] = x$ for all lists x

(ii) Prove that $\text{cons}[x, \text{append}[y, z]] = \text{append}[\text{cons}[x, y], z]$

(iii) Prove that $\text{append}[x, \text{append}[y, z]] = \text{append}[\text{append}[x, y], z]$

Here are two further theorems about S-expressions.

THEOREM 6.6 $\text{reverse}[\text{append}[x, y]] = \text{append}[\text{reverse}[y], \text{reverse}[x]]$.

Proof. We use the following equation, which 'clearly' defines a function:

$$f[x, y] = (\text{null}[x] \to \text{reverse}[y], \text{append}[f[\text{cdr}[x], y],$$
$$\text{cons}[\text{car}[x], \text{NIL}]])$$

Define $g[x, y] = \text{reverse}[\text{append}[x, y]]$; then:

$$g[x, y] = \text{reverse}[\text{append}[x, y]]$$
$$= (\text{null}[x] \to \text{reverse}[y], \text{reverse}[\text{cons}[\text{car}[x],$$
$$\text{append}[\text{cdr}[x], y]]])$$

//definition of append

$$= (\text{null}[x] \to \text{reverse}[y], \text{append}[\text{reverse}[\text{append}[\text{cdr}[x], y]],$$
$$\text{cons}[\text{car}[x], \text{NIL}]])$$

//definition of reverse

$$= (\text{null}[x] \to \text{reverse}[y], \text{append}[g[\text{cdr}[x], y],$$
$$\text{cons}[\text{car}[x], \text{NIL}]])$$

So that g satisfies the equation for f. If $h[x, y] = \text{append}[\text{reverse}[y], \text{reverse}[x]]$, then:

$$h[x, y] = \text{append}[\text{reverse}[y], (\text{null}[x] \to \text{NIL}, \text{append}[\text{reverse}[\text{cdr}[x]],$$
$$\text{cons}[\text{car}[x], \text{NIL}]])]$$

//definition of reverse

$$= (\text{null}[x] \to \text{append}[\text{reverse}[y], \text{NIL}], \text{append}[\text{reverse}[y],$$
$$\text{append}[\text{reverse}[\text{cdr}[x]], \text{cons}[\text{car}[x], \text{NIL}]]])$$

//property of conditional

$$= (\text{null}[x] \to \text{reverse}[y], \text{append}[\text{append}[\text{reverse}[y],$$
$$\text{reverse}[\text{cdr}[x]]], \text{cons}[\text{car}[x], \text{NIL}]])$$

//Checkpoint 6.26

which proves that h also satisfies the equation for f.

The following checkpoint is needed as a lemma in the proof of our final theorem.

CHECKPOINT 6.27 Prove that:

(i) $\text{reverse}[\text{cons}[x, \text{NIL}]] = \text{cons}[x, \text{NIL}]$

(ii) $\text{append}[\text{cons}[x, \text{NIL}], y] = \text{cons}[x, y]$

THEOREM 6.7 $\text{reverse}[\text{reverse}[x]] = x$.

Proof. We use $f[x] = (\text{null}[x] \to \text{NIL}, \text{cons}[\text{car}[x], f[\text{cdr}[x]]])$.

Clearly $g[x] = x$ satisfies the equation for f. Define $h[x] = \text{reverse}[\text{reverse}[x]]$. We have:

$$h[x] = (\text{null}[x] \to \text{reverse}[\text{NIL}], \text{reverse}[\text{append}[\text{reverse}[\text{cdr}[x]],$$
$$\text{cons}[\text{car}[x], \text{NIL}]]])$$

//definition of reverse

$$= (\text{null}[x] \to \text{NIL}, \text{append}[\text{reverse}[\text{cons}[\text{car}[x], \text{NIL}]],$$
$$\text{reverse}[\text{reverse}[\text{cdr}[x]]]])$$

//Theorem 6.6

$$= \text{null}[x] \to \text{NIL}, \text{cons}[\text{car}[x], h[\text{cdr}[x]]])$$

//Checkpoint 6.27

CHECKPOINT 6.28 Prove that $\text{length}[x] = \text{length}[\text{reverse}[x]]$.

The above proofs follow established mathematical practice in that they offer no clue whatsoever regarding the discovery of the crucial equation to define f. It is almost suggested that such clues are not necessary, either because they are not 'part' of mathematics, irrelevant to understanding the proof, or obvious to anybody with the appropriate insight. However, if the reader has attempted any of the checkpoints, he will have quickly realized that the discovery of the equation for f is the most difficult and creative part of the proof!

We remarked on a similar phenomenon in Part 1, in our discussion of Ackermann's function (p. 109) and the Grzegrocyck hierarchy (p. 111). In both cases we showed how the choice of function could be quite readily understood in terms of the use to which it was to be put. In the same spirit, we now offer a number of hints regarding the discovery of proofs by recursion induction. We have not a complete theory of the construction of such proofs; rather we have a number of comments and heuristics which we have found useful in constructing the proofs in this section. [It may well be that such heuristics can be included in a program to construct such proofs, although it is a difficult problem in artificial intelligence. The interested reader is referred to the papers of Boyer and Moore (1975), Bundy (1975), and Moses (1970).]

The most important observation is that the *equation for f was developed hand-in-hand with the construction of the proof*. Secondly, such proofs seem to be constructable only when the algorithms to be proved equivalent have a significant procedural structural similarity.[*] For example, it is very difficult to prove $x^+ + y = (x + y)^+$ (see Checkpoint 6.25) with the definition of addition used in the proof of Theorem 6.2. The problem is that the definition of addition leads to terminal tests of the form '$x^+ = 0 \rightarrow y$', and '$x = 0 \rightarrow y^+$', which are hard to relate. This point is highly reminiscent of Dijkstra's criticism (p. 81) of the functional definition of 'equivalent' considered in Chapter 3.

We now discuss two of the above proofs in greater detail.

(1) $\text{length}[\text{append}[x, y]] = \text{length}[x] + \text{length}[y]$ (Theorem 6.4)

We clearly need to use the definitions of length, append, and addition at some stage of the proof; the problem is to decide when. Expanding addition on the right-hand side yields:

$$h[x, y] = \text{length}[x] + \text{length}[y]$$

$$= (\text{length}[x] = 0 \rightarrow \text{length}[y], \text{length}[x]^- + \text{length}[y]^+) \quad (6.4)$$

It is not immediately clear whether to expand length or append on the left-hand side. Expanding length gives:

$$\text{null}[\text{append}[x, y]] \rightarrow 0, \ldots \tag{6.5}$$

whereas expanding append yields:

$$(\text{null}[x] \rightarrow \text{length}[y], \text{length}[\text{cons}[\text{car}[x], \text{append}[\text{cdr}[x], y]]]) \quad (6.6)$$

The initial tests of (6.4) and (6.6) will match if we can show:

$$\text{null}[x] \text{ iff length}[x] = 0$$

which we prove as a lemma [Lemma 6.5(ii)]. We now have to relate the 'else' parts of (6.4) and (6.6), which, in terms of recursion induction proofs, means looking for similar recursive calls on g and h. (6.4) is not very helpful, but (6.6) suggests working towards the recursive call:

$$\text{length}[\text{append}[\text{cdr}[x], y]], \text{ that is, } g[\text{cdr}[x], y]$$

We first need to remove the call of cons; the various facts about S-expressions suggest Lemma 6.5(ii) and the equation:

$$g[x, y] = (\text{null}[x] \rightarrow \text{length}[y], g[\text{cdr}[x], y]^+) \tag{6.7}$$

---

[*] In line with the footnote on p. 161, this should read: "when the functions to be proved equal are defined structurally similarly".

Matching (6.4) to (6.7) suggests using Theorem 6.2 to put the call to succ in the right place, and finally Lemma 6.5(iii).

The most important part of the discovery/proof process outlined above is the *structural* matching of two conditional expressions which generates (or refers to) a number of lemmas about the properties of S-expressions. Matchers that involve such knowledge of S-expressions are programmable (see Hardy, 1976, for example). The difficult part is knowing when to call appropriate theorems in the proof. This problem is crucial in artificial intelligence; the interested reader is referred to Winograd (1972) and Sussman and McDermott (1973).

(2) reverse[reverse[x]] = x (Theorem 6.7)

In this case we get no clues from the right-hand side, and there are two possible calls of reverse to expand on the left. We obey the heuristic used in the proof above, namely to *expand the innermost call*, whose usefulness stems from the fact that it tends to generate tests of the form 'null[x] →'. In this case we get:

$$g[x] = \text{reverse}[\text{reverse}[x]]$$

$$= \text{reverse}[\text{null}[x] \rightarrow \text{NIL}, \text{append}[\text{reverse}[\text{cdr}[x]], \text{list}[\text{car}[x]]]]$$

where list[y] = cons[y, NIL].

$$= (\text{null}[x] \rightarrow \text{reverse}[\text{NIL}], \text{reverse}[\text{append}[\text{reverse}[\text{cdr}[x]]],$$

$$\text{list}[\text{car}[x]]])$$

which suggests proving reverse[NIL] = NIL. We clearly ought to work towards transforming the '**else**' part into the recursive call:

$$\text{reverse}[\text{reverse}[\text{cdr}[x]]] = g[\text{cdr}[x]]$$

which requires us to move the outer call of reverse past the call to append. Fortunately, Theorem 6.6 tells us how to do this, and leads to:

$$\text{null}[x] \rightarrow \text{NIL}, \text{append}[\text{reverse}[\text{list}[\text{car}[x]], g[\text{cdr}[x]]]]$$

This almost completes the proof; Checkpoint 6.27 allows us to simplify to:

$$f[x] = (\text{null}[x] \rightarrow \text{NIL}, \text{cons}[\text{car}[x], f[\text{cdr}[x]]])$$

which $h[x] = x$ clearly satisfies.

6.5 Application of the formalism: the meaning of programming languages

In Section 1.2 we described the background leading up to the development of BNF as a formalism for the precise specification of the syntax of ALGOL 60 and most subsequent programming languages. The semantics of ALGOL 60 were described in its report (Naur, 1963) in paragraphs of English, which were soon found (Knuth, 1967) to be incomplete and to contain a number of errors and ambiguities. Thus an early problem for the theory of computer science was the development of formalisms analogous to BNF in which semantics could be precisely specified. In this section we discuss McCarthy's contributions (1962a, 1966) to the problem; more recent work will be reviewed in Chapter 8.

In order to give the semantics of a programming language L, we first need some way of specifying the well-formed programs $Prog_L$ in L; that is, we need a (precise) syntactic definition of $Prog_L$. Secondly, we need a set M_L of possible meanings of programs in L, so that if P is in $Prog_L$, the meaning of P is in M_L. Finally, we need some way of associating with any program P its meaning. We normally insist that programs should be deterministic: that they should always evoke the same computation and results when presented with the same data. This suggests modelling the meaning of a programming language L by a function:

$$L\text{-means} : Prog_L \to M_L$$

Actually, since we presumably want to be able to compute effectively the meaning of any program P, we presumably need to insist that L-means should be computable. Secondly, by no means every program *is* deterministic, so it is not reasonable in general to insist that L-means should be a function. However, the vast majority of work done to date on the semantics problem has concerned itself with deterministic programming languages. We shall be content in this volume merely to remark that this is a special case.

We now consider $Prog_L$ and M_L in turn.

$Prog_L$

BNF provides a notation for specifying syntax by a set of Post–Chomsky productions (see Section 3.4.4). Since the ALGOL 60 report, BNF has become *the* standard method for defining the syntax of programming languages; but this does not mean that it is the only way, nor does it even mean that it is the most appropriate way when the aim is not writing programs but giving meaning to them.

BNF productions specify $Prog_L$ as a set of legal *strings of (terminal) symbols.* Now the meaning of a program is to a large extent independent of the particular string of symbols chosen to represent it. The ALGOL 60 reporters realized this (Naur 1963, p. 2), and they specified a 'reference' language (which consisted of a *standard* set of strings to represent the various syntactic constructs) to avoid arguments about the difference between, say, '**begin**', 'BEGIN', 'begin', and so on. (Compare this remark with the idea that there is a standard set of strings of decimal numerals to represent numbers that have all leading zeros suppressed.) But the point is somewhat deeper, since *as far as meaning is concerned* (but not, of course, as far as writing actual programs is concerned) it is essentially irrelevant which of the following five forms one chooses to represent the *same* arithmetical expression:

$7 + 5$
$+ 75$ (Polish prefix)

75 +   (Polish postfix)
VII + V   (Roman)
(PLUS 7 5)   (LISP or applicative)

In each case, one expects that the meaning will be 12 (i.e. twelve or XII!).

A note unrelated point on which we dwelt in Section 3.4.4 in our discussion of Chomsky's approach to syntax is that a program has a *grammatical structure* which, although it may be discernible from the set of BNF productions that specify the grammar of the language, is not reflected in its representation as a string of symbols. Compilers know this of course, and they usually form a parse *tree* which directly represents the grammatical structure. Now there is, quite generally, a substantial relationship between grammatical structure and meaning; in particular, the meaning of a syntactic construct is built up in some way from the meaning of its grammatical components. Consequently, what is appropriate in a definition of Prog_L in order to facilitate a formal specification of L-means is that the grammatical structure should be manifest. If, on the other hand, Prog_L is specified by BNF productions, L-means will need to include something like a particular parsing program (see the EULER system of Wirth and Weber, 1966); we might then ask why *that particular* parsing program is better than any other as far as meaning is concerned.

We can illustrate the above points with reference to a simple language E of arithmetical expressions. A set of BNF productions for E are given in Fig. 6.11.

⟨prog⟩ ::= ⟨term⟩|⟨term⟩ + ⟨prog⟩

⟨term⟩ ::= ⟨simple⟩|⟨simple⟩ * ⟨term⟩

⟨simple⟩ ::= ⟨variable⟩|⟨constant⟩|(⟨prog⟩)

⟨variable⟩ ::= ⟨letter⟩{⟨letter⟩|⟨digit⟩}$_0^*$

⟨constant⟩ ::= {⟨digit⟩}$_1^*$

Fig. 6.11

An example program P in E would be $a * (7 + b)$. Instead of working from this string of seven characters to get the meaning of P, we shall work directly in terms of the structure of P. To introduce the method, we have invented a dialogue (see Fig. 6.12) between 'K', who knows all the salient facts about P, and 'U', who wishes to understand. As a result of the dialogue, U can assert that the value of the program is 40, that its structure can be depicted as in Fig. 6.13, and that one particular symbol string representation of it might be $a * (7 + b)$, where $a = 4$ and $b = 3$.

McCarthy observed that the above dialogue can be made precise to yield an

(1) U: Is it a program?   K: Yes.

(2) U: Is it a sum, product, term, or constant?   K: A product.

(3) U: (knowing that products have a multiplier and a multiplicand)
         What sort of thing is the multiplier?   K: A variable.

(4) U: What is its value?   K: 4.

(5) U: What sort of thing is the multiplicand?   K: A sum.

(6) U: (knowing that sums consist of an addend and an augend)
         What sort of thing is the addend?   K: A constant.

(7) U: Which constant?   K: 7.

(8) U: What sort thing is the augend (of the multiplicand of the
         program)?   K: A variable.

(9) U: What is its value?   K: 3.

Fig. 6.12

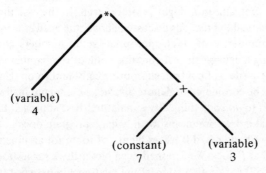

Fig. 6.13

alternative formal specification for syntax that is more appropriate to the problem of giving meaning to programs. The exchanges beginning "what sort of thing
is . . ." can be replaced by four predicates is-sum, is-prod, is-const, and is-vble,
corresponding to the four distinct syntactic structures, so that, at any time, precisely one of them is true. We need two component selectors sel-addend and
sel-augend for the case is-sum is true, and two more sel-mlpr and sel-mpcnd for
the case is-prod is true. In these terms, the eighth question in the dialogue
amounts to:

$$\text{is-var}(\text{sel-augend}(\text{sel-mpcnd}(P)))$$

Fig. 6.14 shows an alternative definition of the syntax of E. It takes the form of
a recursive definition of the predicate is-prog.

is-prog(P) = is-const(P) *or* is-vble(P)

or (is-sum(P) *and* is-prog(sel-addend(P))

and is-prog(sel-augend(P)))

or (is-prod(P) *and* is-prog(sel-mlpr(P))

and is-prog(sel-mpcnd(P)))

Fig. 6.14

CHECKPOINT 6.29 Check that the definition of is-prog really does specify a computable function within the formalism introduced in Section 6.2.

This method of specifying syntax has since been developed by the Vienna Laboratory of IBM (see Section 8.3.4). McCarthy called such a syntactic specification *abstract* and *analytic* in contrast with *concrete* (since it does not fix on a particular external representation) and *synthetic* (since it detailed the analysis of programs rather than their construction or synthesis).

M_L

Having satisfactorily specified the syntax of L, we now turn our attention to the question of what it is that programs in L might possibly mean. In the case that L is the language E of arithmetical expressions discussed above, the answer is fairly obvious: L-means(P) is a number, so M_L is an appropriate set of numbers. But E is not a typical programming language, since it contains none of the familiar commands such as assignment, transfers of control, subroutine calls, and so on. Unlike an expression, which might be considered to denote a *value*, a command *instructs* some executing mechanism to *do* something. Thus, a natural first approach to semantics is to equate 'what a program means' with 'what a program does', although, as we shall see in Chapter 8, this leaves plenty of room for argument about precisely what it is that P does. We foreshadowed McCarthy's suggestion in the preceding section (p. 159) in our discussion of the relationship between iteration and recursion: a program effects a transformation $x_{\text{initial}} \rightarrow x_{\text{final}}$ on a state vector x which describes the association between variables and their values. Thus M_L is the set of functions from states to states, and:

$$L\text{-means}(P)(x_{\text{initial}}) = x_{\text{final}}$$

For the language E of expressions, we can specify E-means as in Fig. 6.15, where lookup (P, x) gives the value associated with the variable P in state x.

CHECKPOINT 6.30 Use E-means to evaluate the program P described in the dialogue shown in Fig. 6.12.

McCarthy (1966) applied this technique to a small subset of ALGOL 60 which had assignment commands and conditional jumps of the form 'if p **then goto** l'. One slight change (which turns out to cause problems for more sophisticated

$$E\text{-means}(P) = \lambda x.(\text{is-const}(P) \rightarrow P,$$

$$\text{is-vble}(P) \rightarrow \text{lookup}(P, x),$$

$$\text{is-sum}(P) \rightarrow E\text{-means(sel-addend}(P), x) +$$

$$E\text{-means(sel-augend}(P), x),$$

$$\text{is-prod}(P) \rightarrow E\text{-means(sel-mlpr}(P), x) *$$

$$E\text{-means(sel-mpcnd}(P), x))$$

Fig. 6.15

languages) was that he had to handle changes of state corresponding to assignment commands. More significantly, the notion of state vector had to be extended to include a program counter in order to handle jumps.

We now present a second example of McCarthy's approach to semantics, this time applied to a very different sort of programming language: the machine language C of a simple one-address computer with a single accumulator (taken from McCarthy and Painter, 1967). Before giving a precise abstract analytic syntax and meaning for C, we informally describe the four commands that comprise it. Notice that there are no commands that cause a transfer of control; as a result, we shall be able to carry over the notion of state used for the expression language E.

LOAD a load the contents of register a into the accumulator
STO a store the contents of the accumulator in the register a
ADD a add the contents of register a into the accumulator
LI x (*L*oad *I*mmediate) place the constant value x in the accumulator

CHECKPOINT 6.31 Write a program in C to place the sum of the squares of the first ten numbers in the accumulator.

Here is a formal syntax for C:

is-cmnd (C) = (is-load (C) *and* is-register(sel-adr (C)))
            or (is-sto (C) *and* is-register(sel-adr (C)))
            or (is-add (C) *and* is-register(sel-adr (C)))
            or (is-li (C) *and* is-value(sel-arg (C)))

A state is a pairing of registers R with values V. Each of the four commands in C cause a change of state, so we have a function:

update $: R \times V \times S \rightarrow S$

so that update(r, v, s) is the state resulting from updating s by planting value v in register r. We can express this by:

lookup$(r_1, \text{update}(r_2, v, s)) = (r_1 = r_2 \rightarrow v, \text{lookup}(r_1, s))$

where, as in the case of E, lookup associates registers with their values.

We observed above that the basis of McCarthy's approach to semantics is to equate what a program means with what it does, so that if P is a program in C (a list of commands in C) C-means(P) describes the outcome of executing P. We define C-means in terms of a function step, which describes the result of executing a single command:

$$\text{step}(c, s) = (\text{is-load}(c) \rightarrow \text{update}(\text{ac}, \text{lookup}(\text{sel-adr}(c), s), s),$$
$$\text{is-sto}(c) \rightarrow \text{update}(\text{sel-adr}(c), \text{lookup}(\text{ac}, s), s),$$
$$\text{is-add}(c) \rightarrow \text{update}(\text{ac}, \text{lookup}(\text{ac}, s) + \text{lookup}(\text{sel-adr}(c), s), s),$$
$$\text{is-li}(c) \rightarrow \text{update}(\text{ac}, \text{sel-arg}(c), s))$$

$$C\text{-means}(P) = \lambda s \cdot \text{null}(P) \rightarrow s, C\text{-means}(\text{rest}(P))(\text{step}(\text{first}(P), s))$$

CHECKPOINT 6.32 Compute C-means(P), where P is the program you wrote to answer Checkpoint 6.31.

CHECKPOINT 6.33 (difficult, but well worth doing) Apply the technique sketched for C above to the machine language of some computer you know. You should begin by deciding what constitutes the 'state' of your computer, and should exclude difficulties such as data transfer commands, interrupts, overflow conditions, etc.

McCarthy's approach to semantics has been substantially developed, particularly by the Vienna Definition Laboratory of IBM Corporation who wanted a precise definition of the highly complex language PL/1, to ensure standard implementations and transportability. The VDL method is sketched in Chapter 8.

As we shall explain in Chapter 7, any precise account of meaning can be used as the basis of an approach to the problem of proving programs correct. McCarthy and Painter (1967) prove the correctness of a compiler from the language E of expressions given above to the machine language C. The proof is notable in that it introduces a proof technique called 'structural induction', which was later developed by Burstall (1969) in his study on correctness. The Vienna Definition Laboratory development of McCarthy's approach has also been used to prove correctness (see Jones and Lucas, 1971).

7 Making Programs Reliable

7.1 Introduction

Many, possibly most, programs in regular use contain bugs. Programmers often complain about bugs in operating systems and compilers, while press accounts of gross mistakes by 'computers', from credit companies blacklisting innocent people, to bills being issued for £0.00 or for massively excessive amounts, are sadly all too familiar. Since it has been estimated (see London 1975, p. 535) that about half the time and cost of any large programming project is currently spent on debugging and testing, it is hard to accuse software companies of not trying to make programs reliable. Unfortunately, current ideas about program building are rather primitive, and the information feedback from most computer systems is extremely sparse, so debugging and testing are haphazard affairs. In particular, it is rarely clear when to stop debugging and pronounce a program reliable; nor can one ever be certain that new bugs have not been introduced into a program while trying to remove old ones.

Often, reliable programs become unreliable when their specifications alter, as a result of their being adapted to a new use or a new environment. Other programs, such as operating systems, never really have fixed specifications; rather the specifications and the program evolve over time. These problems are compounded by the fact that it is notoriously difficult to understand, maintain, modify, or transport a program written by other people.

Altogether, much of current software is unreliable, and unreliability costs a great deal of time, money, resentment, and damage. The advantages to be gained from reliable software have been described by many authors (see, for example, Hoare, 1969, Sections 5 and 6). Typically, they look forward to a time when debugging will be virtually unnecessary, and programs will be cheaper, maintainable, transportable, easily understandable, and modifiable, not to mention more efficient and better structured. In Section 7.5, we reflect on these claims, and offer a rather different interpretation of the work introduced in this chapter.

Let us consider what it might mean to say that a program is 'correct' or 'reliable'.* Since the programs one first meets compute answers, such as roots of

---

* 'correct', 'reliable', 'validated', 'checked', and 'certified' are just some of the terms that have appeared in the literature in connection with reliable software. Hetzel (1974, p. 7) attempts to sort out some of the differences. In what follows, we use 'reliable' and 'correct' interchangably, for we shall argue below that there is in fact no absolute demarcation between testing, which has tended to favour 'reliable', and formal proofs, which use 'correct'.

quadratics, means of distributions, and equations of straight lines, a first guess might be to define a program to be correct if it always gives the right answers. Thus we may assert that:

$$\text{let fac}(n) = n = 0 \to 1, n * \text{fac}(n-1)$$

reliably or correctly computes the factorial function, while:

$$\text{let partlyfac}(n) = (n = 0 \to 1, n = 2 \to 2, n = 5 \to 120, 32)$$

is unreliable or incorrect, since it gives the right answer only if n is 0, 2, or 5. In fact, as Hoare (1969, p. 576) points out, it is not clear that fac should be considered correct, since for any computer installation there is usually a maximum value, say N, that any variable such as n may assume; thus the evaluation of $\text{fac}(N + 1)$ would typically give the wrong answer. However, we shall ignore this problem,[†] since a more serious criticism can be levelled against the 'right answer' definition of 'correct' given above; many programs, such as operating systems, traffic controllers, and chess-playing programs, do not obviously produce answers that are right or wrong; rather, they 'run' or 'behave'. Moreover, even in the case of sorting and searching programs (for example) which do produce answers, it is usually more interesting *how* the answer is produced than the *mere fact* that it is produced. Thus we are led to the idea that a program gives rise to *behaviours*, and we define a program to be reliable or correct if it always behaves as it should. We shall show below how the 'right answer' definition of 'correct' is a special case of this more general definition. For the 'behaviour' definition of 'reliable' to be at all useful, we need to explain further what is meant by 'should', 'behave', and 'always', although at this stage of the development of computer science such a discussion must necessarily remain rather vague and intuitive.

'should'

We suppose that it is possible to assess a behaviour, by comparing it with the specifications of the program or with a prediction of what the behaviour will be. If the predicted and actual behaviour agree, or are consistent, we say that the program behaves as it should.

'behave'

It is difficult to consider program (or human) behaviour other than in terms of its effect on some external environment. The simplest model of a program's behaviour is its input–output characteristics – hence the 'right answer' definition of 'correct' given above. In the case that program behaviour is modelled by input–output characteristics, the specifications of the program are often given by an Entry predicate on the inputs and and Exit predicate on the inputs and outputs; we shall use this in Section 7.3. We also noted above that the input–output

---

[†] The interested reader is referred to Hoare (1969), and the recent Ph.D. thesis by R.L. Sites (1974).

model is inadequate if a program does not generate answers, or if one is concerned with how an answer is generated. In such cases, it is usual to model behaviour by some indication of the program's execution, say by tracing subroutine entries and exits, by recording branches taken at tests or loops executed, or by noting forks in control or traps processed. Additionally, snapshots might be taken of some components of the state at various points during the program execution.

To date, the majority of formal studies of correctness have worked with the input–output model of behaviour, while testing studies have tended to address themselves to programs for which that model of behaviour is inadequate. Nevertheless, it is important to realize that any correctness or reliability study presupposes a commitment to a particular model of program behaviour. In fact, the whole discussion is intimately bound up with what is accepted as the 'meaning' of a program; any model of behaviour implicitly involves a commitment to meaning. Conversely, any precise account of the meaning of programs supports an approach to the problem of proving correctness. Thus McCarthy's state-change function semantics described on p. 172 was used by him, together with J.A. Painter (1967), to prove a compiler for arithmetical expressions and simple assignment commands correct.

Programmers are probably most familiar with the above ideas in relation to debugging. A program has a bug if it fails to behave as it should; that is, if there is a difference between a predicted and actual behaviour. Debugging often involves choosing an appropriate model of behaviour, in which the bug can most simply be inferred from the difference in predicted and actual behaviour.

'always'

Many programs, such as partlyfac above, behave as they should for some inputs, but not for others. If the number of behaviours that a program can give rise to is small, its reliability or correctness can be determined simply by exhaustively considering each behaviour. The problem is that in practice those programs for which reliability is a serious issue tend to give rise to a huge, perhaps even infinite, number of different interesting behaviours, so exhaustive testing is either impractical or impossible. Broadly speaking, there have been two major approaches, known as *testing* and *proving*, to mounting convincing demonstrations that a program *always* behaves as it should. We shall argue below that there is no absolute demarcation between them.

CHECKPOINT 7.1 What do you think could serve as useful meanings of 'should', 'behave', and 'always' for the following programs: (i) a program to compute the roots of a quadratic equation; (ii) a bubble or exchange sorting program; (iii) a compiler; (iv) an operating system; (v) an English-understanding program?

We discuss testing in Section 7.2. One distinguishing aspect of testing is inductively inferring that a program always behaves as it should after considering a carefully chosen small set of behaviours. The problem inherent in the approach is the age-old problem with induction (Hume's problem): no amount of confirming instances can absolutely rule out the possibility that there is an untested non-confirming instance. As a caricature of the problem, one might inductively infer that partlyfac correctly computes the factorial function after testing it on inputs 0, 2, and 5. In practice, large (apparently) reliable programs such as compilers and operating systems have been tested this way.

Since no amount of testing, short of being exhaustive, can absolutely guarantee reliability, the idea arises of *proving* that a program always behaves as it should. In common parlance, a proof is a convincing argument that is very difficult to refute. Thus one may 'prove' to a jury that one did not commit a crime (irrespective of whether or not one did!). Again, in physics, one may 'prove' Newton's inverse square law using Coulomb's apparatus, although relativity theory may cause one to re-think. R.L. London (1970) pioneered the approach of constructing closely reasoned arguments in a mixture of English and mathematics to prove correct a number of programs, such as a program to bid at bridge. Such proofs provide stronger evidence than testing in support of a claim that a program is correct, but do not absolutely guarantee it.

The notion of 'proof' has been formalized within mathematics as 'derivable within a system of logic'. Not surprisingly, a popular view within computer science has been to say that a program has only 'really' been proved correct if it has been proved mathematically. From such a standpoint, London's proofs (such as London, 1970) might be less informal than testing; but they are informal nonetheless. The most successful approach to proving formal correctness to date is the so-called inductive assertion technique of Floyd–Hoare–Manna; we present Floyd and Hoare's work rather informally in Section 7.3, and sketch Manna's formalization of the technique in Section 7.4. The current state of the art in formal correctness proofs is quite advanced; Hoare (1971, with M. Foley; 1972a) has proved his sophisticated Quicksort recursive sorting program and a version of the prime sieve of Eratosthenes correct, while London (1975, p. 543) lists the unification algorithm, a pattern matcher, a parser, an expression compiler, and a verification condition generator by Ragland (1973) consisting of 203 procedures.

We would like to conclude this section by convincing (we only barely avoided saying "proving to"!) the reader that testing and formal proofs are just opposite ends of a continuum of supporting evidence for reliability, with no absolute demarcation between them. It may be that we are more impressed by a mathematical proof of correctness; but that probably reflects our great faith in mathematics, and is in no way an absolute guarantee of reliability. We should be clear what is at issue; a mathematical proof is either correct or not correct, but it may be very difficult to be sure which is the case for any given alleged proof. Indeed, Leavenworth (1970), using testing techniques, uncovered a formatting error in a program previously 'proved correct' by Naur (1969).[*] Moreover, it may be that

---

[*] We cannot resist quoting Hetzel (1974, p. 9), who quotes Davis, who references a book *Erreurs de Mathematique* by Lecat containing over 130 pages of errors of current mathematicians since antiquity.

a proof establishes a result that only partly captures *a priori* beliefs about the behaviour of a program (see Hoare, 1971).

We emphasize that this chapter is not intended to be a survey of the current state of the art. Rather it is an introductory account of some of the problems encountered, and advances made, in trying to make programs reliable. Of necessity, many interesting pieces of work have been omitted or sketchily described. The interested reader is referred to Hetzel (1974), the Proceedings of the International Conference on Reliable Software (1975), or the source articles quoted in this chapter.

7.2 Program testing

This section is a brief review of some of the ideas that have been developed to increase confidence in the correctness of large, practical programs such as compilers, operating systems and inventory, accounting or airline reservation systems. Mostly, they do not propose formal proofs. Rather, they have the status of suggestions, often vague, about how to build programs that can be adequately tested. We include the discussion to reinforce the point made in the preceding section, namely that there is no absolute demarcation between current work on testing and work on formal correctness. Indeed, at the end of the section, we mention two systems currently under construction which appear to span the gap between testing and proving, based on 'symbolic execution'. A more detailed introduction to the testing literature, as well as rather different views about formal correctness from those advanced in this chapter, can be found in the recent collection edited by William C. Hetzel (1974).

Perhaps the only agreement that runs through the entire literature on testing is the idea that the common practice of *first* building a program and *then* testing it, often using two different teams of programmers, is the root cause of much of the expense associated with making software reliable. Instead, it is proposed that programs should be designed and constructed to facilitate adequate testing, the force of the argument being that to include testability as a criterion from the start of a programming project materially affects and improves the program that is eventually constructed. Simply stated, there are two main suggestions, relating respectively to specifications of behaviour and program structure. We now discuss these in turn.

Recall the basic question to which this chapter is addressed: what does it mean to be convinced that a program always behaves as it should? In this question, the word 'should' is meaningful only if there is a set of predicted behaviours or specifications against which the workings of an actual program can be assessed. Hence it is *always* the case that the specifications for a program, however tentative or vague, precede its construction, even when the 'construction' consists of adapting an existing program to a new use. Common sense demands therefore that specifications that are as detailed and precise as possible should be set out in advance of the design and construction of a program. Since program specifications impose conditions on acceptable program behaviour, testing necessarily involves deciding on a model of behaviour that is adequate for comparing predicted and actual behaviour. As with specifications, the model of behaviour should be made explicit and precise.

The problem is that in practice it is often very difficult for such detailed and precise specifications to be given, usually because the programmer and problem specifier improperly understand the problem or are unable to communicate their needs adequately. For example, the specifier may have a poor understanding of the capabilities of computers or may fail to appreciate the significance to the programmer of certain pieces of information. Conversely, the programmer may improperly understand the needs of the specifier, and may be unable to elicit the information he requires. What often happens is that there is a feedback cycle in which the specifications are modified in the light of the behaviour of a preliminary version of the program. For example, it may be decided that the program (correctly!) solves a slightly different problem from that which the specifier 'really' had in mind. Alternatively, it may be that the program suggests new applications to the specifier, who then reformulates his specifications. In any case it seems that we may summarize the preceding discussion by noting that there is a need for specifications and a model of behaviour that are as precise and explicit as possible at each stage in the design and construction of a program.

The second suggestion is that it has been realized that not all kinds of program structure support testing equally, and that obeying certain disciplines leads to the construction of programs that more effectively support testing. Mostly, these suggestions are grouped in the literature under the heading of 'structured programming'. Typically, the following points are made:

(a) Certain kinds of control structure, such as **while**-loops and procedures, should be used, while others, such as **goto**, should be avoided or used with care.

(b) Control and data structures should be appropriately matched (see Hoare, 1972b).

(c) Data structures should be functional. In particular, detailed assumptions about the format of the data should be clearly indicated to facilitate changes in format should they be needed.

(d) The interfaces between the various modules of a program should be 'clean'; a module should do precisely what its specifications say it does, and no more. In particular, changes to non-local variables should be clearly indicated.

As we noted in Section 4.1, it seems that structured programming is really making two points about problem solving:

(1) It observes that a solution to a problem has a structure, and it argues that this structure should be manifest in a program to solve the problem. Clearly a language with a wide range of appropriate control and data structures is more likely to enable the programmer to articulate his program (or problem solution) structure directly. It also suggests that the programmer should discipline himself to use the linguistic structures at his disposal in such a way that the problem solution structure is kept manifest.

Following the appeals of Dijkstra (1968), there has been considerable debate about 'goto-less' programming. It is argued that programs that use goto indiscriminately tend to be error-prone, and difficult to understand, debug, and modify. While it is certainly the case that constructs such as for, while, repeatuntil, and so on, particularly in conjunction with break and loop for unnatural exits, make many loops, that might otherwise be coded as gotos, more explicit, and while 'escapers' can make longjumps such as error handling and recovery clearer, it is still possible, as Knuth (1974) shows, to construct well-structured programs using goto. It seems that the real reason why goto is troublesome is that it can very easily destroy the structure of the program or problem solution, as represented by the program text, and only partly, as has been argued, because it introduces too many control paths to be considered at once.

(2) Structured programming also relates the *activity* of solving a problem algorithmically to the textual development of a program. Dijkstra (1972) seems to argue for top-down problem solving. We have serious reservations about this aspect of structured programming, but a fuller discussion would take us too far from our main concern here, which is program testing.

Vyssotsky (see Hetzel, 1974, p. 47) states the case for discipline by the programmer very well: "I cannot imagine any reasonable way of testing a large PL/1 program written by many people if the implementation had made unrestricted use of base storage, ON conditions, and multitasking".

CHECKPOINT 7.2 [taken from R. Hamming, *Computers and Society* (1972, p. 89)] Write a program to read in triples of numbers and determine whether or not they could be the lengths of the sides of a triangle. In the case that they could, determine whether the triangle is scalene, isosceles, or equilateral. Decide *a priori* how to model the behaviour of your program, and say how many data sets are required to test every logical path through the program. For each data set *predict* what the behaviour will be and then test that the actual behaviour matches it.

Checkpoint 7.2 asked the reader to test *every* possible significantly different behaviour of his program. The problem in practice is that programs for which testing and reliability are really serious issues tend to give rise to a huge, perhaps infinite, number of 'significantly different' interesting behaviours, so exhaustive testing is either impractical or impossible. Faced with such situations, possibly the most obvious course of action, which has probably been followed at some stage by all programmers, is carefully to select a small number of actual behaviours, and, if they agree with the predicted behaviours, inductively infer that the program will always behave as it should. In certain circumstances, this approach works well. For example, the problem specifier may set a number of 'benchmark' behaviours, which are taken as evidence that his problem has been solved. Alternatively, there may be sufficient experience with similar problems to lead to the adoption of a standard data set, which concentrates on these pieces of program that have traditionally been prone to error. Thus compilers for block-structured programming languages tend to make mistakes on variable binding, so a standard data set to test such a compiler would probably include a program that repeatedly rebound the same name. The United States Air Force seems to have used this approach with great success for testing COBOL compilers. In general, however, the inductive generalization approach to testing has not worked very well (see Hetzel, 1974, p. 22), largely because it is often not obvious how to choose 'carefully' a small set of typical behaviours.

In situations where a reasonably small standard data set cannot be chosen, the tendency has been to follow other industries, particularly engineering industries, in which design and testing are also serious problems, and use *statistical sampling*. Statistics essentially derives its importance from the fact that before the advent of computers it was the only (or, at least, the most powerful) way of bringing mathematical analysis to bear on problems involving huge amounts of data, for example, for assessing the results of experiments in which many measurements are taken. Unfortunately, in order to be reasonably tractable, statistical analysis tends to insist upon a number of often unwarranted assumptions, such as that data are distributed randomly in some space, or that certain factors or parameters of interest are mutually independent. Moreover, analysis typically proceeds by collapsing a huge amount of information into a relatively small number of numerical measures, such as the mean or variance.

Here is the crux of the problem: programs evoke huge numbers of different interesting behaviours, but we are usually not so much interested in statements about the *aggregate* of behaviours as about *all individual* behaviours. Naturally, statistical analysis has been valuable in situations in which its assumptions (approximately) hold, such as in simulations of systems for time-sharing or traffic control. Nevertheless, it may be conjectured that, since computing offers a different way of analyzing large amounts of complex data, statitical sampling will become a less and less important testing tool.

We conclude this section with a brief discussion of two systems currently under construction, by James C. King (1975) of IBM and by Boyer, Elspas, and Levitt (1975) of Stanford Research Institute. Both systems are based on *symbolic execution*, which is a way of testing a large number of behaviours simultaneously, and which can be extended to a formal proof technique using an induction principle first isolated by Topor and Burstall (1973).

Consider the following (meaningless) piece of program:

read(x);

read(y);

$z := 2 * x + y$;

test $z = 0$ **then** $x := 1$

   or $x := 1/z + 1/y$

We observe that there are two possible logical paths through the program, determined by the condition $z = 0$. The important point is that we do not need to know the particular values read into x and y in order to reason about the program. Suppose that the value read into x is m, so that m is a fixed but unknown value, much like a mathematical (or universally quantified) variable. Suppose that the value read into y is n; then we may denote the value assigned to z by $2 * m + n$. It follows that the branch taken at the test command is completely determined by the truth or falsity of the algebraic expression $2 * m + n = 0$. In particular, choosing to follow one of the branches of the test command imposes a constraint $2 * m + n = 0$ or $2 * m + n \neq 0$ on the symbolic variables m and n.

If $2 * m + n = 0$, x is assigned the value 1 and execution halts normally. We may ask if it is possible to choose m and n so that this logical path will in fact be taken, that is, to satisfy the constraint $2 * m + n = 0$. If it is not, we can replace the entire test command by the assignment command $x := 1/z + 1/y$. However, it is easy to satisfy $2 * m + n = 0$, say by $m = n = 0$.

If $2 * m + n \neq 0$, x is assigned $1/z + 1/y$, that is to say, $1/(2 * m + n) + 1/n$. Clearly an error occurs if $n = 0$ or $2 * m + n = 0$, so we ask if this can happen. Now, it is obviously not possible for $2 * m + n$ to be zero after a test that guarantees $2 * m + n \neq 0$, but it is possible simultaneously to satisfy $2 * m + n \neq 0$ and $n = 0$, namely by choosing $m \neq 0$. It follows that there is a bug in the program unless the overall program specifications explicitly prevent n being zero.

The above example is very simple, but it illustrates the main ideas:

(a) Symbols, or algebraic expressions, are used as values for variables. Assignment commands assign algebraic expressions to variables.

(b) Choosing to follow a particular branch at a test command imposes a constraint on the symbols which may, or may not, be satisfiable.

(c) A symbolic execution corresponds to a whole set, often infinite, of individual executions. This advantage is gained at the cost of not being able to take advantage of the particular (e.g. numerical) attributes of an individual value which a symbol may assume.

King (1975) and Boyer, Elspas, and Levitt (1975) describe interactive systems in which the programmer can choose branches at tests, interrupt computations, examine the state, and display the constraints on his symbols. Boyer et al. include a special-purpose constraint satisfaction program which attempts to generate test data for paths chosen by the programmer. As an example, we follow Boyer et al. (1975, pp. 239–240) and denote a control path by a sequence of constraints imposed on the program symbols at the tests, and a program state by a pairing of names and symbolic values. The program to be discussed is an erroneous version of an algorithm due to Wensley for finding the square root of a number $p, 0 \leqslant p < 1$, to an approximation err, $0 \leqslant e < 1$.

```
let Wensley.square.root(p, err) = valof

$(WSR
        let d = 1
```

```
        let ans = 0
        let tt = 0
        let c = 2 * p
        //compute √p, 0 ≤ p < 1, to accuracy err, 0 ≤ err < 1
        if c ≥ 2 do resultis 0    //Branch point A
                                  //Ensure p < 1
$(R
        if d ≤ err do resultis ans //Branch point B
        d : = 0.5 * d
        tt := c − (d + 2 * ans)
        test tt ≥ 0   //Branch point C
        then ans := ans + d ⟨⟩                  //these two lines
             c := 2 * (c − (2 * ans + d))   //should be interchanged
        or c := 2 * c

$)R    repeat

$)WSR
```

We have labelled the three decision points A, B, and C. Consider the execution sequence ⟨ false at A, false at B, true at C, true at B, exit ⟩. The condition imposed on the symbolic values p and err by taking the false branch at A is $p < 1$. Following false at B imposes the further constraint err < 1. The reader should check that the constraints imposed by the entire sequence are:

$$p < 1, \text{err} < 1, 2p - 0.5 \geq 0, \text{err} \geq 0.5$$

at which point the state is:

$$\{d = 0.5, \text{ans} = 0.5, \text{tt} = 2p - 0.5, c = 4p - 3\}$$

It is in fact possible simultaneously to satisfy the four state constraints,[*] for example by setting $p = \text{err} = 0.9995$, which is consistent with the intention that:

$$0.5 = \text{ans} \leq \sqrt{p} \pm \text{err}$$

However, consider the execution sequence ⟨ false at A, false at B, true at C, false at B ⟩ at the point just after the second test at B. The path condition is:

$$p < 1, \text{err} < 1, 2p - 0.5 \geq 0, \text{err} < 0.5$$

and the state is as above. By the time branch point C is reached, the state has become:

$$\{d = 0.25, \text{ans} = 0.5, \text{tt} = 4p - 4.25, c = 4p - 3\}$$

---

[*] Boyer *et al.* (1975, p. 239) use a program to generate these values.

Since $p < 1$, and tt $= 4p - 4.25$, we have tt < 0 and so there is *no option* but to follow the false branch at C, and execute $c := 2 * c$. If we then choose to exit via the true branch at B, we have path condition:

$$p < 1, \text{err} < 0.5, 2p - 0.55 \leqslant 1, 0.25 \leqslant \text{err}$$

and state:

$$\{d = 0.25, \text{ans} = 0.5, \text{tt} = 4p - 4.25, c = 8p - 6\}$$

It is again possible simultaneously to satisfy these constraints, say by $p = 0.9995$ and $e = 0.4995$; but then:

$$0.5 = \text{ans} > \sqrt{p} - \text{err}$$

and the *fact* of a bug has been discovered. It is far from obvious how to isolate the bug, or what use the symbolic execution technique is in this respect.

CHECKPOINT 7.3 What is the relationship between symbolic execution and program schemas, as described in Chapter 3 (p. 75)?

CHECKPOINT 7.4 Symbolically execute the program you wrote in answer to Checkpoint 7.2.

We conclude this section with a brief description of Topor and Burstall's continuation induction technique of extending symbolic exeuction to a formal proof method. Consider the following program:

```
entry : I := 1
      R := 1
loop : if I < N then begin I := I + 1
                      R := R * I
                      goto loop
              end
exit :
```

We denote by:

$$L : x = \text{expn}, \dots$$

the assertion that there is a computational state, which arises from control being at the label L, in which the identifier x has as symbolic value the algebraic expression expn. We shall prove that the above program computes the factorial function. More precisely, we prove:

PROPOSITION 7.1 If $n \geqslant 0$ and entry : $N = n$, then exit : $N = n, I = n$, $R = n!$

Proof. Suppose that entry : $N = n$. Symbolically executing the first two commands in the program leads to:

$$\text{loop} : N = n, I = 1, R = 1$$

We shall prove by induction that if $1 \leqslant i \leqslant n$;

$$\text{loop} : N = n, I = i, R = i!$$

We have already proved the case $i = 1$, so suppose it has been proved for $1 \leqslant j \leqslant i < n$. We shall prove it true for $i + 1$. Since $i < n$, the test at the label loop evaluates to true, and so we have no option but to execute the three statements in the loop, returning once more to loop with symbolic values:

$$\text{loop} : N = n, I = i + 1, R = i! * (i + 1)$$

which completes the proof by induction. Finally, in the case $i = n$, the loop test fails and we reach exit with:

$$\text{exit} : N = n, I = n, R = n!$$

as desired.

CHECKPOINT 7.5 Prove that entry : $N = n$ implies exit : $P = 2^n$ (for $n \geqslant 0$), for the program:

entry : $p := 1$

loop : **if** $n > 0$ **then begin** $p := 2 * p; n := n - 1;$ **goto** loop **end**

exit :

For further details of the proof method, the interested reader is referred to Topor and Burstall (1973), Burstall (1974), or Topor (1975). In his Ph.D. thesis, Topor (1975) shows how to prove that an actual program simulates the behaviour of a virtual program that expresses its effect.

7.3 The inductive assertion technique for proving programs correct

7.3.1 Introduction: Floyd's work

The vast majority of program listings contain comments, as well as program statements, despite the fact that they are normally totally ignored by the processor. Clearly, such comments are not aimed at the compiler or interpreter, but at a programmer. The point is that, unlike the processor, which typically executes program statements unquestioningly until it is either finished or interrupted, programmers *interpret* program behaviour, often in terms of some *a priori* problem. Now, it is usually the case that long uncommented programs are difficult to interpret or understand; it is doubly difficult to reach a level of understanding that inspires confidence. Comments help by describing in a more expressive *assertion language* how a particular piece of program is supposed to behave or what the important properties of the computational state are expected to be at some point.

One of the earliest suggestions for making software *provably* correct or reliable

was to write comments not in English but in a formal mathematical notation
such as first-order logic, and to infer the correctness of the program from *both*
the program text *and* the formalized comments. Knuth (1972, p. 18) attributes
the idea to von Neumann and Goldstine in 1946! It also seems to have attracted
pioneer workers such as Turing, Wilkes, Perlis, and Gorn. However, the first
widely distributed published versions appeared independenty from P. Naur
(1966) and R.W. Floyd (1967). The presentation that follows is closer to Floyd's,
although we incorporate some suggestions of J.C. King (1969).

Floyd (1967) called formalized comments 'assertions' or 'tags', and required
that they be written in first-order predicate logic (from now on abbreviated to
FOL). Consider the simple flowchart program in Fig. 7.1, in which every edge
between commands has an attached assertion.

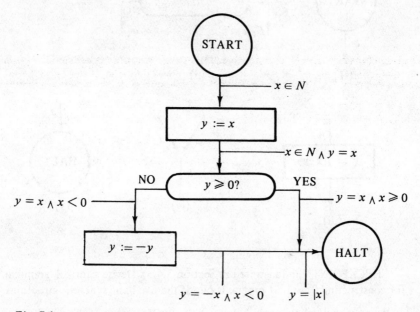

Fig. 7.1

The intention is that the assertions, which formalize aspects of the programmer's intuitive understanding of his program, should be true whenever
control flows along the edge to which they are attached. Consider the fragment:

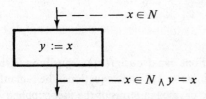

Since it is not provable (or generally true) that '$x \in N \wedge y = x$' *before* the assignment command, it clearly must be provable *afterwards* because of the effect of the assignment command '$y := x$' and the state of affairs beforehand, as represented by the assertion '$x \in N$'. Clearly, we need a model of computing phenomena, such as assignment comands, from which to deduce the effect of program statements. Since the assertion language is FOL, the natural solution is to give a semantics for the flowchart language also in FOL. Floyd isolated the following five basic syntactic structures in the flowchart language:

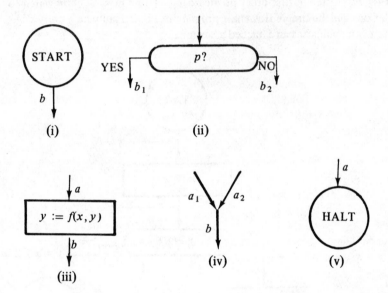

(i)   (ii)

(iii)   (iv)   (v)

CHECKPOINT 7.6 (answered in Section 3.4.3) Devise a formal 'grammar' for constructing flowchart programs out of the five basic syntactic structures.

We now consider the intended meaning in FOL of each of these syntactic structures. We suppose that incoming edges a_i and outgoing edges b_j have associated assertions $I(a_i)$ and $I(b_j)$. The *branch command* (ii) routes control either along b_1 or b_2 depending on the result of the test p. Thus, if p is true, we expect to be able to infer the assertion $I(b_1)$ from p and $I(a)$. This reasoning suggests the following FOL semantics for a branch command:

$$I(a) \wedge p \vdash I(b_1)$$
$$I(a) \wedge -p \vdash I(b_2)$$

[This notation means: from $I(a)$ and p one can deduce $I(b_1)$ (actually *in* FOL).]

It may be objected that it is rather loose to call these equations 'the semantics' of the branch command, since they are phrased in terms of the user-supplied assertions $I(a)$, $I(b_1)$, and $I(b_2)$. Rather, the equations *implicitly embody* the semantics of the branch command and impose a necessary *path condition* (*or verrification condtion*) on the assertions $I(a)$, $I(b_1)$, and $I(b_2)$. That is to say, the path condition is not so much an expression of the meaning of the branch command as a theorem in the flowchart language about the branch command, based on some (here unspecified) formulation of semantics. We shall take this point up again when discussing Hoare's logic of programs, and in Chapter 8.

Similar reasoning leads to:

$$I(a_1) \vee I(a_2) \vdash I(b)$$

as the path condition for the join 'command' (iv). Notice how the path conditions model flow of control directly by chains of inferences. Floyd (1967, 25) argues that the path condition for the start (i) and halt (v) 'commands' should be the constant assertion 'true'; we shall suppose instead that there are input and output assertions, which we shall denote by Entry and Exit. Entry defines the preconditions of the program, and Exit defines the relations holding at the end. As we pointed out in Section 7.1, in those cases where Entry and Exit assertions can quite naturally be supplied, they establish basic specifications for the program to be correct.

Lastly, consider the assignment command (iii). Two FOL expressions have been proposed as its path condition:

(a) *Forward substitution*

Suppose $I(a)$ is the assertion $R(x, y_{init})$, where y_{init} is the value of y before the assignment command. Since the effect of the assignment is to change the value of y from y_{init} to $f(x, y_{init})$, it will not in general be true that $R(x, y)$ holds afterwards. All we can be sure of is that it held before:

$$(\exists y_{init})(y = f(x, y_{init}) \wedge R(x, y_{init}))$$

For example, if $R(y_{init})$ is '$y_{init} = 4$', and we execute $y := y + 1$, the forward substitution rule enables us to conclude:

$$(\exists y_{init})(y = y_{init} + 1 \wedge y_{init} = 4)$$

from which it follows that $y = 5$. There is a slight disadvantage with forward substitution, which becomes more of an issue when we later consider a single path condition for an entire sequence of statements. A sequence of n assignment statements generates a path condition with n nested $\exists$'s, which becomes fairly incomprehensible as soon as n is large (say greater than 2!). Generally speaking, since Floyd (1967) introduced forward substitution, the alternative path condition, backward substitution, has been preferred.

(b) *Backward substitution*

Suppose that $I(b)$ is $S(x, y)$. Since the value of y is then $f(x, y_{init})$, clearly $S(x, f(x, y_{init}))$ held before the assignment, where $S(x, f(x, y))$ denotes the result of substituting the *text* $f(x.y)$ for the variable y throughout the *text* $S(x,y)$. As an example, suppose that $S(x,y)$ is '$y = 5$'. Backward substitution enables us to infer $(y + 1) = 5$ before $y := y + 1$. If backward substitution has the advantage of avoiding '∃' and increasingly complex assertions, it has the disadvantage of pulling an assertion backwards *against* the flow of control unlike the other path conditions given above.

In the final analysis, it does not much matter which path condition is used, since they are logically equivalent. In both cases, the essential idea is to model assignment by logical substitutivity. This presents a problem for assignment to components of data structures, but we defer discussion until Section 7.3.2.

Having given a FOL semantics for the flowchart language, we can set about proving the example program in Fig. 7.1 correct. For example, the (forward substitution) path condition for assignment requires us to prove:

$$x \in N \wedge (\exists y_{\text{init}})(y = x \wedge x \in N) \vdash y = x \wedge x \in N$$

which is obvious.

CHECKPOINT 7.7 Write down and prove all the other path conditions for the program in Fig. 7.1.

CHECKPOINT 7.8 Write down and prove all the path conditions for the program in Fig. 7.2.

CHECKPOINT 7.9 The un-commented program in Fig. 7.3 is supposed to locate the index minind (between l and r) of an array $A[1:n]$, such that $A[\text{minind}]$ is the least element of $A[l] \ldots A[r]$. Invent appropriate assertions for each edge which describe the computational state, and prove the path conditions for each statement.

The reader may well have found it difficult to supply a set of assertions in answer to Checkpoint 7.9. To some extent this may be because he is not used to using FOL. It may also be because FOL is not a very expressive language; it is often difficult to articulate intuitions about a program in FOL, a point to which we shall return on p. 202 when discussing data structures. However, it may be symptomatic of something that is claimed as an advantage by proponents of correctness proofs: requiring a programmer to make precise statements about his program may have the beneficial side-effect of causing him to understand his program more deeply than he otherwise would. In particular, it may prevent a lot of bugs. For example, most programmers 'know' Euclid's algorithm (Fig. 7.2) for finding the greatest common divisor of a pair a, b of numbers. But it is also probably true that few could prove formally why it works, or, to put it another way, could supply the assertion attached to the 'no' branch of $x_4 = 0$ in Fig. 7.2.

The lack of expressive power of FOL means that complex assertions have to be written down to express the simplest of intuitions. The dangers caused by this are manifold; a sentence may incorrectly express an intuition or be difficult to understand when trying to prove a path condition. Also, as Hoare (1971a,

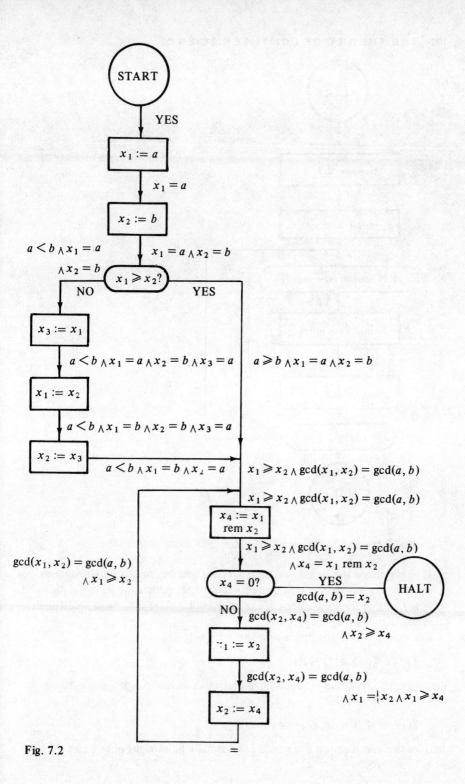

Fig. 7.2

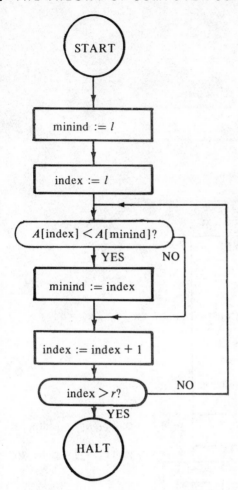

Fig. 7.3

p. 45) has pointed out, it may be far from clear whether or not FOL assertions completely express an intuition or specification. Altogether, we have the disturbing fact that the expressions of the assertion language may be more difficult to debug than the original program!

For example, it might be thought that:

$$(1 \leqslant i < n \supset A[i] \leqslant A[i+1])$$

is an adequate specification for a program to sort an array A. In fact, as Hoare (1971a, p. 45) observes:

for $i = 1$ **to** n **do** $A[i] := i$

satisfies this specification but would not normally be thought of as a sort

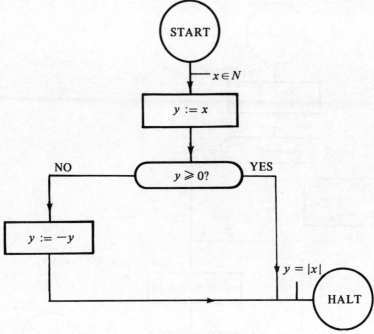

Fig. 7.4(a)

program! We need to specify further that, after sorting, the elements of A are a permutation of what they were initially. The sentences required to state this in FOL are rather complex. Recently, Suzuki (1975) has shown how this problem can be reduced by making the assertion language more expressive, without sacrificing the desirable logical properties of FOL.

One of the drawbacks of the method as we have described it thus far is that there are simply too many assertions. Unlike real program comments, which are used sparingly and strategically, we have insisted on assertions everywhere. In particular, no distinction is drawn between those assertions that are most helpful in finding a proof and trivial ones, such as alleging $x = 0$ after $x := 0$, which could safely be omitted. We may draw an analogy with proofs in mathematics books, which list the important steps in a proof but omit the intermediate steps as details which could 'obviously' be supplied but which would make the proof 'as a whole' more difficult to grasp. Of course, as the number of proof steps provided is reduced, the danger is increased that a non-obvious step-to-step inference is included. In practice, that is to say in mathematics books and journals, a compromise is struck, although it is usually not made explicit. For reasons that are given below, it *is* made explicit for inductive assertion proofs:

    (i) There should be Entry and Exit assertions.

    (ii) There should be at least one assertion to 'cut' each loop.

Assertions may be given at other points, but only if they are particularly

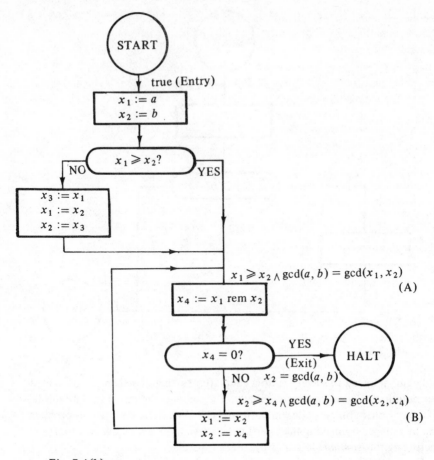

Fig. 7.4(b)

informative. The programs given above in Fig. 7.1 and 7.2 are shown again in Fig. 7.4 with the less crucial assertions omitted. Notice that in Fig. 7.4(b) two different and crucial assertions cut the single loop.

CHECKPOINT 7.10 Prune the less crucial assertions from the flowchart program you annotated in Checkpoint 7.9.

Following King (1969), we define a *path* between assertions X and Y to be a sequence of statements which could be executed starting at X, finishing at Y, and passing no other assertion. The idea is that the paths together describe the flow of control through the program. In Fig. 7.4(b) there is a single path from A to Exit, namely the sequence $\langle x_4 := x_1 \text{ rem } x_2; x_4 = 0 \rangle$. There is a single path from A to B and B back to A, but no path from either B or Entry to Exit. There are *two* paths from Entry to A, and in Fig. 7.4(a) there are two paths from Entry to Exit, since the flow of control is determined by the result of the test in the branch command. It might be thought that it would be better to distinguish these two paths so as to get a one–one correspondence between pairs of assertions and sequences of statements; but the really crucial observation is that, since every loop is cut by an assertion, there is a *finite* number of paths each consisting of a *finite* sequence of statements. The FOL semantics for the flow-chart language enable a single compound *path condition* (also called a 'verification condition') to be derived for each of the paths *p* from A to B to express the idea that the assertion at A and the net effect of the sequence of statements in *p* should together imply the assertion at B. Thus there are a finite number of finite path conditions.

CHECKPOINT 7.11 How many paths would there be if the assertions at A and B were omitted from Fig. 7.4(b)?

CHECKPOINT 7.12 Write down path conditions for the programs in Fig. 7.4.

CHECKPOINT 7.13 The reader should revisit the discussion of the pros and cons of forward and backward substitution given on p. 189 and write down the path conditions for a sequence of five assignment statements.

We observe that loops are singled out above solely because they are the only control structure in the flowchart language that can generate an infinite number of paths between two assertions. One might conjecture that more sophisticated control structures would necessitate further disciplines to be imposed on the placing of assertions. The reader might like to ponder what they would be for procedures, coroutines, parallel tasking, and software interrupts.

The preceding discussion has probably left the impression that a proof of correctness consists of proving a finite number of finite path conditions. Unfortunately, this is not the whole story. To exemplify the problem consider a slightly emasculated version of the gcd program in Fig. 7.4(b) (see Fig. 7.5), in which two of the loop statements and the assertion at B are removed, and the Exit assertion is slightly modified.

There are still two paths from Entry to A and one from A to Exit, but there is also a single path from A to A. The reader should prove that, despite the fact that the four path conditions hold, the program is not correct because it terminates if and only if *b* divides *a*. It will never give an incorrect answer (it could not because of the truth of the path conditions) but it often gives no answer at all. We say that the program is *partially correct* but not correct.

Thus provable path conditions are no guarantee that the program is correct, because they are no guarantee that the program terminates. Floyd (1967, p. 30) suggested that a proof of termination might be given separately by an induction argument[*] on a well-ordered set, usually by considering the sequence of values taken by the variables determining the flow of control through the loops in the

---

[*] Often called 'computational induction' since it refers to the length of certain control flows.

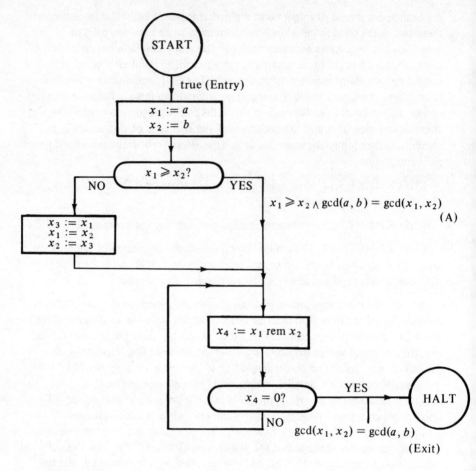

Fig. 7.5

program. For example, in Fig. 7.4(b), the sequence of values of x_4 is:

$$x_4(1) = a \textbf{ rem } b$$

$$x_4(2) = b \textbf{ rem } (a \textbf{ rem } b)$$

$$x_4(k + 1) = x_4(k - 1) \textbf{ rem } x_4(k), k > 1$$

It is easy to show that:

(i) for all $k, x_4(k) \geqslant 0$

(ii) for all $k > 1, x_4(k) > x_4(k + 1)$ or $x_4(k) = 0$

Appealing to the well-order principle, there must be some minimum l such that:

$$x_4(l) = 0$$

so that the loop is executed precisely l times. On the other hand, the sequence of values taken by x_4 in Fig. 7.5 is $a \text{ rem } b, a \text{ rem } b, a \text{ rem } b, \ldots$.

Notice that this reasoning essentially amounts to 'executing' the program twice: once to be sure that it terminates, and once to reason about the value it computes. (See Section 5.2 for a similar phenomenon.) The reader may well suspect that proving termination is a special case of proving partial correctness – this result (due to Zohar Manna) is stated formally in Section 7.4 (p. 213).

To summarize: Floyd's approach to proving the correctness of flowchart programs requires the following:

(1) Place a number of assertions on the program, including an Entry and Exit assertion and an assertion to cut each loop. Prove a path condition for each path between assertions. A program satisfying this is said to be *partially correct*.

(2) Prove that the program terminates by induction on a well-ordered set of numbers (or tuples of numbers).

CHECKPOINT 7.14 Write down Entry and Exit assertions for a program to locate an element x known *a priori* to be a member of an array $A[1:n]$. Write programs to satisfy these assertions using:

 (i) binary chop (assuming A is sorted),

 (ii) linear re-hash of the index.

Prove each of the programs correct by Floyd's method. What difference does it make to the programs and proofs if it is not known *a priori* that x is in A?

CHECKPOINT 7.15 The correspondence between programs and logic suggests that programs are analogous to theorems and subroutines to lemmas. To explore this idea, consider the program in Fig. 7.3 (Checkpoint 7.9) as a subroutine getminindex(A, l, r, minind). Write Entry and Exit assertions for getminindex. Prove that the sorting program in Fig. 7.6 is correct.

7.3.2 *Hoare's logic of programs*

Floyd's work was a first step towards systems in which useful programs in practical programming languages could be proved correct. The flowchart language is a particularly simple programming language, and Floyd (1967, pp. 26–30) was well aware of the kind of problems that would have to be solved in order to extend the approach to a substantial portion of commonly used programming concepts:

 (i) There are no data structures.

 (ii) There is a minimal procedure facility (see Checkpoint 7.15). Questions of parameter passing and global, local, and **own** variables had not been faced.

 (iii) There is no block structure. In particular there are no scope and extent problems or other interactions with storage allocation. There are no troublesome interactions with control structures such as unnatural block or procedure exits using **goto**.

(iv) Storage allocation is primitive. There is no heap, common, or **own** (static) storage.

(v) There are no nondeterministic control structures such as coroutines, parallelism, or software interrupts.

In a continuing series of papers, C.A.R. Hoare and his associates have made significant contributions to the problem of clarifying the connection between logic and programs and providing a formal semantics for a substantial portion of ALGOL 60 and PASCAL (Hoare and Wirth, 1972). Also, Hoare has presented a number of impressive demonstrations of how to apply his 'logic of programs' and his ideas on structured programming (Hoare, 1972b) to construct correct programs,[*] and the reader is urged to study his find (Hoare, 1971) and Quicksort (Hoare and Foley, 1971) programs. Quicksort in particular is a highly efficient recursive sort program, and the demonstration effectively silences those critics who believe that only 'toy' programs can be proved correct.

Hoare's approach is to define the semantics of basic statements and declarations to be axioms, and structured statments and declarations to be rules of inference that directly relate proof structure to syntactic structure. For example, the axiom for the 'basic' assignment statement is based on the backwards substitution reasoning described above:

$$R^x_{\text{expn}}\{x := \text{expn}\}\, R$$

in which R^x_{expn} denotes the substitution of expn for x in R,[†] and the notation:

$$P\{C\}\, Q$$

means that if P is true before the command C is executed, and if the execution of C terminates, then Q is true afterwards. The rule of inference defining the meaning of sequencing (in the fashion of ALGOL 60) is:

$$P\{C_1\}\, Q, Q\{C_2\}\, R \vdash P\{C_1; C_2\}\, R$$

We now consider the semantics of the command '**while** B **do** S' in more detail. Hoare (1969, p. 578) argues as follows: "In executing this statement, a computer first tests the condition B. If this is false, S is omitted, and execution of the loop is complete. Otherwise, S is executed and B is tested again. This action is repeated until B is found to be false. The reasoning which leads to a formulation of an inference rule for iteration is as follows. Suppose P to be an assertion which is always true on completion of S, provided that it is also true on initiation. Then obviously P will still be true after any number of iterations of the statement S (even no iterations). Furthermore, it is known that the controlling condition B is false when the iteration finally terminates. A slightly more powerful formulation

---

[*] To be precise, this should say "to construct programs for which the proof is straightforward". The distinction does not really seem to be worth stressing.

[†] Note that here, and throughout our discussion of Hoare's work, we assume that there are no side effects during the evaluation of an expression.

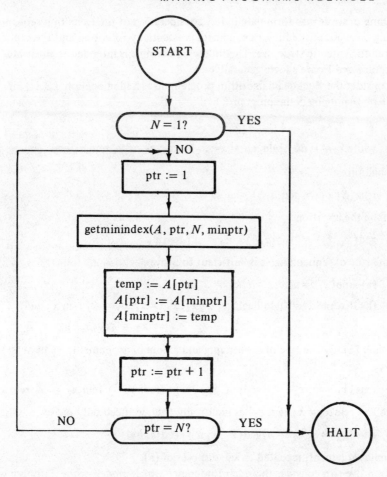

Fig. 7.6

is possible in light of the fact that B may be assumed to be true on initiation of S":

$$P \wedge B\{S\}P \vdash P\{\text{while } B \text{ do } S\}P \wedge -B$$

The remark made on p. 188 about Floyd 'semantics' really being theorems involving the semantics also applies here. Indeed, in Section 8 we offer a proof of the **while** rule of inference using the mathematical semantics of Scott and Strachey.

We wish to make two comments about this semantics for **while**. Firstly, Hoare's description of the execution of '**while** B **do** S' implicitly disallows an unnatural exit from within S, and it is not immediately clear whether such an exit is permitted by the rule. Secondly, in contrast to a Floyd proof, where chains of inferences directly model the flow of control in a program, control is *implicit* in a Hoare proof in the sense that, although the rule defining the meaning of **while** was formulated after consideration of the execution sequence, having once established the rule, control is essentially forgotten and the proof is related to syntactic structure. The following example is intended to illustrate this point and Hoare's logic generally.

Consider the Euclidean algorithm program discussed in Section 7.3.1 [Fig. 7.4(b)]. Denote by S the program:

$$x_1 := a; x_2 := b, x_3 := x_1 \text{ rem } x_2;$$

$$\textbf{while } x_3 \neq 0 \textbf{ do begin } x_1 := x_2; x_2 := x_3; x_3 := x_1 \text{ rem } x_2 \textbf{ end}$$

We shall prove:

$$\text{true}\{S\} x_2 = \gcd(a, b)$$

Let P be the assertion:

$$\gcd(x_1, x_2) = \gcd(a, b) \wedge x_3 = x_1 \text{ rem } x_2$$

By the rule of sequencing, it is sufficient to prove:

(a) $\text{true}\{x_1 := a; x_2 := b; x_3 := x_1 \text{ rem } x_2\} P$

and

(b) $P\{\textbf{while } x_3 \neq 0 \textbf{ do begin } x_1 := x_2; x_2 := x_3; x_3 := x_1 \text{ rem } x_2 \textbf{ end}\}$
$$x_2 = \gcd(a, b)$$

Consider (a). By the rule of sequencing and axiom of assignment, we have to prove:

$$\text{true}\{x_1 := a; x_2 := b\}\gcd(x_1, x_2) = \gcd(a, b) \wedge x_1 \text{ rem } x_2 = x_1 \text{ rem } x_2$$

Since "$x_1 \text{ rem } x_2 = x_1 \text{ rem } x_2$" is identically true, we need only prove:

$$\text{true}\{x_1 := a; x_2 := b\}\gcd(x_1, x_2) = \gcd(a, b)$$

A similar argument, repeated twice, disposes of (a).

To prove (b), consider the rule of inference which models **while**. Suppose we have already proved the invariance of P:

$$P \wedge x_3 \neq 0 \{x_1 := x_2; x_2 := x_3; x_3 := x_1 \text{ rem } x_2\} P$$

By the **while** rule, we may deduce that:

$$P\{\textbf{while } x_3 \neq 0 \textbf{ do begin } x_1 := x_2; x_2 := x_3; x_3 := x_1 \textbf{ end}\} P \wedge x_3 = 0$$

It is straightforward to show that $P \wedge x_3 = 0$ implies $x_2 = \gcd(a, b)$. We are left to prove the invariance of P. As we pointed out in Section 7.3.1 (p. 190) the crucial step is to realize that:

$$x_3 \neq 0 \wedge x_3 = x_1 \text{ rem } x_2 \text{ implies } \gcd(x_1, x_2) = \gcd(x_2, x_3)$$

The rest of the proof is left as an exercise.

CHECKPOINT 7.16   Write a program to compute, for given a, b, the largest number n such that a^n divides b. Prove your program correct using Hoare's logic.

CHECKPOINT 7.17 Write a program to compute the median element of an array $A[1:n]$, and prove it correct.

CHECKPOINT 7.18 Perform an analysis of the execution of: (a) S **repeatuntil** B, (b) S **repeat**, (c) **for** $i=1$ **to** n **do** S, and propose semantics for each analogous to **while**. In fact, (c) is rather difficult; you may wish to impose restrictions on the **for** statement in order to keep the rule relatively simple.

The connection between **while** program structures and invariants is exploited by Hoare (1971a). He argues that at the time that a programmer decides to use a **while** construct he is subconsciously aware of the appropriate invariant; making it explicit leads simultaneously to the development of a better and correct program.

We wish to make two remarks about the above correctness proof. Firstly, the proof was very straightforward once the assertion P had been introduced at the appropriate place. Indeed, it might be conjectured that the proof of (a) could be mechanized, thereby removing much of the effort involved in formal proofs. We shall return to this suggestion in Section 7.3.3.

Secondly, we observe that the correctness proof for the gcd program S proceeded in a 'top-down' fashion; given a statement:

$$\text{true}\{S\}\, x_2 = \gcd(a, b)$$

of the goal, and an assertion P, we noted that it was sufficient (by the rule of sequencing) to achieve two subgoals:

(i) $\text{true}\{x_1 := a; x_2 := b; x_3 := x_1 \text{ rem } x_2\}\, P$

(ii) $P\{\text{while } x_3 \neq 0 \text{ do begin } x_1 := x_2; x_2 := x_3; x_3 := x_1 \text{ rem } x_2 \text{ end}\}$

$$x_2 = \gcd(a, b)$$

Hoare and Wirth (1972, p. 345) observe that they consciously formulated the rules of inference defining PASCAL so as to facilitate such top-down proofs. Further discussion of this point, in particular its relationship to different ways of formulating equivalent grammars in compiling (Gries, 1971, Section 4.2), the PLANNER language (Hewitt, 1969), and structured programming (Dahl *et al.*, 1972), are beyond the scope of this introductory text.

Hoare-style logical semantics have been proposed for a wide class of programming constructs including procedures, coroutines, and user-defined data structures such as records. The majority of the semantics of PASCAL have been defined formally in this way (Hoare and Wirth, 1972), and the set of useful programs amenable to proofs like that given above is now very large.

However, a number of problems have been encountered with several of the programming constructs defined, and this has led to restrictions being imposed within the logic on constructs, either in order that a meaning can be defined at all, or can be defined in a way that is relatively natural and straightforward to use. For example, side effects are disallowed in expressions, jumps are restricted to be Landin-style 'escapers' (Clint and Hoare, 1972) and the control variable and limits of a **for** loop may not be altered (Hoare and Wirth, 1972, p. 347). We shall find in Chapter 8 that this is a familiar pattern; similar problems arise whenever one attempts mathematically to define a semantics for real programming languages. In what follows, we shall discuss assignment commands and procedures, to show how functions and logical substitution inadequately model those computing phenomena. Our presentation will of necessity be brief; the interested reader is referred to Hoare (1971b), Hoare and Wirth (1972), and Burstall (1972).

Assignment
There are two problems: one with data structures, and one with side-effects. The axiom of assignment is:

$$R_e^x \{x := e\} R$$

where R_e^x denotes the textual substitution of e for x in R.
    Following Burstall (1972), denote:

$$1 \leqslant i \leqslant 9 \wedge (1 \leqslant x \leqslant 100 \supset A[x] = x)$$

by P, and consider:

$$P\{A[(A[i]^2 + 2)] := 0\} A[i^2 + 2] \neq i^2 + 2$$

Now, it is certainly true that if P is true before the assignment command then '$A[i^2 + 2] \neq i^2 + 2$' will be true afterwards. The rule for assignment suggests substituting 0 for the *text* '$A[(A[i]^2 + 2)]$' in the *text* '$A[i^2 + 2] \neq i^2 + 2$', which leaves it unchanged, and then trying to prove:

$$P \vdash A[i^2 + 2] \neq i^2 + 2$$

which is not possible. The problem is that logical substitution fails to capture the idea of evaluating an expression, in this case $(A[i]^2 + 2)$, to yield the component of the data structure A to be assigned a new value. One way to solve the problem is separately to define an axiom of array assignment that defines the 'new' array A_{new} in terms of the 'old' array A_{old} and the assignment command. For example:

$$A_{old}\{A[i] := x\} A_{new}[j] = (j = i \to x, A_{old}[j])$$

Hoare and Wirth (1972, p. 345) give four different assignment axioms depending on the data structure assigned to. In any case, a clear distinction is made between 'simple' assignment and assignment to data structures, which is intuitively unsatisfactory since *all* assignment statements invoke the same process [see Strachey (1967) or Stoy (1975, Chapter 10)]:
    (1) Evaluate the left-hand side to yield a location.
    (2) Evaluate the right-hand side to yield a value.
    (3) Cause the location determined by (1) to contain the value determined by (2).
    What varies between assignment statements is the effort necessitated by (1) and (2).

It is tempting to think that the word 'evaluate' in (1) and (2) refers to the familiar mathematical notion. However, the inclusion of commands in functions or in **valof** constructions ought to dispel the idea. Floyd (1967, p. 29) considers how the command:

$$A := C + \textbf{valof } \$(\ C := C + 1; \textbf{resultis } C\ \$) + C$$

might be modelled in FOL and finds that he is forced to "reluctantly postulate a processor", in which case the semantics become less "transparent". Hoare and Wirth (1972, p. 337) expressly forbid such side-effects.

Procedures

Hoare (1971b) bases his expression of the meaning of procedures on a discussion of parameterless procedures. Consider such a procedure F with body C:

procedure F; **begin** C **end** F;

Intuitively, the effect of a call:

call F;

of F is to replace the command '**call** F' by the body C of F and then to execute it. Thus it is natural to model procedure invokation by:

$$P\{C\}R \vdash P\{\textbf{call } F\}R$$

Normally, procedures have parameters, say:

procedure $F(x)$; **begin** C **end**;

called by:

call $F(a)$;

with actual parameter a. Suppose that:

$$P\{C\}R$$

in which P and R are expressions involving the formal parameter x. The call to F with actual parameter a requires that a be substituted for x and the body C executed. Thus it is 'natural' to model parameter passing by logical substitution:

$$P\{C\}R \vdash P_a^x\{\textbf{call } F(a)\}R_a^x \tag{7.1}$$

For example, consider:

procedure ohno(x, y); **begin** $x := 3; y := 4$ **end**;

for which:

$$\text{true}\{x := 3; y := 4\}x = 3 \wedge y = 4$$

According to the proposed rule (7.1):

$$\text{true}\{\textbf{call } \text{ohno}(a, b)\}a = 3 \wedge b = 4.$$

Unfortunately, there are problems with rule (7.1). Firstly, if the *same* actual parameter a is substituted for *both* x and y, it implies that:

$$\text{true}\{\textbf{call } \text{ohno}(a, a)\}a \;=\; 3 \wedge a = 4$$

which is clearly absurd. Now, one way to solve a problem is to ensure that it never occurs! Thus Hoare (1971b, p.106) imposes the restriction that no two actual parameters which are assigned to in the body of F should be the same. He argues that, far from revealing a shortcoming with his approach, the problem is actually evidence in support of it, since the restriction is in line with ISO standard Fortran. It may be true that calling a procedure with the same actual parameter substituted for several formal parameters is inherently error-prone since one can never be sure that two apparently different variables will in fact always be different. But the imposition of a restriction raises the spectre that the only programs amemable to a proof of correctness are those having a seal of approval. It seems more satisfactory to try to develop a system in which *all* programs can be proved correct, but in which different proofs involving the same linguistic structure vary in their difficulty. As with assignment, it is difficult to imagine a system that could handle ohno(a, a) which did not 'postulate a processor', and first execute $a := 3$ and then overwrite its effect by executing $a := 4$.

Even if we accept Hoare's restriction, there is still a problem, illustrated by the following example, taken from Hoare (1971b, p. 106):

$$\textbf{procedure } \text{notagain}(x, v); x := v + 1;$$

for which:

$$\text{true}\{x := v + 1\}x \;=\; v + 1$$

Calling notagain with the same actual parameter a substituted for both x and v gives:

$$\text{true}\{\textbf{call } \text{notagain}(a, a)\}a \;=\; a + 1$$

which is absurd. It is important to realize that this is *not* a different version of the problem discussed above in connection with ohno. The problem this time really stems from the fact that (in ALGOL 60 terminology) v is passed by value whereas x is not, and two very different parameter passing mechanisms are both modelled in the logic by logical substitution. Hoare (1971b, p. 106) ensures that the problem never arises by imposing the restriction that no non-value parameter may also be a value parameter. Hoare and Wirth (1972) apparently accepted that this is an unreasonable restriction which avoided the real issue, and they proposed instead to model name parameters by functions that describe the way they are changed, and to model a procedure call as a simultaneous assignment to the name parameters.

More precisely, suppose that:

$$\textbf{procedure } F(x, v); \textbf{ value } v; C;$$

have value parameters v, and non-value parameters x. Suppose further that:

$$P\{C\}R$$

where in general the assertions P and R involve x and v. Each non-value parameter x_i is altered as a result of a call $F(a, b)$ of F; let the function f_i model its change in value, so that the value of x_i after call $F(a, b)$ is $f_i(a, b)$. The formal properties of the functions f_i may only be deduced from the fact that the assertion R refers to the changed values:

$$P \vdash R^x_{f(x, v)}$$

where $R^x_{f(x, v)}$ denotes the simultaneous substitution of $f_i(x, v)$ for x_i in R, for each i. The rule proposed by Hoare and Wirth (1972, p. 354) to model procedure invokation is:

$$Q^a_{f(a, b)}\{\textbf{call } F(a, b)\}Q$$

As an example, consider the troublesome procedure notagain discussed above:

procedure notagain(x, v); **value** v; $x := v + 1$;

in which v is a value, and x a non-value, parameter. We have:

$$\text{true}\{x := v + 1\}x = v + 1$$

Introducing the function f to describe the effect of a call to notagain on x we get:

$$\text{true} \vdash (x = v + 1)^x_{f(x)}$$

that is:

$$\text{true} \vdash f(x) = v + 1$$

Now we can prove:

$$a = 4\{\textbf{call } \text{notagain}(a, a)\}a = 5$$

as follows; by the rule of invokation, we have to show:

$$a = 4 \vdash (a = 5)^a_{f(a)}$$

that is to say:

$$a = 4 \vdash f(a) = 5$$
where
$$f(a) = a + 1$$

The proof is obvious.

CHECKPOINT 7.19 Prove that $a = 3 \wedge b = 1 \{\textbf{call } \text{silly}(a, b, a, b)\}a = 4 \wedge b = 2$, where silly is declared to be:

procedure silly(x, y, m, n); **value** m, n;

begin $x := m + n$; $y := m - n$ **end**;

Show that the technique does not solve the 'ohno' problem, by considering **call** silly(a, a, a, a).

This treatment of procedures still ignores the distinction between call by name and call by reference, as well as local, **own** (or static), and non-local (free) variables. In fact, Hoare and Wirth (1972, Section 11.2) model non-locals as extra name parameters, but there are a number of problems with the approach. Hoare and Wirth (1972, p. 337) admit that they "are not wholly satisfied with the axioms presented for . . . procedures . . ." and they note that "This may be due either to the inadequacy of the axiomatization or to genuine logical complexity of (this feature) the language". The reader might like to work on the following (research) problem:

CHECKPOINT 7.20 [rated at about 50 on the Knuth (1972, p. xviii) scale] By considering **call** swap$(i, A[i])$, where swap is defined by:

procedure swap(x, y);

begin new z;

$z := x; x := y; y := z$

end;

derive a Hoare-style semantics for call by name and call by reference.

7.3.3 Towards automatic proofs of correctness

Recently a good deal of attention has been focussed on the problem of making proofs of correctness for useful programs more feasible by automating various aspects of the inductive assertion technique. This section is intended to convey the flavour of current work and to point the interested reader to the literature.

Recall the correctness proof of the gcd program S in Section 7.3.2 (p. 200). As well as Entry and Exit assertions, we required an invariant or loop assertion P to 'cut' the **while** loop. Hoare's logic of programs enabled subgoals or lemmas to be generated from the program S and the three assertions, analogous to Floyd's *path* (*or verification*) *conditions*. The first observation to be made is that the generation of the path conditions can often be automated, although it is by no means trivial, since several rules of Hoare and Wirth (1972) may be simultaneously applicable. Igarishi, London, and Luckham (1973) note that it is possible to re-formulate the axioms for PASCAL so that at any given point in a proof just one rule is applicable. This is guaranteed if no two rules have common substitution instances.

The second observation is that many of the path conditions can be proved automatically using only the simplest of facts about operators such as $+$ and $<$; for example, $a + 0 = a$ or $a^1 = a$. By way of illustration, consider the following 'asserted' program: [this example implicitly answers Checkpoint 7.16.]

entry $a \leqslant b$;

$n := 1$;

assert $a^n \leqslant b$;

while $a^{n+1} \leqslant b$ do $n := n + 1$;

exit $a^n \leqslant b \wedge a^{n+1} > b$;

The invariant assertion cutting the **while** loop is $a^n \leqslant b$. The path condition for **entry** to **assert**, derived from the axiom of assignment, is:

$$a \leqslant b \vdash a^1 \leqslant b$$

This is easy to prove, and relies solely on two basic facts:

(i) $a = a^1$

(ii) $x = x', x \leqslant y \vdash x' \leqslant y$

Fact (ii), which is a special case of the substitutivity of equals for equals, has in the past caused severe problems for automatic theorem provers. The path condition for **assert** to **exit**, derived from the rule defining the **while** loop, is:

$$a^n \leqslant b \wedge \sim a^{n+1} \leqslant b \vdash a^n \leqslant b \wedge a^{n+1} > b$$

which relies on substitutivity of equals, and the relation:

$$\sim x \leqslant y \equiv x > y$$

holding between $\leqslant$ and $>$ on a totally-ordered set such as the integers. Finally, the path condition for the loop, from assert to assert, derived from the rule for the **while** loop and the axiom of assignment, is:

$$a^n \leqslant b \wedge a^{n+1} \leqslant b \vdash a^{n+1} \leqslant b$$

This requires the additional fact that:

$$a^{n+1} \leqslant b \vdash a^n \leqslant b$$

Igarishi, London, and Luckham (1973), Suzuki (1975), King (1969), Deutsch (1973), and Ragland (1973) describe simplification systems, or special purpose theorem-provers, capable of generating and proving each of the above path conditions. The Igarishi, London, and Luckham system simplifies all path conditions as far as possible, and then leaves the programmer to supply proofs for those few (crucial) path conditions not proved automatically. Alternatively, the unproved path conditions may be submitted to an automatic theorem prover which is slower but more sophisticated and more general than the simplifier. von Henke and Luckham (1975) and Good, London, and Bledsoe (1975) describe systems that extend Igarishi, London, and Luckham (1973).

As a final remark, Igarishi, London, and Luckham (1973, p. 5) (note that the performance of their path condition generator is largely determined by the (correctness and) quality of the user-supplied assertions. They regard this as a problem to be solved by making the generator more sophisticated. An alternative view of the problem, and indeed of the entire rationale of the Igarishi, London, and Luckham system (and its descendents), is given in Section 7.5.

The perceptive (or sceptical) reader will have observed, *apropos* the previous remark, that the automatic systems described thus far work on 'asserted' programs, that is to say, on programs for which assertions have been supplied. In fact, a number of papers have addressed the problem of automatically supplying the assertions, particularly the loop invariant assertions, although only Caplain (1975) seems to have implemented his suggestion. Wegbreit (1973, 1974) shows how loop assertions might in certain circumstances be heuristically derived from the entry and exit assertions. Katz and Manna (1973) discuss how an independently-discovered Wegbreit-like technique might be combined with a technique of inductively inferring the loop invariant from the loop body. Elspas (1974), Cooper (1971), German (1974), and Greif and Waldinger (1974) have also considered the problem.

7.4   The foundational studies of Zohar Manna

7.4.1   *Introduction*

Floyd's inductive assertion approach to proving the correctness of flowchart programs involves the following two steps (see Section 7.3.1):

(a) Assertions are placed on the program, including Entry and Exit assertions, and an assertion to cut each loop. A finite number of path conditions between assertions are derived and proved; the program is then said to be 'partially correct'.

(b) An inductive proof that the program terminates is given by considering a well-ordered set of (n-tuples of) numbers, usually derived from considering the sequence of values taken by variables controlling the flow of control through the loops in the program.

A program is correct if it is partially correct and terminates.

Suppose that P is a partially correct program, and that we are trying to prove that it terminates. If we can discover an appropriate induction proof, then we may be sure that P terminates and is correct. If, on the other hand, we cannot discover a proof of termination, it may either be because P does not in fact terminate, so that it is impossible for *anybody* to find a proof, or it may be that, despite the fact that in reality P does terminate, *we* are not capable of finding a proof. It seems therefore that, if termination is defined at all in Floyd's method, it is only defined in terms of a programmer's ability to construct mathematical proofs! An analogous remark can be made about the definition of partial correctness: if we can supply proofs for the path conditions, all well and good; if not, it may be either because no proofs exist or because *we* are incapable of discovering them.

The ideas introduced in this section, which is an extremely brief overview of much of Manna's (1974) book on the theory of computation, were initially aimed at providing a sound mathematical basis for Floyd's method by framing precise definitions for termination and partial correctness in terms of the function p computed by a program P. In the next sub-section, we show how Manna:

(1) defined the function p : Inputs → Outputs computed by a flowchart program P, in terms of the execution sequence of P.

(2) defined the partial correctness, termination, and correctness of P with respect to Entry and Exit assertions.

(3) showed how a logical formula W_P[Entry, Exit] could be generated algorithmically from the program P and the assertions Entry, Exit, so that W_p[Entry, Exit] is satisfiable if and only if P is partially correct with respect to Entry and Exit.

Notice that Manna does not require intermediate assertions that embody the programmer's intuition about the state of his program. As we pointed out in Section 7.2, it is difficult to understand what could be meant by 'correctness' or 'reliability' other than with respect to a set of prior specifications of program behaviour; the functional semantics implicit in the Floyd–Hoare–Manna work mean that program behaviour is most naturally modelled by Entry and Exit assertions.

Manna's concern with the foundational question of framing a precise mathematical definition of the intuitive notion of 'correctness' is analogous to Turing's (say) concern with framing a precise definition of 'computable'. Exploiting this analogy, we note that Manna's ideas naturally lead to 'meta-'results such as the undecidability of certain questions about correctness and termination, and the discovery of relationships between termination, correctness, equivalence, and so on. Furthermore, although nobody would seriously suggest Turing machines as a way of carrying out practical computations, they are nonetheless capable of so doing. Analogously, Manna's approach does support real correctness proofs, as we shall demonstrate in Section 7.4.2. In fact, Manna (1969a, 1970b) seems to have believed that his approach *would* be useful in practice, since programmers could appeal to well-known results in logic and could make use of automatic theorem provers, particularly those based on Robinson's resolution principle. Elspas *et al.* (1972) also advance this argument in their early survey paper. It is doubtful that they, or Manna, still adhere to that view.

7.4.2 *The correctness of flowchart programs*

Consider the annotated (or asserted) flowchart program [taken from King (1969)] in Fig. 7.7, which is amenable to being proved correct by Floyd's approach.

CHECKPOINT 7.21 Use Floyd's method to prove that the program in Fig. 7.7 is correct.

We now illustrate Manna's formalization of Floyd's inductive assertion

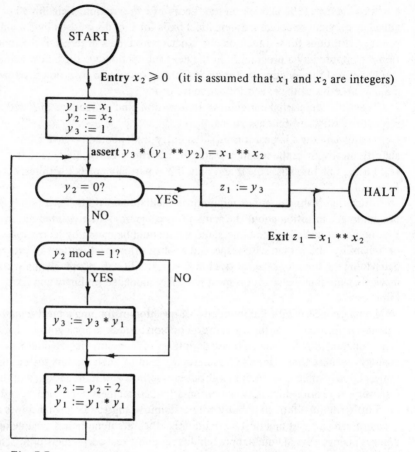

Fig. 7.7

approach by abstracting various aspects of the program in Fig. 7.7. Firstly, observe that the six variables mentioned in the program fall naturally into three disjoint classes:

(1) y_1, y_2, and y_3 are *program variables*, whose values are manipulated, tested, and changed during the execution of the program.

(2) x_1 and x_2 are *input variables*, whose values satisfy an input assertion Entry(x_1, x_2), which in the case of Fig. 7.7 is '$x_2 \geqslant 0$'. Observe that the values of x_1 and x_2 are unaltered during the execution of the program, and that they are used to initialize the program variables.

(3) z_1 is an *output variable*, whose value is assigned just prior to the program execution HALTing. As its name implies, it is used to deliver the output or results of the computation determined by the input variables.

Secondly, observe that, if and when the execution of the program halts, the input and output variables satisfy an assertion Exit(x, z), which in the case

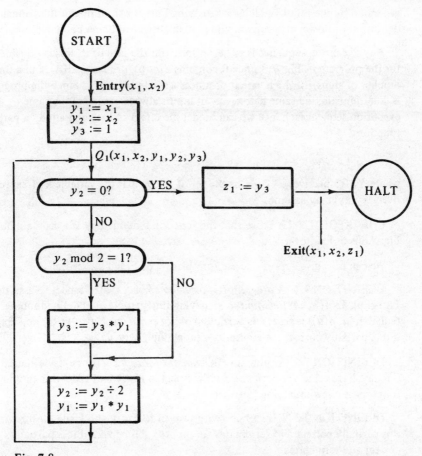

Fig. 7.8

of Fig. 7.7 is '$z_1 = x_1 ** x_2$'. Finally, there is a single intermediate assertion which relates the program and input variables. More generally, there are n assertions $Q_i(x, y)$, $1 \le i \le n$. The abstracted flowchart program is shown in Fig. 7.8.

Clearly, we could generalize the *particular* tests '$y_2 = 0$' and 'y_2 mod $2 = 1$' to $P_i(x, y)$, and could generalize the *particular* assignment commands to $y_i := f_j(x, y)$. If we did, we would basically be left with the information detailing the flow of control in the program, which is what we earlier called a *schema* (see Chapter 3, p. 75). Manna (1969b) supplies the details; suffice it to say that most of what follows can be carried over to schemas.

Instead, we continue our account of Manna's work by noting that we can define for any pair x_1, x_2 of inputs satisfying Entry(x_1, x_2) the *execution sequence* which they generate.

CHECKPOINT 7.22 Give a precise definition of the execution sequence generated by the input variables x satisfying Entry(x) in terms of the formal definition of flowchart program you gave in answer to Checkpoint 7.6.

Any execution sequence is either infinite (on the face of it, this is possible for the program in Fig. 7.8 since it contains a loop), or reaches HALT in a finite number of steps, in which case it produces a single output z_1. Since the program is deterministic, the same pair x_1, x_2 of inputs always generates the same execution sequences; hence we can model the effect of the program by a partial function:

$$p : X_1 \times X_2 \rightarrow Z_1$$

where X_1 (respectively X_2, Z_1) is the set of values that the variable x_1 (respectively x_2, z_1) may assume.

CHECKPOINT 7.23 Prove that the function p defined by the program in Fig. 7.8 is in fact total.

We can now give a more precise formulation of Floyd's approach:

DEFINITION 7.1 A program P is *partially correct* (with respect to assertions Entry(x), Exit(x, z)) *for input* u, satisfying Entry(u), if $p(u)$ defined implies that Exit$(u, p(u))$ is true. P is *partially correct* (with respect to Entry and Exit) if it is partially correct for all inputs u satisfying Entry(u).

DEFINITION 7.2 A program P *terminates for input* u if $p(u)$ is defined, that is to say, has a value. P *terminates* (with respect to Entry and Exit) if it terminates for every input u satisfying Entry(u).

DEFINITION 7.3 P is *correct* (with respect to Entry and Exit) *for input* u if it is partially correct and terminates for input u. P is *correct* if it is partially correct and terminates.

To prove partial correctness, Floyd suggests generating path conditions; for the program in Fig. 7.8, they are:

Entry to Q_1: $\forall x(\text{Entry}(x_1, x_2) \supset Q_1(x_1, x_2, x_1, x_2, 1))$

Q_1 to Exit: $\forall x, y(Q_1(x_1, x_2, y_1, y_2, y_3) \wedge y_2 = 0 \supset \text{Exit}(x_1, x_2, y_3))$

Q_1 to Q_1: $\forall x, y(Q_1(x_1, x_2, y_1, 2 * y_2' + 1, y_3) \supset$
via Yes $Q_1(x_1, x_2, y_1 * y_1, y_2', y_1 * y_3))$

Q_1 to Q_1: $\forall x, y(Q_1(x_1, x_2, y_1, 2 * y_2', y_3) \wedge y_2' \neq 0 \supset$
via No $Q_1(x_1, x_2, y_1 * y_1, y_2', y_3))$

In what follows, we refer to these four path conditions respectively as $E_n Q_1$, $Q_1 E_x$, $Q_1 Q_1 Y$, and $Q_1 Q_1 N$.

Manna (1969a) observed, as we did in Section 7.3.1, that the path conditions $E_n Q_1, Q_1 E_x, Q_1 Q_1 Y$, and $Q_1 Q_1 N$ implicitly define the flow of control through the program. Moreover, if $W_P[$Entry, Exit$]$ denotes the logical formula:

$$\text{Entry}(x) \supset (E_n Q_1 \wedge Q_1 E_x \wedge Q_1 Q_1 Y \wedge Q_1 Q_1 N)$$

then $W_p[$Entry, Exit$]$ is satisfiable if and only if P is partially correct with respect to Entry and Exit. In fact, Manna (1969b) showed how to generate $W_p[$Entry, Exit$]$ algorithmically for an arbitrary program P and assertions Entry and Exit, and he proved the following theorem:

THEOREM 7.1 For any flowchart program P, and any pair Entry, Exit of assertions placed at the entry and exit points of P, there is an algorithmically-constructable logical formula $W_P[$Entry, Exit$]$ such that $W_p[$Entry, Exit$]$ is satisfiable if and only if P is partially correct with respect to Entry, Exit.

We hinted above (see p. 197) that the notions of termination and partial correctness might be related; this is made precise in the following theorem (Manna, 1970a, p. 5):

THEOREM 7.2 P does *not* terminate for input x if and only if P is partially correct with respect to Entry and false.

Proof. By Definition 7.1, P is partially correct for input x with respect to Entry and false if and only if ($p(x)$ defined $\supset$ false) is true. But by definition of '$\supset$', this is true if and only if $p(x)$ is not defined, that is, if and only if P does not terminate for x.

This theorem captures the intuition, expressed on p. 197, that both the 'assertion' and 'inductive' parts of the Floyd approach involve reasoning about the same execution sequence.

In a number of other papers, Manna (1970a, 1970b, 1970c) has modelled a variety of computational phenomena, such as equivalence of programs and non-deterministic programs, and related them to each other by a set of results like Theorem 7.2.

We now show how Manna's ideas can be applied to prove a program, such as that given in Fig. 7.8, partially correct for a given pair of inputs, say $x_1 = 2$, $x_2 = 6$. We suppose that Entry(x_1, x_2) is $x_2 \geqslant 0$ and Exit(x_1, x_2, z_1) is $z_1 = x_1 ** x_2$, as shown in Fig. 7.7; but we do *not* assume that $Q_1(x_1, x_2, y_1, y_2, y_3)$ is known. Since $x_2 = 6 \geqslant 0$, Entry(x_1, x_2) is true, so by $E_n Q_1$:

$$Q_1(2, 6, 2, 6, 1)$$

holds. Since $y_2 = 6 \neq 0$ and 6 mod 2 = 0, $Q_1 Q_1 N$ enables us to infer:

$$Q_1(2, 6, 4, 3, 1)$$

Similarly $Q_1 Q_1 Y$ leads to:

$$Q_1(2, 6, 16, 1, 4)$$

and then to:

$Q_1(2, 6, 256, 0, 64)$

Finally, $y_2 = 0$, so that $Q_1 E_x$ enables us finally to infer:

$$64 = 2 ** 6$$

which is true. Hence P is partially correct with respect to $x_2 \geqslant 0$ and $z_1 = x_1 ** x_2$ for inputs 2, 6.

Ashcroft and Manna (1969) and Manna and Pnueli (1970) extended Manna's work to a more substantial subset of ALGOL 60, in the same way that Hoare extended Floyd's work. Not surprisingly, many of the problems referred to in Section 7.3.2 had to be faced. The interested reader is particularly recommended to read Manna and McCarthy (1970), which attempts to couple Manna's correctness studies and McCarthy's S-expressions (see Chapter 6) to prove recursive LISP-like programs correct.

In conclusion, we note that a number of simple decidability and undecidability results can be proved using Manna's approach. The following is typical:

THEOREM 7.3 Manna (1969b, p. 252) It is decidable whether or not a program terminates if it has a single program variable y_1 (a *single* program variable!?), and all assignment statements of the form $y_1 := const$ (where const is a constant) or $y_1 := f(y_1)$.

7.5 Reflections

In this final section, we reconsider the claims reported in Section 7.1 for the completely reliable software of the future, and, perhaps radically, suggest that the work introduced in this chapter should be interpreted somwehat differently. Recall that it was predicted (see p. 175) that: "debugging will be virtually unnecessary, and programs will be cheaper, maintainable, transportable, easily modfiable and understandable, not to mention more efficient and better structured".

There does not seem to be much evidence that there are significantly fewer software reliability problems (per program) today than there were fifteen years ago (say), despite the enormous efforts that have been made in the meantime to solve or control them. But that does not mean that all the work has been useless or beside the point, since many of the programs that motivated reliability studies then are today programmed very reliably, very frequently. For example, it is now quite common for compilers for ALGOL 60, or time sharing operating systems, to behave as they should for months, or even years. To a very large extent, this observed reliability on the severe problems of yesteryear is a corollary to the general advance in computer science; we understand the problems involved in building such programs, especially compilers, much better now, and have a richer programming environment to work in.

The point is that, as computer science has advanced, so the demands on computers have become greater. Often, the problems that have exposed the limitations of programming technology, including reliability, have been those that have pushed it to its limits. There does not seem to be any reason to suppose that this will not always be the case; we will *always* be able to say that yesterday's major problems can now be solved reliably, but we will not be so confident about today's. Apparently, we are doomed to chase forever the shadow of absolutely reliable software. Since there is no more reason to believe in absolutely reliable software than in the absolute truth of mathematics, it is worth asking whether the work described in this chapter should be re-interpreted.

Let us restate the belief that greater reliability on yesterday's problems is an inevitable consequence of the development of computer science; not only do we understand many of the problems much better, but, necessarily and inevitably, we have richer programming systems to work in, and better ways of building programs. Significantly, both the testing literature and formal correctness studies emphasize that structured programs are more reliable than unstructured ones. Several programming languages, notably PASCAL (Wirth, 1971) and NUCLEUS (D.I. Good and Ragland, 1974) have been consciously designed for the construction of structured reliable programs. The growth of time-sharing has led to the development of interactive languages such as LISP (McCarthy *et al.*, 1962) and POP2 (Burstall, Collins, and Popplestone, 1971), in which programs are 'naturally' modular, with independently compilable and testable modules. Probably the most convivial programming environment constructed to date is Interlisp (Teitelmann *et al.*, 1974), which, amongst its many features, provides the programmer with a break package, do-what-I-mean feature, and editor, to make debugging highly effective.

We suggest that the work described in this chapter is best interpreted as a significant contribution to the development of the next generation of programming systems, which, following Winograd (1974), we call *programming assistants*. In support of our argument, we briefly review some of the main developments in formal correctness proofs.

The Floyd–Hoare inductive assertion technique enables an existing program to be proved correct. Once it is proved correct, it can be run, presumably reliably. Similarly. Section 7.2 referred (critically) to the basic testing practice of first building, and then testing, programs. We may picture both of these ways of developing reliable programs as in Fig. 7.9(a).

Hoare (1971a, 1972a) and Hoare and Foley (1971) have presented a number of convincing demonstrations in support of their argument that programs should be built and proved correct at the same time. In particular, Hoare (1971a) argues that assertions (of loop invariants) significantly aid program construction by forcing the programmer to make explicit what he is already subconsciously aware of. Igarishi, London, and Luckham (1973) introduce the **assert** command into PASCAL, to help their verification condition generation and simplifier; however, it is still treated as a comment by the PASCAL system when the program is eventually run. Suzuki (1975) has shown how the assertion language, and hence the **assert** commands, can be made more expressive. Igarishi, London,

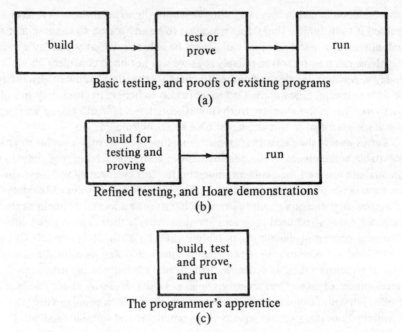

Basic testing, and proofs of existing programs

(a)

Refined testing, and Hoare demonstrations

(b)

The programmer's apprentice

(c)

Fig. 7.9

and Luckham (1973), Suzuki (1975), Luckham and von Henke (1975), and to a lesser extent Snowdon (1974), describe interactive intelligent systems that facilitate the simultaneous construction of a program and proof of its correctness; since a subroutine can be specified by its Entry and Exit assertions, the system leads naturally to structured programs. We may picture such systems as in Fig. 7.9(b).

The systems described in the preceding paragraph still make a clear distinction between the activities of building/proving and running; **assert** is treated as a comment by the PASCAL processor. The final step in our argument [see Fig. 7.9(c)] is to suggest that this distinction should be dropped, and to consider the effect of combining a PASCAL interpreter and a verification system such as that of Igarishi, London, and Luckham (1973). Faced with such a system, the programmer would build up an information structure that would not only define how a program is supposed to operate but also what problem it is to solve. **Assert** comments would be as much a part of the information structure as commands. The programmer's apprentice would be capable of helping the programmer in all the ways noted in this chapter- executing his program (perhaps symbolically), checking the consistency of a routine with its specifications, testing whether certain relations are true at points which the programmer designates, proving many of the simple path conditions, and cooperating with the programmer to prove the difficult ones. A really helpful assistant would have to draw on most of the systems we have described in this chapter, and several we have omitted. Tentative steps towards aspects of such systems can be seen in the work of King (1969), Deutsch (1973), Igarishi, London, and Luckham (1973) (and their descendants), PEARL (Snowdon, 1974), ABSET (Elcock *et al.*, 1971), the symbolic execution systems described in Section 7.2, and the LCF proof assistant (Milner, 1973). The programmer's assistant can be seen as merely the latest development in the evolution of high-level programming languages; the ideas described above appear in embryonic form in automated floating point arithmetic and type checking!

Does it really make any difference how the work on software reliability is interpreted? The thrust of our argument that it does is the belief that one's rationale for working on a problem significantly affects the work that is done, the importance accorded to subproblems, and the directions in which scarce effort is deployed. Substantial problems will have to be solved to interface a PASCAL interpreter (say) and the Igarishi, London, and Luckham system in order to produce a prototype programmer's assistant. Those problems are unlikely to be solved, or even considered worthy of solution, if people continue to work towards absolutely reliable software. From the standpoint of the programmer's assistant, we would *expect* 'assert' commands to be as helpful and detailed as possible; certainly we would not view the 'great reliance' placed on assertions to be a problem, as Igarishi, London, and Luckham (1973, p. 5) apparently do (see p. 207).

8 Questions of Meaning

8.1 Introduction

In this final chapter, we briefly describe some of the more important developments that have occurred over the past fifteen years aimed at giving a satisfactory precise account of the meaning of programs and programming languages. We have already indicated in Sections 1.3 and 7.1 the central importance of such questions of meaning for computing science and practice:

(i) The portability of programs requires (at least) consistent implementations of programming languages. The experience of ALGOL 60, as discussed in Section 1.3, suggests that a formal specification of the semantics of a programming language, replacing ALGOL 60's paragraphs of English, could be a significant step towards this end. Certainly, IBM Corporation seem to have been persuaded by this argument when they initiated the project of formally defining the language PL/1 at their Vienna laboratory (see Section 8.3.4).

(ii) As we pointed out in Section 1.3 and Chapter 7, suggestions for making programs more reliable implicitly embody, or define, notions of meaning. Thus, in order to prove that a program always behaves as it should, it is necessary first to define 'behaviour', and this is essentially a commitment to a definition of meaning. The path (or verification) conditions of Floyd and Hoare can be viewed either as logical formulations of, or statements about, meaning.

(iii) The development of more expressive, more systematic, programming languages has proceeded, and can be expected to continue to proceed, hand in hand with techniques for defining and analysing languages. For example, Landin's (1965) modelling of ALGOL 60 in terms of IAEs (see Section 8.3) led to the idea of streams, and to the isolation of escapers as a structured way of expressing (a class of) jumps out of routines. Similarly, Strachey's (1966, 1967) λ-calculus analysis of ALGOL 60 showed clearly that **arrays**, **procedures**, and labels had the status of 'second class citizens' relative to **real**, **integer**, and **boolean** variables. Language designers were naturally led to consider the consequences for programming, and implementation, or removing such 'injustices'.

Despite its centrality, and the relatively large amount of attention that formal semantics has attracted, the subject is still very undeveloped. The vast majority of work has centred on deterministic programming languages such as ALGOL 60, and has (essentially) modelled linguistic constructs such as assignment, iteration, conditional execution, **gotos**, and, implicitly, whole programs, by state-transforming functions $s_{init} \rightarrow s_{final}$. In fact, such a model has several obvious shortcomings:

(a) All programs that give rise to the same state-transforming function are deemed to be equivalent. Thus, for example, no difference can be made between a polyphase sort, bubble sort, and quicksort, despite the fact that they embody very different sorting processes. On the other hand, a central concern of data processing is to analyse which process is most effective in any given situation.

(b) [example taken from Milner (1975)] Many programs, including all operating systems, are nondeterministic, and therefore presumably need to be modelled (at least) by relations not functions. Again, operating systems contain a number of programs for accounting, device handling, and timing, whose top level structure can be abstracted to:

write(read(   )) **repeat**

Since such programs are *designed* not to terminate, there is no s_{final}, and so all such functions, *qua* state-transformers, compute the empty function. This is clearly unsatisfactory.

(c) The interaction between a program and its environment, in particular the problem that the program is intended to solve, are completely ignored. On the other hand, it is reasonable to ascribe to a picture processing program (for example) a meaning that refers to visual processes and relations, and it may be extremely difficult to render such a notion of meaning in terms of states and state transformations. The meaning of a robot pressing its finger on the nuclear button is hardly best expressed by a state detailing the forces on its tactile sensors! Indeed, it may be preferable to give separate related definitions of the meaning of a programming language and the meaning of any individual program in that language. It may also be possible to devise an appropriate notion of meaning of an algorithm, which is largely independent of any particular programming language; in this way, computer science might begin to get to grips formally with what are currently vague ideas about the suitability of a particular programming language for coding a particular algorithm. To date, these issues have not been tackled.

Most programmers are introduced to their trade, or to a new programming language, through manuals, journal articles, or lecture courses. These are almost always couched in a natural language such as English, together with example behaviours of language fragments such as **while** B **do** S or **valof** S. [See Appendix B, the ALGOL 60 report (Naur, 1963), or the first paper on the programming language SNOBOL (Farber, Griswold, and Polonsky, 1964).] Despite this imprecision, such introductions usually manage to instil an adequate level of understanding. Indeed, many programmers, who are introduced to their trade in this way, can, on the basis of their experience of using a paricular language, either learn to implement languages, or design better ones.

It might be argued that a formal semantics would make programming languages even easier to learn, would lead to an even deeper understanding of a programming language, would simplify the job of implementation, and would enable even better languages to be designed. Notice the qualifier 'even' on the comparative forms; there is no absolute understanding, just as there is no single absolute notion of correctness (see Section 7.1). We now want to put the claims for a formal semantics in perspective, by reconsidering the argument about the ALGOL 60 report which motivated our study of semantics.

The semantic descriptions in the ALGOL 60 report were not the usual sloppy, loosely worded, hopelessly ambiguous paragraphs of everyday English. Rather, they were carefully drafted in a highly stylized way by some of the most redoubtable figures in computing. Nevertheless, the report was incomplete, ambiguous, and, in some cases, apparently proposed constructs that were either difficult to comprehend (such as dynamic **own arrays**), or were incredibly difficult or inefficient to implement. (For example, the report proposes that **if** B **then** S should be equivalent to **dummy** if B is false. Since B may be a **boolean procedure** whose evaluation can involve a number of 'side effects', this implies that the previous computational state has to be remembered and perhaps reinstated.) Certainly, a more precise definition of ALGOL 60 would have avoided many of the problems, but it is nevertheless a fact that the vast majority of apparently competent ALGOL 60 programmers have either been made aware of their existence by subsequent English descriptions, have hardly suffered from its known problems, or remain blissfully ignorant of their existence. Since it is difficult to imagine anybody wanting to use dynamic **own arrays**, it is not surprising that programmers have hardly suffered from the fact that they were not expressly disallowed in the report. Again, so long as ambiguous linguistic constructs such as the **for** command (see Knuth, 1967) continue to give rise to behaviours that are consistent with a programmer's expectations, he may justifiably believe that his understanding of that construct is confirmed as correct, even when it is incorrect.

There is no guarantee that a mathematical semantics would not also be incomplete, and certainly no guarantee that it would not propose linguistic constructs that would be difficult to comprehend or implement. However, the high precision of mathematics, relative even to stylized English, is such that many of the problems might have been avoided. There is a price to be paid of course: the mathematical descriptions of meaning would themselves probably be couched in a notation that would itself be difficult to comprehend, and would certainly be less familiar than English. It is hardly profound to observe that in order to describe a language (the 'object' language) one has to use another language (the 'metalanguage'). [Clearly one has to understand the metalanguage in order to understand the object language. It has frequently been pointed out that there is a danger of an infinite regress: to understand the metalanguage requires a meta-metalanguage, and so on. The only reply is that understanding can only be based on prior knowledge. McCarthy (1966, p. 7) pithily observed that nothing can be explained to a stone.] Thus the trade-off is between familiarity and precision in the metalanguage. This situation is common throughout science; one gives an intuitive description in a familiar natural language, and then a formal mathematical description to remove any problems caused by the intuitive description.

Perhaps the most important lesson to be learned from the ALGOL 60 experience is the danger inherent in introducing too many new concepts at the same time. Most programming languages break considerably less new ground than ALGOL 60 did, so there is usually much less new to explain in terms of what is already known. Similar remarks apply to the development of set theory and the infinitesimal calculus.

One of the most important contributions of ALGOL 60 has been the large number of techniques that have had to be developed in order to implement it. Indeed, most of the inadequacies of the report were discovered in the course of designing implementations. The relationship between implementation and meaning is controversial. For example, the Oxford 'school' headed by Strachey and Scott have argued that implementation is necessarily derivative of meaning. According to their view, any implementer is obviously guided by a clear intuitive notion of what has to be achieved, and they saw their task primarily in terms of making that intuition precise and explicit. On the other hand, Milner (1975, p. 9) argues that "languages are always designed in the first place operationally; it is only by specifying some evaluation mechanism . . . that we can be sure that a language can be practically implemented". At the end of this chapter, we shall argue that the preceding evidence strongly supports a view diametrically opposite to that argued by the Oxford school; we believe that implementation ideas (suitably abstracted) are a necessary part of the meaning of current programming languages.

There has been a variety of formalisms proposed for defining the meaning of programming languages, and implementers, working programmers, language designers, and theorists would have different opinions about the attractiveness of them. Different needs are better catered for by different formalisms. For example, Hoare's logic of programs (Hoare and Wirth, 1972) is a convenient vehicle for proving programs correct, but less useful to an implementer or language designer. Generally speaking, there is not one formal 'essence' of meaning from which all others can be derived; rather there are related formalisms which relate to the problems that prompted the need for an account of meaning.

How can a precise account of the semantics of a programming language be given? Since any implementation of a programming language is, in the final analysis, just a program, and since a program is usually thought of as a precise statement, it has been very tempting to suggest using a compiler or interpreter to define meaning. Thus BCPL originally had a single standard compiler to a simple one-address machine code, called OCODE, of a 'virtual' machine. Implementing BCPL consisted in large part of simulating the OCODE machine on a more or less unfriendly real machine, which for example might have a small number of fast registers. Similarly, EULER (Wirth and Weber, 1966) had its semantics defined by a compiler to a 'basic' machine code which was described informally. The problem with using a real program, such as a compiler, is that a number of detailed decisions have to be taken in its construction which are (apparently) almost wholly irrelevant to understanding the language being compiled. For example, most compilers model the symbol information structure as a table or as a binary tree. If a symbol table is used, it is common to use internal re-hashing or hash plus chaining to look up information in the table. If internal rehashing is used, a good deal of thought has to be given to the choice of rehashing function. Moreover, a real compiler has to interface with the host operating system to handle interrupts, program tracing, runtime storage allocation, as well as input and output.

The considerations lead us to propose that by a 'precise' account of the semantics of a programming language is meant a mathematical account. Notice that this does not rule out an approach to semantics based on a compiler (or interpreter). Instead of a real compiler to a real (or virtual) machine, an *abstract machine* is defined as a mathematical object, which ignores many of the details referred to above. For example, finite state machines, Minsky machines, and Elgot and Robinson RASPs discussed in Chapter 2 could be simple abstract machines. Given an abstract machine, an abstract compiler function can be defined that associates with each fragment of the object language a piece of behaviour of the abstract machine.

In Section 8.3 we shall describe how P.J. Landin defined an abstract machine called the CSEDM machine, whose states had five components: Control, Stack, Environment, Dump, and Memory. He showed how an abstract compiler function could be defined from (most of) ALGOL 60 into 'imperative applicative expressions' (IAEs), and showed how each IAE could be interpreted as a state to state transformation of the CSEDM machine.

This approach to formal semantics has been called *operational* since it explicitly involves an abstract machine, which interprets constructs as sequences of operations. As we pointed out above, it has been argued by proponents of *mathematical semantics* (with which it is usually contrasted), and by the Oxford school in particular, that an operational semantics is a definition not only (or, not so much) of a language, but also of a specific implementation of it. It is argued that it defines just one of a number of possible implementations, and that it is preferable to abstract the implementation component out and concentrate on the essential meaning. We wish to make two observations about this argument.

Firstly, implementations refer to real compilers, whereas operational semantics involves compiler *functions* and abstract *mathematical machines*. Thus an operational semantics is as much mathematical as any other semantics. The argument really refers to the *formulation* or *description* of the function (which is ultimately just a set of ordered pairs) which is proposed as meaning. It may be that an operational semantics is inspired by, or directly suggests, an implementation based on a real program, and it may well be that it is difficult to carry out certain kinds of analysis, or prove certain kinds of theorems, with the meaning function formulated operationally, but that is not the same as saying that it does not define the same function as any other formulation of meaning.

Secondly, most of the argument about the involvement of implementation issues in questions of meaning is emotive, and neglects to specify what is meant by 'implementation'. The point is that implementation does not only refer to 'bit pushing', choices of hash functions, and similar highly detailed decisions. As well as being concerned with making statements about such issues, implementers (see Gries, 1971) are much more concerned with issues like: what kind of environment is needed to execute a procedure in, how is it accessed, how is the environment restored after jumping out of a procedure, how are call by name, value, or reference implemented?

A central issue in giving a formal semantics for programming languages is whether, and to what extent, such abstract ideas about implementation are necessarily a part of meaning. Is it *possible* to understand call by name in ALGOL 60 without involving procedures ('thunks')? Is it possible to understand **goto** without postulating composite label values that enable the appropriate environment to be set up? We shall argue in Section 8.4 that there has been a convergence between operational and mathematical semantics, and that the difference between them is essentially a matter of degree: the extent to which an abstract machine is represented in the semantics.

The other major alternative approach to semantics, currently called *mathematical semantics*, is to associate directly a mathematical function with each linguistic construct, rather than have it evoke a mathematical model of a computational behaviour. This idea, essentially based on Tarski's notion of semantics of mathematical logics, was initiated by Strachey (1966). He observed (Strachey, 1964, p. 201): "It is the aim of this paper to show that with the introduction of a few new basic concepts it is possible to describe . . . a programming language in terms of applicative expressions . . . . As a result, it is no longer an essential part of the basic semantic description of the language to postulate an 'evaluating mechanism', or notional computer, however abstract". Unfortunately, Strachey's (1966) model contained a number of mathematical uncertainties, specifically relating to the self-application problems discussed in Section 1.2, and the lack (in 1966) of a mathematical (in the Fregean or Tarskian sense) model of the λ-calculus. Dana Scott provided such a model in 1970, and began a collaboration with Strachey on the development of a mathematical semantics. Sadly, the research project they began was hampered by Strachey's untimely death in 1975. In Section 8.4, we shall briefly introduce the Oxford school's approach to semantics, and shall question whether Strachey's stated aim (above) of purging the notional computer has been achieved. Since both Sections 8.3 and 8.4 require a somewhat greater familiarity with the λ-calculus than can be reasonably expected of the reader, we give an informal introduction to it in Section 8.2.

This chapter, like the preceding one, necessarily represents the author's selection of a tiny fragment of the work that has been concentrated on the question of meaning. We nevertheless believe that we have discussed most of the more important issues. Further references can be 'chased' from the source articles quoted in Sections 8.3 and 8.4, and the anthology edited by Engeler (1971).

8.2 The λ-calculus

The introductions to operational and mathematical semantics that follow in
Sections 8.3 and 8.4 are largely based on the work of P.J. Landin and the Oxford
University program research group, which was founded by C. Strachey. Both
Landin (1964) and Strachey (1966, 1967) developed their analyses from the
observation that there is a 'natural' correspondence between many of the linguistic
constructs of ALGOL-like programming languages and expressions of Church's
λ-calculus. This section is intended to provide sufficient background information
about the λ-calculus to make the discussions in Sections 8.3 and 8.4 self-contained.
However, shortage of space dictates a number of omissions, principally: a proof
of the Church–Rosser theorem, a discussion of Curry and Fey's (1958) combinators, and details of Scott's (1970) construction of a model of the λ-calculus.
Surprisingly, there does not seem to be a good, widely-available, account of the
λ-calculus and its relevance to computer science. Wegner (1968, Sections 3.5–
3.11) is considerably more detailed than the account given here, but is hardly
fuller. The most satisfactory account that the author has found is J.G. Sanderson's
tutorial "The λ-calculus, lattice theory, and reflexive domains", which is included
as a supplement to Stoy's (1975) overview of the work of the Oxford school.
Hindley, Lercher, and Seldin (1973) provide a good standard account.

In Section 6.2, we presented λ-*notation* as a uniform way of providing
standard default names for all computable functions. Thus the function:

has
$$x, y \mapsto x^2 + y$$
$$\lambda(x, y) \cdot x^2 + y$$

as its standard λ-name. We also introduced λ-abstraction as a way of discovering
the (default) λ-name from an equation defining a function, and showed how
Curry's paradoxical combinator Y enabled λ-abstraction to be applied to self-
referential equations.

The λ-calculus is not just a notation. It was introduced by Church (1941) as
one of the first formal systems to propose a precise definition of 'computable',
as outlined in Chapter 1. It is possible to give a formal syntax for it, and a model,
which associates with each syntactic construct a value from an appropriate
domain. As our presentation is relatively informal, we shall allow ourselves the
following generous syntax:

$$\langle \lambda \text{expn} \rangle ::= \langle \text{ident} \rangle \mid \langle \lambda \text{expn} \rangle (\langle \lambda \text{expn} \rangle) \mid \langle \text{number} \rangle$$
$$\mid \lambda \langle \text{bvpart} \rangle \cdot \langle \lambda \text{expn} \rangle$$

$$\langle \text{bvpart} \rangle ::= \langle \text{ident} \rangle \mid (\ ) \mid (\langle \text{ident} \rangle \{, \langle \text{ident} \rangle\}_1^*)$$

We shall also allow ourselves the luxury of numbers and functions such as squaring and (integer) halving which will always be named by obvious mnemonics. We
shall also feel free to facilitate the parsing of λ-expressions by including bracket
pairs { }. In fact, the details of the λ-calculus and its model are considerably

easier to work out if identifiers and numbers are omitted, and only functions considered. Wegner (1968, p. 191) discusses Church's representation of the integers as functions. Similarly, it is simpler to work with functions of one variable, that is, to disallow all but the ⟨ident⟩ alternative form of ⟨bvpart⟩. There have been a number of proposals for achieving functions of several arguments in the λ-calculus. Reynolds (1971) suggests viewing sequences such as (x, y) as functions, so that, for example, the function add is thought of as a function of one argument, which is a sequence function (x, y), which when applied to 1 yields x, etc. An alternative approach, described below, is called "currying" (after H.B. Curry; actually, the technique was invented by Schönfinkel).

The second alternative form of λ-expression is called a *combination*. If $E_1(E_2)$ is a combination, E_1 is the *operator* and E_2 is the *operand*. The final alternative form of λ-expression is a *function*. If $\lambda(x, y, z) \cdot E$ is a function, (x, y, z) is the *bound-variable part* and E is the *body*. Anticipating the discussions of semantics in Sections 8.3 and 8.4, we now exploit a correspondence between ALGOL 60 and the λ-calculus to explain various aspects of the λ-calculus. This is intended to emphasize the points made in Section 8.1; in this section we are relying on the reader's presumed prior knowledge of ALGOL 60, and using it as a metalanguage to describe the λ-calculus. In Sections 8.3 and 8.4 the roles will be reversed, and the λ-calculus will be used as a metalanguage to investigate ALGOL 60.

Our first example introduces the most persuasive correspondence, that holding between functions and ALGOL(type) procedures. The bound variable part corresponds to the procedure's parameter list, and the function body to the procedure body. For example, consider the pair:

$$\lambda(x, y) \cdot x^2 + y \qquad \textbf{integer procedure } \text{sum1}(x, y); \textbf{integer } x, y;$$
$$\text{sum1} := x^2 + y;$$

The ALGOL 60 report insists that formal parameters should be pairwise distinct. A familiar observation about the formal parameters of a procedure is that they can generally be given alternative names without affecting the meaning of the procedure. However, consider the ALGOL block:

```
begin integer x;
        integer procedure sum2(y); integer y;
                sum2 := x + y;
        x := 2; print(sum2(4))
end
```

in which x is a global, or free, variable of the procedure sum2. If we rename the formal parameter of sum2 to be x instead of y, the procedure will always return twice its actual parameter, and not 2 plus it as before. This suggests that a formal parameter should not be renamed if it leads to a previously free variable occurrence becoming bound. Exactly the same considerations apply to the λ-calculus. For example, the body of the λ-function:

$$\lambda y \cdot x + y$$

has a free occurrence of x and a bound occurrence of y. The bound variable y may be given any other name except x without altering the function named. In fact, as we shall see below, this *renaming conversion* is a very important (textual) transformation on λ-expressions.

CHECKPOINT 8.1 Try to frame precise definitions of free and bound occurrences of identifiers in λ-expressions. [Hint: The λ-expression:

$$\lambda f \cdot f(y)(\lambda y \cdot f(y))$$

illustrates most of the problems.]

Our second example correspondence relates combinations and procedure calls:

$$\{\lambda(x, y) \cdot x^2 + y\}(3, 4)$$ **begin integer procedure** sum1(x, y);

                                     integer x, y;

                           sum1 $:= x^2 + y$;

                print(sum1$(3, 4)$)

              end

The invocation sum1$(3, 4)$ results in 3 being substituted for x, 4 being substituted for y, and the body being executed. Analogously, a combination can be *reduced* by substituting the operands for the bound variables. Thus:

$$\{\lambda(x, y) \cdot x^2 + y\}(3, 4)$$

can be reduced to:

$$3^2 + 4$$

Again, care has to be taken with accidentally binding free variables. Consider:

$$\{\lambda f \cdot \lambda y \cdot f(y)\}(y)$$

which unfortunately reduces to:

$$\lambda y \cdot y(y)$$

The problem can be solved by appealing to the renaming operation sketched above, and we insist that a combination:

$$\lambda \text{bv} \cdot \text{body}(\text{arg})$$

may only be *reduced*, by substituting (the text) arg for the bound variable bv in (the text) body, if arg contains no free occurrences of variables bound in body.

Using reduction, we can demonstrate the λ-calculus's completely free-wheeling attitude to functions. Consider the λ-function and ALGOL 60 procedure:

$$\lambda f \cdot \{f(0) + f(1)\} \qquad \textbf{integer procedure } \text{sum2}(f); \textbf{ integer procedure } f;$$
$$\text{sum2} := f(0) + f(1);$$

An application of the **integer procedure** sum2 involves binding an actual parameter, which is iteself an integer procedure, to f. Similarly, we can form the λ-combinations:

$$\lambda f \cdot \{f(0) + f(1)\}(\text{sq})$$
$$\lambda f \cdot \{f(0) + f(1)\}(\lambda x \cdot 5)$$

in which the operand is itself a λ-function.

But the λ-calculus is more liberal than ALGOL 60 in its treatment of functions. Consider the λ-function:

$$\lambda x \cdot \lambda y \cdot x + y$$

which, when applied to 5 say, reduces to:

$$\lambda y \cdot 5 + y$$

which is also a λ-function. ALGOL 60 has to be extended to express the corresponding procedure, for example by introducing **integer procedure procedures**.

The previous example illustrates 'currying', which is a technique for replacing functions of several variables by a complex function of one variable. The λ-function $\lambda(x, y) \cdot x + y$ of two variables is replaced by $\lambda x \cdot \lambda y \cdot x + y$, which, when applied to 5 (say), reduces to a function $\lambda y \cdot 5 + y$, which, when applied to 7 (say), reduces to 12.

The basic evaluation mechanism of the λ-calculus is reduction (applying an operator to an operand), with preparatory renaming to avoid free variables becoming bound. Consider the λ-expression:

$$\{\lambda x \cdot \text{half}(\text{sq}(x))\}(\{\lambda y \cdot \text{sq}(\text{half}(y))\}(5))$$

One evaluation sequence for this expression corresponds closely to ALGOL 60's call by value: first evaluate the operand, then evaluate the operator body with the value of the operand substituted for the bound variable:

$$\{\lambda x \cdot \text{half}(\text{sq}(x))\}(\{\lambda y \cdot \text{sq}(\text{half}(y))\}(5))$$

reduces to:

$$\{\lambda x \cdot \text{half}(\text{sq}(x))\}(\text{sq}(\text{half}(5)))$$

which is:

$$\{\lambda x \cdot \text{half}(\text{sq}(x))\}(4)$$

This reduces to:

$$\text{half}(\text{sq}(4))$$

which is 8. There is a serious problem with self-application. Consider the λ-function

$\lambda u \cdot u(u)$, which has the strange property that when it is applied to itself reduces to itself applied to itself:

$$\{\lambda u \cdot u(u)\}(\lambda u \cdot u(u)) \text{ reduces to } \{\lambda u \cdot u(u)\}(\lambda u \cdot u(u))$$

It is tempting to think of $\{\lambda u \cdot u(u)\}(\lambda u \cdot u(u))$ as naming a non-terminating computation. In particular, the call by value evaluation sequence can be non-terminating:

$$\{\lambda x \cdot \text{sq}(\text{half}(x))\}(\{\lambda u \cdot u(u)\}(\lambda u \cdot u(u)))$$

and this occurs even in extreme cases where the value of the operand is not needed in the evaluation of the operator body:

$$\{\lambda x \cdot 5\}(\{\lambda u \cdot u(u)\}(\lambda u \cdot u(u)))$$

Readers familiar with ALGOL 60 will note that the latter example can be evaluated, to yield 5, by using call by name, which calls for systematic substitution of the operand text for the bound variable in the operation body, yielding 5 in this instance. It follows that there are several different evaluation sequences for λ-expressions, each of which may or may not produce an answer. It is not clear whether all evaluation sequences which do produce answers actually produce the same answer. The Church–Rosser theorem guarantees that they do. First, define a λ-expression to be 'reduced' if no further reductions are possible, and to be 'irreducible' if no finite sequence of reductions can lead to a reduced form. On p. 71 we noted that it is undecidable whether or not a λ-expression is irreducible; in view of the discussion of $\{\lambda u \cdot u(u)\}(\lambda u \cdot u(u))$ above, it should come as no surprise to the reader that this result is equivalent to the halting problem for Turing machines.

THEOREM 8.1 (Church–Rosser) If two different evaluation sequences for a given λ-expression result in reduced expressions, then the two reduced expressions are equivalent up to renaming of bound variables.

In fact, it is possible to specify a complete search strategy called 'normal order', which will discover the reduced form if and only if one exists. Normal order, which is rather like call by name, requires that, at each stage in the evaluation sequence, the leftmost operator–operand combination should be reduced.

THEOREM 8.2 (Church–Rosser) The normal order evaluation sequence of an λ-expression terminates on a reduced form if and only if the λ-expression has a reduced form.

We conclude this brief discussion of the λ-calculus by considering a model for it. So far, our intuition has been that $\lambda x \cdot 5$ names the constant function that always returns 5. Similarly, we have thought of $\epsilon_1(\epsilon_2)$ as naming the application of the function named by ϵ_1 to the value named by ϵ_2. To formalize these intuitions, we try to supply a model, by associating with each well-formed

λ-expression ϵ a value, say val$[\epsilon]$.* We require that:

$$\text{val}[\epsilon_1(\epsilon_2)] \ = \ \text{val}[\epsilon_1][\text{val}[\epsilon_2]]$$

and that:

$$\text{val}[\lambda x \cdot \epsilon] \ = \ f$$

where f is the function whose value for an argument v is:

$$\text{val}[\epsilon_v^x]$$

where ϵ_v^x is the result of substituting v for x in ϵ. Clearly val associates functions or numbers with λ-expressions, which are viewed as pieces of text. The snag is that it is by no means clear what, if any, function could serve as the value of the λ-expression:

$$\lambda u \cdot u(u)$$

and others like it. Presumably:

$$\text{val}[\lambda u \cdot u(u)] \ = \ \text{selfapplic}$$

where selfapplic is the self-application function. However, as we pointed out in Chapter 1, before Scott's (1970) construction, it was not certain that selfapplic was a definable function. Consequently, it was far from certain that a model could be provided for the λ-calculus, and so by the 1960's the λ-calculus had fallen into disrepute with logicians. In 1970, Dana Scott showed how to construct a model for the λ-calculus. The basic idea is to define a domain D with the property that:

$$D \cong (D \to D)$$

where $D \to D$ is the domain of computable functions from D to itself. The isomorphism of D and $D \to D$ means that D is precisely the kind of value set that is needed for a model of the λ-calculus. The definition of D is based on a notion of approximation, which, mathematically, amounts to insisting that D should be a complete lattice (see Scott, 1970). The computable functions from one domain to another are defined to be the lattice-theoretic continuous functions. The attraction of complete lattices and continuous functions is a result [see, for example, Scott (1971, p. 312)] due to Tarski and Knaster which guarantees that any continuous function from D to itself has a fixed point. This fact is exploited by Scott (1971) and Scott and Strachey (see Section 8.4) to guarantee the existence of a solution to recursive equations, and to give a meaning for constructs such as **while** commands. The construction of the domain D involves a 'retraction' sequence of increasingly complex lattices $D_0, D_1, \ldots$, and seems at first sight to be far too abstract to be relevant to computer science. In

---

* We use square brackets to avoid confusion with the metalinguistic brackets
  (,) of the λ-calculus syntax.

fact, the construction can be applied much more generally to guarantee the existence of a wide range of domains of interest to computer scientists. For example, it is easy to define a domain S of S-expressions such that:

$$S \simeq A + S \times S$$

This is highly reminiscent of the syntax for S-expressions given on p. 149. However, the elements of S are not restricted to finite binary trees (dotted pairs), but can account for circular constructs such as:

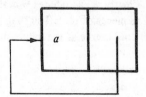

Again, Scott and Strachey (1971, p. 31) discuss a space V of values for procedures to manipulate:

$$V = T + N + L + C + P$$

where T, N, L, C, and P are respectively domains of truth values, numbers, locations, commands, and procedures. They argue that the application of a procedure to a value v in a given state s will return a value v', and possibly alter the state s'. Thus (with due regard to currying) they model P by:

$$[V \rightarrow [S \rightarrow V \times S]]$$

where S is the domain of states. Putting the equations for V and P together yields:

$$V = T + N + L + C + [V \rightarrow [S \rightarrow V \times S]]$$

which is a domain that we can be assured can be constructed by the retraction sequence technique.

The main mathematical contribution of Scott's work to computer science is not so much that he provided a model for the λ-calculus; rather it is that the way in which the λ-calculus model was constructed can be more generally applied to construct reflexive domains of interest to computer science. We shall take up this issue again in Section 8.4. Details of Scott's retraction sequence construction can be found in Scott (1970, 1971) and Stoy (1975).

We need to make one final observation before considering the meaning of programming languages. The Church–Rosser theorem refers to reduction and renaming of λ-expressions. Both reduction and renaming can be defined purely syntactically, as transformations on λ-expressions considered as uninterpreted pieces of text. Indeed, before a model was provided for the λ-calculus, reduction and renaming *had to be* defined as syntactic transformations. Once a model val : ⟨λexpn⟩ → D is available, we can prove the correctness of reduction and renaming by showing, for example:

$$\epsilon_0 \text{ reduces to } \epsilon_1 \text{ implies } \text{val}[\epsilon_0] = \text{val}[\epsilon_1]$$

Stoy (1975, p. 123) supplies the details.

8.3 Operational semantics: making the machine explicit

8.3.1 *Observing the basic correspondence*

The preceding section exploited a correspondence between various aspects of programming languages and the λ-calculus, in order to introduce the λ-calculus. It should be clearly understood that the correspondence was used merely as a pedagogical device to relate the problems surrounding renaming, reduction, and evaluation sequences to the reader's presumed prior knowledge of similar aspects of ALGOL 60, namely renaming bound variables, procedure calling, and call by name or value. It should also be clearly understood that it is possible, indeed more usual, to define the syntax and semantics of the λ-calculus without reference to ALGOL 60, or any other programming language. This section (and the following) stem from the same observed correspondence being made the other way round: if the λ-calculus is considered *a priori* understood, then various aspects of ALGOL 60 (for example) can be explained in terms of it.

Strictly speaking, we did not describe λ-expressions in Section 8.2, but a generalization which included numbers, identifiers, λ-functions, lists of identifiers, numbers or functions, lists of lists of numbers, and so on. Following Landin (1964), we call these generalizations *applicative expressions* (from now on abbreviated to AEs), and note that using Church's encoding of the integers as λ-functions, and currying, it is clear that AEs could be replaced by λ-expressions in what follows. Such parsimony is, however, unnecessary.

The preceding section related formal parameter lists to bound variable parts, (typed) **procedures** to λ-functions, and procedure applications to λ-combinations. Our discussion of evaluation sequences for λ-expressions related call by name to normal order, and call by value to operand-then-operator order. (Actually, we shall discuss call by name in a little more detail below.) Moreover, in Section 6.2, we showed how recursive function declarations could be λ-abstracted to equivalent AE forms, using Curry's paradoxical combinator Y. Several other aspects of programming languages correspond equally directly with λ-expressions, including declarations, conditional expressions, environments, and closures.

The BCPL declaration and expression:

    let $x = 6$

    $x + y$

corresponds closely to $\{\lambda x \cdot x + y\}(6)$. ALGOL 60 declarations are typed, and

Landin (1965, p. 96) showed how Curry's combinators could be used to give an interpretive definition of type.

The conditional expression **if** p **then** a **else** b requires p to be evaluated in order to select the value of either a or b as the value of the whole expression. This reasoning suggests describing the conditional expression by the λ-expression:

$$\{\text{ifasfn}(p)\}(a, b)$$

where ifasfn is a λ-function which returns a function first, which selects a, or a function second, which selects b. More precisely, define:

$$\text{ifasfn(true)} \;=\; \text{first \textbf{where} first} \;=\; \lambda(x, y) \cdot x$$
and
$$\text{ifasfn(false)} \;=\; \text{second \textbf{where} second} \;=\; \lambda(x, y) \cdot y$$

This model satisfactorily handles the conditional expression **if** $3 = 2$ **then** 5 **else** 6, for:

$$\{\text{ifasfn}(3 = 2)\}(5, 6),$$
$$= \text{second}(5, 6),$$
$$= 6$$

Unfortunately, the description is not capable of coping with expressions of the form **if** $a = 0$ **then** 1 **else** $(1/a)$. The point is that, as well as deciding whether to return the value of the conclusion or the alternative as the value of the entire conditional expression, it is important to delay the evaluation of both. A better description is based on the idea that $\lambda(\ ) \cdot 1/0$ is a well-defined function, even if any attempt to apply it leads to an error. [The point is that a function is a set of ordered pairs, and $\lambda(\ ) \cdot 1/0$ is a well-defined set – the empty set.] We can now render **if** p **then** a **else** b more adequately by:

$$\{\{\text{ifasfn}(p)\}(\lambda(\ ) \cdot a, \lambda(\ ) \cdot b)\}(\ ) \qquad\qquad (8.1)$$

Consider the expression **if** $a = 0$ **then** 1 **else** $1/a$, in the case that a is zero. Equation (8.1) reduces to:

$$\{\text{first}(\lambda(\ ) \cdot 1, \text{emptyfunction})\}(\ )$$

which is:

$$\{\lambda(\ ) \cdot 1\}(\ )$$

that is to say;

1

The same technique can be exploited to impute a meaning to **for** commands, and call by name. In 1961, P.Z. Ingerman invented a technique for implementing call by name based on procedures known as 'thunks'. This idea is used in rendering call by name in terms of AEs. If we have the declaration:

integer procedure simple(x); **integer** x;

   simple $:= x + 2$;

the body is transformed into simple $:= x(\ ) + 2$, and a call simple($a + b$) transformed into simple($\lambda(\ ) \cdot a + b$).

CHECKPOINT 8.2   What is the relationship between this rendering of call by name and that used by Hoare and Wirth in their logic of programs (p. 204)?

ALGOL 60, in common with many other programming languages, allows free variables in procedures. Unlike LISP, POP-2, or APL, ALGOL 60 binds these variables statically; that is, it can be decided at compile time what ALGOL variable (= location) a free variable is bound to. Thus the program:

begin integer a;

   integer procedure peep; print(a);

   $a := 2$; peep;

   $a := 3$; peep;

   begin integer a; $a := 27$; peep **end**
end

causes $2, 3, 3$ to be printed, *not* $2, 3, 27$. A full discussion of this issue is beyond the scope of this introduction (see Gries, 1971, Chapter 8), except for two remarks. Firstly, there is clearly more to the procedure peep than its code body; it also consists of a binding of the free variable a. Such a 'binding' of the variable a is called an *environment*, and is usually implemented via a link (known as the static link) or a display technique. The bundle of information consisting of the body of peep and its environment is called a *closure*, and may be thought of as the 'value' of peep. (We discuss this in more detail in Section 8.4, p. 243. The second remark is that environments and closures occur in the λ-calculus too. For example, evaluating the λ-combination sq(a) requires background information about the value of a. Furthermore, in an environment in which y is bound to 27, the value of the λ-combination:

$$\{\lambda f \cdot \{\lambda y \cdot f(y)\}(2)\}(\lambda x \cdot y)$$

is 27, not 2. Clearly, the value bound to f is a closure consisting of $\lambda x \cdot y$ and the environment $y = 27$.

The extensive correspondence between aspects of ALGOL 60 and AEs suggests a two-stage approach to defining the meaning of ALGOL 60:

(i) Define an (abstract) compiler function from ALGOL 60 to AEs.

(ii) Define the meaning of AEs.

It may be noted that the use of the λ-calculus, or something similar, is not unexpected in defining the semantics of programming languages. We expect that any algorithm can be coded in any programming language L; thus we expect that the set of meanings of programs in L will comprise all computable functions. Church's λ-calculus was introduced precisely to give a formal definition of 'computable'. We may also note that the fact that some aspect of a programming language *can* be described in the λ-calculus does not necessarily prescribe *how* it is described. Consider recursive function definitions and conditional expressions; the latter were defined so that the usual evaluation sequence for:

$$\{\text{ifasfn}(p)(\lambda(\ )\cdot a, \lambda(\ )\cdot b)\}(\ )$$

follows closely the computation of **if** p **then** a **else** b. On the other hand, the explanation of recursive functions in terms of the paradoxical combinator Y bears little resemblance to the way such functions are computed by machine. We shall revisit this issue later.

The following two subsections develop the approach to meaning sketched above: in Section 8.3.2 we consider the meaning of AEs, and in Section 8.3.3 we consider the translation of ALGOL 60 into AEs.

8.3.2 *Evaluating AEs*

We observed in Section 8.2 that the value of an AE $\lambda x \cdot 5$ is a function C5 (say), that, when applied to any number, always yields 5. Thus the most direct approach to defining the value of AEs is to define a function $\text{val}(X)$ giving the value of an AE X. We noted in the previous subsection that, in general, $\text{val}(X)$ depends upon the environment that binds the free variables of X. Mathematically, an environment is just a function, say E, that gives the value of free variables (identifiers) in X. Thus we define:[*]

$$\text{val}(E, X) = \text{is-ident}(X) \to E(X),$$
$$\text{is-comb}(X) \to \{\text{val}(E, \text{sel-opr}(X))\}[\text{val}(E, \text{sel-opd}(X))]$$
$$\text{is-}\lambda\text{fn}(X) \to f$$
$$\textbf{where } f(u) = \text{val}(E_{\text{new}}, \text{sel-body}(X))$$
$$\textbf{where } E_{\text{new}} = \text{extend}(E, u, \text{sel-bv}(X))$$

The function extend updates the environment E by binding u to the bound variable part of X:

$$\text{extend}(E, u, x) = \lambda y \cdot y = x \to u, E(y)$$

CHECKPOINT 8.3   Use val to evaluate sq(3), half(sq(4)), $\{\lambda x \cdot \text{half}(\text{sq}(x))\}(4)$, $\{\lambda f \cdot \{\lambda y \cdot f(y)\}(2)\}(\lambda x \cdot y)$, the latter in the environment in which y is bound to 27.

CHECKPOINT 8.4   Use val to evaluate the AE renderings of **if** $3 = 2$ **then** 5 **else** 6 and **if** $a = 0$ **then** 1 **else** $1/a$.

We wish to make two remarks about val, both of which will be discussed

[*] In the style of McCarthy, Section 6.5. For example, is-comb is a predicate, sel-opd is a selector.

transform($\langle S, E, C, D \rangle$)=

   null(C) $\to$ $\langle$hd(S) :: $S', E', C', D'\rangle$ **where** $D = \langle S', E', C', D'\rangle$,

   (**let** x = hd(C)

   is-ident(x) $\to$ $\langle$lookup(E, x) :: S, E, tl(C), $D\rangle$,

   is-comb(x) $\to$ $\langle S, E, C_{new}, D\rangle$

           where C_{new} = sel-opd(x) :: (sel-opr(x) :: (**ap** :: tl(C))),

   is-λexp(x) $\to$ $\langle$mk-closure(x, E) :: S, E, tl(C), $D\rangle$,

   x = **ap** $\to$

       (**let** f = hd(S)

       not isclosure(f) $\to$ $\langle S_{new}, E$, tl(C), $D\rangle$

               where S_{new} = f(2nd(S)) :: tl(tl(S)),

       (**let** cl-body = sel-body(f)   //the body of the closure

       let cl-bv = sel-bvpart(f)   //the bv-part

       let cl-env = sel-envpart(f)   //the environment

       $\langle$[ ], extend(cl-env, 2nd(S), cl-bv), cl-body, $D_{new}\rangle$

           where D_{new} = $\langle$tl(tl(S)), E, tl(C), $D\rangle$

       )))

Fig. 8.1

again later. Firstly, it offers no suggestions, and imposes no restrictions, on the order in which the operand and operator of a combination should be evaluated. Secondly, val is apparently a model of AEs, and therefore of the λ-calculus, even though it was mooted by Landin in 1964, six years before a model was formally shown to exist!

Whatever the merits of val, it is certainly not obviously related to the way AEs can be evaluated by machine. Recall that the approach to meaning sketched above calls for a language to be compiled into AEs; continuing that analogy, we may ask how AEs might be 'run'. Landin (1964, p. 316) defined a set of states, and a function transform : state $\to$ state, such that repeated application of transform described mathematically a sequence of steps to evaluate an AE. A state $\langle S, E, C, D \rangle$ consisted of four components: a Stack, Environment, Control, and Dump. [In terms of the runtime storage structure of ALGOL 60 (see Gries, 1971, Chapter 8), which consists of a stack of procedure 'frames', the 'control' C is the code being executed, the 'stack' S is the current frame, the 'dump' D is the frame stack up to, and including, the previous frame, and the 'environment' E is the static link or display. This close analogy underlies the argument of the mathematical semanticists, referred to in Section 8.1, that the SECD 'machine' is a definition of an implementation.] The definition of transform is given in Fig. 8.1. To 'operate' transform, we start with an empty stack and dump, the AE to be evaluated on control, and the initial environment as the environment component of the state. The function transform is repeatedly applied until the control and dump are empty. A full description of the operation of transform is given by Landin (1964, p. 317); we illustrate it with two examples.

Most of the complexity of transform is in the application of closures (corresponding to starting a new runtime stack frame) in the case $x = $ **ap**. Our first example is a simple combination not involving closures; we evaluate sq(a) in the environment $[a \cdot 3]$ which binds a to 3. Fig. 8.2 shows successive snapshots of the state as transform is applied. Note that for clarity we ignore obvious details such as the fact that the environment also binds 3 to 3 and sq to the squaring function.

$\langle [\ ], [a \cdot 3], \text{sq}(a), [\ ] \rangle$

$\langle [\ ], [a \cdot 3], [a \text{ sq } \textbf{ap}], [\ ] \rangle$ //a combination

$\langle [3], [a \cdot 3], [\text{sq } \textbf{ap}], [\ ] \rangle$ //the value of a is 3

$\langle [\text{sq } 3], [a \cdot 3], [\textbf{ap}], [\ ] \rangle$ //sq is the squaring function

$\langle [9], [a \cdot 3], [\ ], [\ ] \rangle$ //$3^2 = 9$

Fig. 8.2

This example clearly demonstrates that, unlike val, transform specifies the way in which a combination is to be evaluated: first evaluate the operand, then the operator, then apply the latter to the former.

Our second example illustrates most of the environment handling problems; it calls for the evaluation of $U(\lambda x \cdot y)$ in an environment that binds y to 27, where U is $\lambda f \cdot \{\lambda y \cdot f(y)\}(2)$. The sequence of states is shown in Fig. 8.3.

CHECKPOINT 8.5 Use the SECD machine to evaluate half(sq(4)) and $\{\lambda x \cdot \text{half}(\text{sq}(x))\}(4)$.

We now show how the transform function of the SECD 'machine' can be used to define a function mechanical $\cdot$ val, which evaluates an AE X in an environment E. First, we define a function iterate, which repeatedly applies a function f to a state S:

$$\langle[\ ], [y \cdot 27], U(\lambda x \cdot y), [\ ]\rangle$$

$$\langle[\ ], [y \cdot 27], [\lambda x \cdot y\ U\ \mathbf{ap}], [\ ]\rangle$$

$$\langle[\text{Aclosure}], [y \cdot 27], [U\ \mathbf{ap}], [\ ]\rangle$$

where Aclosure has function $\lambda x \cdot y$, and environment $[y \cdot 27]$.

$$\langle[\text{Bclosure Aclosure}], [y \cdot 27], [\mathbf{ap}], [\ ]\rangle$$

where Bclosure is the function $\lambda f \cdot \{\lambda y \cdot f(y)\}(2)$ with environment $[y \cdot 27]$.

$$\langle[\ ], [f \cdot \text{Aclosure}\ y \cdot 27], \{\lambda y \cdot f(y)\}(2), D_1\rangle$$

where D_1 is $\langle[\ ], [y \cdot 27], [\ ], [\ ]\rangle$.

$$\langle[2], [f \cdot \text{Aclosure}\ y \cdot 27], [\lambda y \cdot f(y)\ \mathbf{ap}], D_1\rangle$$

$$\langle[\text{Cclosure}\ 2], [f \cdot \text{Aclosure}\ y \cdot 27], [\mathbf{ap}], D_1\rangle$$

where Cclosure has function $\lambda y \cdot f(y)$ and environment $[f \cdot \text{Aclosure}\ y \cdot 27]$.

$$\langle[\ ], [y \cdot 2\,f \cdot \text{Aclosure}\ y \cdot 27], f(y), D_2\rangle,$$

where D_2 is $\langle[\ ], [f \cdot \text{Aclosure}\ y \cdot 27], [\ ], D_1\rangle$

$$\langle[2], [y \cdot 2\,f \cdot \text{Aclosure}\ y \cdot 27], [f\ \mathbf{ap}], D_2\rangle$$

$$\langle[\text{Aclosure}\ 2], [y \cdot 2\,f \cdot \text{Aclosure}\ y \cdot 27], [\mathbf{ap}], D_2\rangle$$

$$\langle[\ ], [x \cdot 2\,y \cdot 27], y, D_3\rangle$$

where $D_3 = \langle[\ ], [y \cdot 2\,f \cdot \text{Aclosure}\ y \cdot 27], [\ ], D_2\rangle$. Notice how the environment binding y to 27 has been reinstated from the closure Aclosure. Now we load 27 onto the stack and unwind the whole way:

$$\langle[27], [x \cdot 2\,y \cdot 27], [\ ], D_3\rangle$$

$$\langle[27], [y \cdot 2\,f \cdot \text{Aclosure}\ y \cdot 27], [\ ], D_2\rangle$$

$$\langle[27], [f \cdot \text{Aclosure}\ y \cdot 27], [\ ], D_1\rangle$$

$$\langle[27], [y \cdot 27], [\ ], [\ ]\rangle$$

Fig. 8.3

```
iterate(f, S) =  null(sel-control(S)) →
                    (null(sel-dump(S)) → sel-stack(S),   //the answer
                    iterate(f, reinstatedump(S)),        //reinstate dump
                    iterate(f, f(S))   //otherwise apply f and start again
                    where reinstatedump(S) = consontostack
                        (sel-stack(S), sel-dump(S))
```

Next, we define a function loadAE, which loads an AE X in an environment E into an SECD state:

$$\text{loadAE}(E, X) = \langle \, [], E, X, [] \, \rangle$$

Finally, we define:

$$\text{mechanical} \cdot \text{val}(E, X) = \text{iterate}(\text{transform}, \text{loadAE}(E, X))$$

Clearly, mechanical · val, just like val, is a function from ⟨ environment, AE ⟩ pairs to AE-values. However, most writers on semantics, including Landin (1964), view val as the 'real' meaning of AEs, and think of mechanical · val not as a definition of the meaning of AEs, but as a description of an implementation of AEs. There is good reason for this; we pointed out above that the four components of an SECD state are closely related to features of the common runtime stack implementation of recursive languages such as ALGOL. Moreover, *if* mechanical · val(E, X) is computed in the 'usual' way, by repeatedly applying transform, then it is seen that a specific order of evaluation for combinations has been chosen:

(i) Evaluate the operand.

(ii) Evaluate the operator.

(iii) Apply the result of (ii) to the result of (i).

However, as a function, mechanical · val is as much a set of ordered ⟨⟨ Environment, AE ⟩, AE value ⟩ pairs as is val. We repeat the point made in Section 6.1: current mathematics does not admit discussion of the process by which a function application is to be evaluated. For example $\lambda x \cdot \text{pred}(\text{succ}(x))$ is the identity function, and there is nothing in mathematics that insists that pred(succ(4)), for example, should be evaluated by first applying succ, and then applying pred, although most people would. Strictly speaking, mechanical · val and val are different *descriptions* of the same function. The description of mechanical · val is inspired by, and suggests, a particular way to evaluate AEs; but that does not alter its status, *qua* set of ordered pairs, as a function.

8.3.3 *Translating ALGOL 60 into (imperative) AEs*

The parts of ALGOL 60 (say) that featured in Section 8.3.1 in the correspondence with the λ-calculus were declarations, expression evaluation, and function application. Not surprisingly, they are precisely the features of ALGOL 60 that are most reminiscent of schoolroom mathematics. Following Landin (1964), it has been customary to call such aspects of a programming language the 'declarative' (or 'applicative', 'definitional') part, in contrast to such 'obviously' non-mathematical, computer-ish, notions as assignment and **goto**. The difficulty of explicating **goto** and assignment in terms of AEs was 'solved' by Landin as follows:

(i) Extend AEs to 'imperative' AEs (from now on abbreviated to IAEs), and compile ALGOL 60 into IAEs.

(ii) Extend the SECD machine by incorporating a memory component (which

plays the role of the symbol table in an ALGOL 60 implementation); thus the
SECD machine becomes the SECDM machine.*

The crucial point is that no function analogous to val was defined. It is precisely that to which Strachey referred in the quotation given on p. 223, and
which we shall take up in Section 8.4. The new kinds of IAE were assigners
(Landin, 1965, p. 92) to render assignments, and program points (Landin, 1966,
p. 269) to explicate jumps. Full details of the compiler from ALGOL 60 into
IAEs may be found in Landin (1965).

One of the major contributions of Landin's correspondence study has been
to the systematic design of programming languages. It is hardly surprising that
a rigorous analysis of a programming language points up its shortcomings or
suggests linguistic generalizations. Two of the more interesting contributions of
Landin's study arose from the explication of jumps and **for** commands.

Jumps are essentially modelled by defining label values to be a part of an
SECDM state (see Reynolds, 1971, p. 316. Landin (1965, p. 91) showed how
an operator J could be defined that neatly transformed a closure into a program
closure, and provided a wide range of useful unnatural exits from procedures
and blocks in a structured way. Program closures have since been called 'escapers',
and are discussed by Reynolds (1972). Interestingly, the operator J, and program closures, can be defined in the SECD framework, and thereby provide a
sort of 'alarm' exit during expression evaluation. A program closure differs from
a closure in that it also contains a dump component; when it is evaluated, the
dump is reinstated.

The rendering of the **for** command (Landin, 1965, p. 95):

for $v := a$ **step** b **until** c, d, e **while** p **do** T

has to reflect the idea that the control variable v takes on a sequence of values,
which may be affected by the execution of T, and which may not therefore b
be predicted statically. This consideration applies particularly to the **while** variant
of step elements. Landin's solution was to exploit the technique described above
for rendering conditional expressions; a step element is rendered as a *stream*,
which is a λ-function of no arguments, which, when applied, yields the first element of the stream and a λ-function that represents the rest of the stream. Thus
the static list $[a\ b\ c]$ can be turned into the stream:

$\lambda(\ ) \cdot \langle a, s_1 \rangle$
    where $s_1 = \lambda(\ ) \cdot \langle b, s_2 \rangle$
    where $s_2 = \lambda(\ ) \cdot \langle c, \text{nullstream} \rangle$

Streams have turned out to be a useful linguistic structure in their own right;

---

* Landin (1965, p. 92) actually described a 'sharing' machine. Details of the
CSEDM machine (it is not clear why the components were re-ordered) were
never published, but were circulated. See also Reynolds (1972).

they are provided in POP2 as dynamic lists, discussed in Reynolds's (1971) GEDANKEN, and BCPL input–output is based on them. Milner's (1975) processes generalize streams.

Landin's work suggests designing programming languages by grafting appropriate imperative features onto a fixed declarative hull. GEDANKEN, ISWIM (Landin, 1966), and POP2 were consciously designed in this way.

CHECKPOINT 8.6 Give stream definitions for the various kinds of step element allowed by ALGOL 60.

8.3.4 *Postscript on operational semantics: VDL*

One of the outstanding early achievements in formal semantics was the IBM Vienna laboratories definition of the complex programming language PL/1. The project was initiated in 1965, and a formal definition of the full language was completed by 1968 (Lucas and Walk, 1969). PL/1 was developed by IBM, mainly as a successor to COBOL in the field of business data processing, for which transportability of programs is a fundamental requirement. The project was based on Landin's explication of ALGOL 60 in terms of AEs and McCarthy's abstract syntax/state transformation semantics, described in Section 6.5. PL/1, like ALGOL 60, allows a certain amount of freedom in the order in which subexpressions must be evaluated, and commands executed, to enable implementers to optimize code generation by exploiting features of the target machine (see Gries 1971, Chapters 17 and 18). The overall aim of the Vienna definition project was to lay down precise and detailed conditions which had to be met by an implementation.

The over-riding concern for consistent implementations is reflected in the Vienna laboratories definition of 'meaning' as 'the entire sequence of states corresponding to a program run'. Clearly this has the advantage of spelling out in the finest detail possible the steps any implementer has to achieve. It has the disadvantage that it is extremely difficult to think about, or reason about, the behaviour of a program, a point to which we shall return below.

Lucas (1971) pointed out that the state of a Landin, McCarthy, or Vienna-style approach to semantics depends crucially on the language being defined, and he discussed a correlation between the complexity of the state needed to define a language using the Vienna machine and the complexity (in some unspecified sense) of the language. Certainly, the runtime storage structures required to implement PL/1 necessitate an extremely complex state.

Following McCarthy and Landin, the Vienna definition interprets an abstract syntax representation of a program. One of the contributions of the Vienna work was a calculus of structured objects (see Lucas, Lauer, and Stigleitner, 1968) which is applicable equally to machine states and abstract syntax trees. The corner stone of the calculus is a powerful replacement operator μ. As in the case of the SECD machine, one of the state components is a control, consisting of the piece of program currently being interpreted. Since the order in which expressions are evaluated is deliberately left partially unspecified, the control component is itself a tree, and is represented as a structured object, with instructions at the tree nodes. Any of the instructions at the leaves of the control tree is a candidate to be executed, so that there is generally a set of possible next states. Thus the function analogous to the SECD machine transform returns a set of successor states, and a program execution is a sequence:

$$s_1 s_2 \ldots$$

of states such that $s_{i+1} \in \text{transform}(s_i)$. An execution step modifies the state and, in particular, the control tree. Two commonly occurring modifications to the control tree are: (i) delete the current node and pass an appropriate value to higher nodes in the three; (ii) replace the current node by a tree.

However valuable the Vienna work was for guiding implementers, it was found to be unsatisfactory for reasoning about programs (see Allen, Chapman, and Jones, 1972, p. 1). Part of the problem seems to be that the sequence of states is completely unstructured. In order to reason about a program it is usually desirable to group a sequence of states together as one entity (such as: this sequence corresponds to executing $A[i, j + k] := 2 * c - 4$), and this is difficult to do in the Vienna work. There is, however, scope for modifying the Vienna work since the control tree really is a tree. The author believes that a neat account of coroutines can be given using Vienna techniques with structure imposed on the state sequence. An account of these ideas is beyond the scope of this introduction.

8.4 Mathematical semantics: de-emphasizing the machine

What is currently usually referred to as 'mathematical semantics' has its origins in the work of Strachey (1966, 1967). The goal of his research, as quoted on p. 223, was to discover an appropriate set of mathematical concepts to serve as primitive semantic building blocks for even the imperative aspects of programming languages. Given such a set of mathematical concepts, it would be possible to define a function, say $L \cdot$ val, to associate each construct in a programming language L directly with its 'meaning', a mathematical object. Strachey firmly believed that it was possible to define $L \cdot$ val more like the AE-meaning function val than the SECD-based formulation mechanical $\cdot$ val (see Section 8.3.3). In particular, the meaning of a language such as ALGOL 60 could be defined precisely and satisfactorily without suggesting an implementation based on stacks, dumps, and symbol tables. We shall return to a discussion of this conjecture at the end of the section.

Strachey's (1966, 1967) analysis proposed a fundamental distinction between two different sorts of programming constructs: an *expression* is evaluated to yield a value, while *commands* are executed to effect a change of state in a machine. In fact, as ALGOL 60 type procedures and BCPL's **valof** construction show, the evaluation of an expression generally also causes a change of state. Thus a fundamental postulate of the Strachey semantics is that it is possible to define a set[*] S of states, and set V of expression values, and two functions:

$$C\text{-means} : \text{Commands} \to (S \to S)$$

and

$$E\text{-means} : \text{Expressions} \to (S \to V \times S)$$

so that C-means(c) and E-means(e) are the meaning of the command c and expression e. If s_{init} is a state, and:

$$C\text{-means}(c)(s_{\text{init}}) = s_{\text{final}}$$

we say that the execution of the command c transforms the state from s_{init} to s_{final}. Similarly, if:

$$E\text{-means}(e)(s_{\text{init}}) = \langle v, s_{\text{final}} \rangle$$

we say that the value of the expression e in state s_{init} is v. If, additionally, $s_{\text{init}} \neq s_{\text{final}}$, we say that the evaluation of e causes a 'side-effect'.

Strachey's (1966, 1967) initial skirmishes with semantics are most famous for his analysis of assignment commands. He pointed out that assignment commands assume instances of the general form:

$$e_1 := e_2$$

where e_1 and e_2 are expressions. Actually, most programming languages impose severe restrictions on the allowable forms of expression e_i, particularly on the left-hand side. In order to make sense of commonly occurring commands such as:

$$x := x + 1$$

it is necessary to realize that the occurrence of the variable x on the left-hand side refers to a different object from that referred to on the right-hand side. The left-side referent, intuitively a location in the case of simple variables, Strachey called the *L-value* of x. The right-side referent, intuitively a bit-string (perhaps interpreted as a number, or truth value, etc.), Strachey called the *R-value* of x. A further postulate is that there are sets ID of names, L of L-values, and R of R-values. One of the attributes of ALGOL 60, which distinguishes it from LISP (for example) in a most profound way, is that an identifier such as x *denotes* an L-value which *possesses* an R-value. We may picture the properties of the variable a and closure peep discussed on p. 233 as in Fig. 8.4.

Reynolds (1971) argues that the relationship between names, objects, and values is of fundamental importance in determining the structure of a programming language. Laski and Brady (1975) agree, but take issue with some of Reynolds's conclusions.

---

[*] We shall see later that it is not sufficient merely to require that S and V are sets.

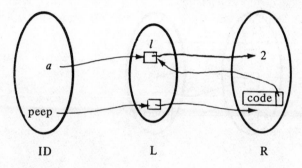

Fig. 8.4

L-values are not to be thought of as single words in a computer memory; generally speaking, current computer architectures require a much greater area of storage to hold the value of a procedure or data structure. Indeed, the restrictions that programming languages impose on the forms that left-sides of assignment commands may assume usually correspond to implementation simplicity of the corresponding *L*-value. (Restrictions on *R*-values usually derive from similar considerations; thus ALGOL forbids *R*-values that are entire arrays, procedures, or labels.) The *R*-value possessed by an *L*-value is determined by consulting the store, which, mathematically, is a function sto : $L \to R$. A basic property of an ordinary assignment command such as $a := 3$ (refer to Fig. 8.4) is that it leaves a denoting l but changes the value possessed by l to 3. The *L*-value denoted by a name may be changed in various ways, including redeclaration in an inner block. The *L*-value/*R*-value model is already rich enough to explain neatly the peep program discussed on p. 233; the important point to note is that the closure, which is the value of peep (see Fig. 8.4), includes not the *name* a, but the *L*-value l denoted by a at the time peep is declared. Entering the inner block causes a to denote a new *L*-value, say l', which is made to possess 27 (see Fig. 8.5), but peep still accesses l and prints 3. Many other computational phenomena are elegantly described in Strachey (1967), several of them in terms of the correspondence with λ-calculus expressions discussed in the preceding section.

Strachey (1966) concluded that *L*-value and *R*-value are primitive semantic notions in terms of which assignment commands may be formalized. However, the above discussion is far from precise, and it is in trying to make it precise that difficulties arise, especially the self-application problem noted in Section 1.2. Furthermore, we eventually have to consider the sets *V* of expression values and *S* of states in more detail. As we pointed out in Section 8.2, if the values in *V* are to be accepted and returned from procedures, then we require something like:

$$V = \ldots + (V \to V)$$

which is impossible to solve if $V \to V$ includes all set-theoretical functions on *V* and *V* has more than one element! Thus it was by no means certain that the sets

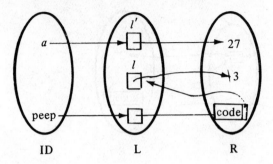

Fig. 8.5

postulated by Strachey could actually be defined, and so his mathematical
semantics were based on insecure foundations.

Section 8.2 described how Scott solved a similar problem for the λ-calculus
by developing a reflexive domain D isomorphic to $D \to D$. The essence of the
approach is to work not with sets but with domains (complete lattices), and to
insist that $D \to D$ contains only continuous functions on D. Scott's retraction
sequence construction enables the definition of many other domains, and
provides precisely the mathematical underpinnings needed to formalize
Strachey's intuitions about semantics. Indeed, from 1970 until his death in
1975, Strachey, together with his colleagues Scott, Stoy, Wadsworth, Milne, and
Mosses, of the Programming Research Group at Oxford University, developed
Scott's mathematical insights and applied them to formalize the analysis that
Strachey had started in 1966. Good accounts of the Oxford group's work are in
Stoy (1975) and the very recently published Milne and Strachey (1976).

In the remainder of this section, we follow Scott and Strachey's (1971)
example, and develop a number of increasingly sophisticated models of a simple
programming language. It will become clear that the method entails writing
down semantic equations, whose (fixed point)* solutions are guaranteed to exist
because they involve continuous functions on complete lattices. Such a function
always has a least fixed point, and it is possible to develop methods for computing it (see Stoy, 1975, Chapter 5). As was the case with McCarthy's approach to
semantics, sketched in Section 6.5, the meaning of a construct depends func-
tionally on the meaning of its parts, the connection between the parts being
discoverable through the syntactic specification of the language.

It is important to realize that Scott's work, and the idea of semantic equations, do *not* depend upon Strachey's (1966, 1967) intuitions about semantics,
but can be harnessed to render other views precise. For example, Milner (1973,
1975) has recently adopted a very different stance on meaning, based on a

---

* See p. 146 for a gentle introduction to the use of fixed points as solutions of
 recursive equations.

formalization of the intuitive notion of 'process'; his work also rests on Scott's theory of computability and exploits semantic equations.

The formal treatment of assignment commands turns out to be rather difficult in all but the simplest cases, and is not discussed further in this introduction. The interested reader is referred to Stoy (1975, Chapter 10) for an account of current thinking. The other major simplifying assumption we shall make in our example language is to use expressions only to route control in **test** and **while** commands; thus (for the moment) expression values all belong to the domain T of truth values. Notice that T is *not* the set {**true, false**} of truth values, since T is a (complete lattice) domain, and thus needs additional top and bottom elements (see Stoy, 1975, Chapter 5). We propose the BNF syntax given in Fig. 8.6 for our language. Informally, the expressions $\cdot$ TRUE $\cdot$ and $\cdot$ FALSE $\cdot$ evaluate to *true*, *false* (in T), and cause no change of state. Likewise, the command *dummy* has no effect on the state. The $\langle$ prim $\cdot$ expn $\rangle$ variant of expressions serve to delay consideration of user supplied names; an example might be random, which generates *true* or *false*, and changes state. Similar remarks apply to $\langle$ prim $\cdot$ command $\rangle$. The other syntactic constructions have their expected meaning (see Appendix B for an informal description).

$\langle$command$\rangle$ ::= **dummy** |$\langle$prim $\cdot$ command$\rangle$|$\langle$command$\rangle$;$\langle$command$\rangle$

|**test** $\langle$expn$\rangle$ **then** $\langle$command$\rangle$ **or** $\langle$command$\rangle$

|**while** $\langle$expn$\rangle$ **do** $\langle$command$\rangle$

$\langle$expn$\rangle$ ::= $\cdot$ TRUE $\cdot$ | $\cdot$ FALSE $\cdot$ |$\langle$prim $\cdot$ expn$\rangle$

|$\langle$expn $\rightarrow$ $\langle$expn$\rangle$, $\langle$expn$\rangle$

Fig. 8.6

According to the Strachey semantics, we need to postulate a domain S of 'states', and meaning functions:

C-means : $\langle$ command $\rangle \rightarrow (S \rightarrow S)$

and

E-means : $\langle$ expn $\rangle \rightarrow (S \rightarrow T \times S)$

The definition of E-means is given in Fig. 8.7. It gives the meaning of an expression e, in a state s_{init} by cases on the syntactic class of e. The **cases** notation is due to Burstall (1969). The meaning of conditional expressions is a reformulation of the λ-calculus rendering given on p. 232. To aid readability, we use the notation **let** $x = M$ *in* N as a mathematically equivalent form for the expression $\{\lambda x \cdot N\} M$. Notice that the strictly sequential interpretation of **let** $x = M$ *in* N,

$E\text{-means}(e)(s_{init}) = \textbf{cases } e:$

   $\cdot \text{TRUE} \cdot : \langle true, s_{init} \rangle$

   $\cdot \text{FALSE} \cdot : \langle false, s_{init} \rangle$

   $\langle \text{prim} \cdot \text{expn} \rangle : e(s_{init})$ //primitive expressions are *a priori* given

                                   //continuous functions $S \rightarrow T \times S$

   $e_{prem} \rightarrow e_{conc}, e_{altr} : (\textbf{let } E\text{-means}(e_{prem})(s_{init}) = \langle \text{tval}, s_{next} \rangle$

                     $\textbf{in}\{\text{ifasfn}(\text{tval})(E\text{-means}(e_{conc}), E\text{-means}(e_{altr}))\}(s_{next}))$

Fig. 8.7

$C\text{-means}(c)(s_{init}) = \textbf{cases } c:$

$\textbf{dummy} : s_{init}$

$\langle \text{prim} \cdot \text{command} \rangle : c(s_{init})$

$c_1 ; c_2 : C\text{-means}(c_2)\{C\text{-means}(c_1)(s_{init})\}$

$\textbf{test } e \textbf{ then } c_1 \textbf{ or } c_2 : (\textbf{let } E\text{-means}(e)(s_{init}) = \langle \text{tval}, s_{next} \rangle$

                $\textbf{in}\{\text{ifasfn}(\text{tval})(C\text{-means}(c_1), C\text{-means}(c_2))\}(s_{next}))$

$\textbf{while } e \textbf{ do } c : (\textbf{let } E\text{-means}(e)(s_{init}) = \langle \text{tval}, s_{next} \rangle$

           $\textbf{in}\{\text{ifasfn}(\text{tval})(C\text{-means}(c ; \textbf{while } e \textbf{ do } c), C\text{-means}(\textbf{dummy}))\} (s_{next}))$

Fig. 8.8

which calls for M to be evaluated and then N, may *not* yield the same value as $\{\lambda x \cdot N\}(M)$ in the case that the evaluation of M involves a side-effect (change of state).

The definition of C-means is given in Fig. 8.8. Notice that, as in Chapters 4, 6, and 7, the sequencing operation ';' is modelled by function nesting. The equation for **test** commands is similar to that for conditional expressions. The important point to notice in the definition of C-means is that the meaning of a **while** command is self-referential; since we can prove that C-means is continuous, we can guarantee that the meaning function exists.

CHECKPOINT 8.7 Introduce the commands **if** e **do** c, and c **repeatwhile** e into the language, and write down the corresponding semantic equations.

CHECKPOINT 8.8 What difficulties arise if you attempt to introduce the logical operators $\cdot \text{NOT} \cdot$, $\cdot \text{AND} \cdot$, and $\cdot \text{OR} \cdot$ into the language?

Let us now say that two commands are equivalent, written $c_1 \equiv c_2$, if they have the same meaning.

THEOREM 8.3 **while** e **do** $c \equiv$ **test** e **then**$(c;$ **while** e **do** $c)$
or dummy

Proof.

$$C\text{-means}(\textbf{while } e \textbf{ do } c)(s_{\text{init}}) = (\textbf{let } E\text{-means}(c)(s_{\text{init}}) = \langle \text{tval}, s_{\text{next}} \rangle$$
$$\textbf{in}\{\text{ifasfn}(\text{tval})(C\text{-means}(c; \textbf{while } e \textbf{ do } c),$$
$$C\text{-means}(\textbf{dummy}))\}(s_{\text{next}}))$$

$$= C\text{-means}(\textbf{test } e \textbf{ then}(c; \textbf{while } e \textbf{ do } c)\textbf{ or dummy})$$

CHECKPOINT 8.9 Prove that **if** e **do** $c \equiv$ **test** e **then** c **or dummy**.

CHECKPOINT 8.10 Prove that c **repeatwhile** $e \equiv c;$ **while** e **do** c.

Proofs of equivalence are proofs that two continuous functions f_1 and f_2 on domains are equal. The proofs of Theorem 8.3 (and the checkpoints) are particularly easy since we can derive the same expression for f_1 and f_2; but things are not always so convenient. Accordingly, a number of techniques have been developed for proving the equality of two continuous functions. Without the lattice-theoretic background, it is not possible to describe these techniques here. The interested reader is referred to Stoy (1975, p. 190ff) for discussions of fixed point, computational, and numerical induction. We note in passing that fixed point induction is closely related to the recursion induction proof technique discussed in Section 6.4.

Given a definition of the meaning of **while** e **do** c, we may ask if it is possible to prove Hoare's axiomatic semantic **while**-rule (see p. 199) as a theorem. We recall that side-effects are disallowed by Hoare, so for all expressions e, and all states s:

$$E\text{-means}(e)(s) = \langle \text{tval}, s \rangle$$

The **while**-rule is:

$$P \wedge e\{c\}P \vdash P\{\textbf{while } e \textbf{ do } c\}P \wedge \sim e$$

In the rule, P is an assertion about the state (presumably a continuous function in $S \rightarrow T$), and e is used both as an expression of the language and as an assertion about the state, which is reasonable since barring side-effects enables us to define expressions as assertions as follows:

$$\text{Expnasassertion}(e, s) = \text{first}(E\text{-means}(e)(s))$$

THEOREM 8.4 If $P(s_{\text{init}})$, $E\text{-means}(e)(s_{\text{init}}) = \langle \textbf{true}, s_{\text{init}} \rangle$ and $C\text{-means}(c)(s_{\text{init}}) = s_{\text{next}}$ together imply $P(s_{\text{next}})$, then from $P(s_{\text{init}})$ and $C\text{-means}(\textbf{while } e \textbf{ do } c)(s_{\text{init}}) = s_{\text{final}}$ we may deduce $P(s_{\text{final}})$ and $E\text{-means}(e)(s_{\text{final}}) = \langle \textbf{false}, s_{\text{final}} \rangle$

Proof. By definition of the $P\{c\}Q$ notation, the computation of c terminates in a finite number of steps. The meaning of **while** e **do** c is given by:

$$C\text{-means}(\textbf{while } e \textbf{ do } c)(s_{\text{init}}) = (\textbf{let } E\text{-means}(e)(s_{\text{init}}) = \langle \text{tval}, s_{\text{init}} \rangle$$
$$\textbf{in}\,\{\text{ifasfn}\,(C\text{-means}(c; \textbf{while } e \textbf{ do } c),$$
$$C\text{-means}(\textbf{dummy}))\}(s_{\text{init}}))$$

To terminate, the evaluation of C-means(**while** e **do** c)(s_{init}) must apply C-means(**dummy**) to s_{init} (yielding s_{init}) after a finite number k of steps. The proof is by induction on k. If k is zero, $s_{\text{init}} = s_{\text{final}}$, and it is trivial to show $P(s_{\text{final}})$ and E-means(e)(s_{final}) = $\langle$ false, s_{final} $\rangle$. Suppose $s_{\text{init}} \neq s_{\text{final}}$, so that E-means(e)(s_{init}) = $\langle$ true, s_{init} $\rangle$. Then, by definition of the meaning of ';':

$$C\text{-means}(\textbf{while } e \textbf{ do } c)(s_{\text{init}}) = C\text{-means}(\textbf{while } e \textbf{ do } c)(s_{\text{next}})$$

where s_{next} is C-means(c)(s_{init}). The conditions of the premiss are fulfilled, and so we may deduce $P(s_{\text{next}})$. By induction we deduce $P(s_{\text{final}})$.

The fact that proofs of equivalence can be given so straightforwardly is clearly an attractive property of mathematical semantics. A more considered assessment of its suitability for this purpose is, however, outside the scope of this introduction, since we have not got to grips with imperative features, unnatural exits, and so on.

We now make the model a shade more complex by supposing that $\langle$ prim · command $\rangle$s are named by the programmer. Accordingly, we need an environment that associates with each name in ID a state change (continuous) function. Thus we have:

$$\text{ENV} = \text{ID} \rightarrow (S \rightarrow S)$$

and denote environments by env. Since commands are executed, and expressions evaluated, in a specific environment, we need to modify the definitions of C-means and E-means slightly. As is the case with the λ-calculus, it is preferable on technical grounds to deal with 'curried' functions which apply a single argument at a time. Thus we modify the functionality of C-means, E-means to be:

$$C\text{-means} : \langle \text{command} \rangle \rightarrow (\text{Env} \rightarrow (S \rightarrow S))$$
and
$$E\text{-means} : \langle \text{expn} \rangle \rightarrow (\text{Env} \rightarrow (S \rightarrow T \times S))$$

The clauses of the definitions of C-means and E-means are virtually unchanged, since there are no procedures or declarations in the language that necessitate environment modification. We shall have to modify environments slightly below, in order to declare labels. The fact that C-means and E-means are curried reflects the compile-then-run structure of languages such as ALGOL 60; if e is an expression, and env is an environment, E-means(e)(env) is a function from states to $\langle$ value, state $\rangle$ pairs. Thus we may discover the structure of e, and handle all environment problems, before 'running' e in a specific state.

Our final modification to the language calls for the inclusion of a simple form of jumps and labels. Specifically, we shall allow two additional forms of commands:

goto ⟨ expn ⟩

and the simple compound command:

begin ⟨ command ⟩ ; ⟨ label ⟩ : ⟨ command ⟩ **end**

where ⟨ label ⟩ is a new kind of ⟨ expn ⟩. Clearly the value of an ⟨ expn ⟩ can no longer be restricted to T, since we need ⟨ label ⟩ values. We shall consider what they might be in a moment, but first of all we investigate the effect of introducing gotos and labelled compound commands on the rest of the language. Consider the sequence of commands $c_1 ; c_2$, whose meaning was previously defined by function nesting:

$$C\text{-means}(c_1 ; c_2)(\text{env})(s_{\text{init}}) = C\text{-means}(c_2)(\text{env})\{s_{\text{next}}\}$$
$$\textbf{where } s_{\text{next}} = C\text{-means}(c_1)(\text{env})(s_{\text{init}})$$

The crucial point to note is that in this model $C\text{-means}(c_2)$ is ALWAYS applied, and that this is an unsatisfactory account of (say):

goto $l ; c_2 ; l$:

in which the intension is that c_2 is *not* executed, that is to say, $C\text{-means}(c_2)$ is not applied. The problem ultimately reduces to modelling control mathematically. We have in fact confronted control already, in dealing with conditional expressions and conditional commands, but there was a simple solution available in that case. A solution to the **goto** problem, proposed by C.P. Wadsworth and F.L. Morris (see Strachey and Wadsworth, 1974) is to give an extra argument to $C\text{-means}$ and $E\text{-means}$ called a *continuation*, which describes 'the effect of the rest of the program'.[*] Mathematically, a continuation is a (continuous) function in $(S \rightarrow S)$, and the control implications of a command are defined as the change the command makes to its continuation argument. Thus if c_1 is a non-**goto** command, the continuation from just before c_1 is executed is equal to the effect of c_1 and the continuation from just after c_1 (see Fig. 8.9). The functionality of $C\text{-means}$ is now:

⟨ command ⟩ → (Env → (Cont → $(S \rightarrow S)$)))

and

$C\text{-means}(c)(\text{env})(\text{cont})(s)$

is the state resulting from executing c in an environment env, with continuation cont, starting in state s. We shall rewrite the continuation clause defining the

----

[*] Continuations are closely related to 'tail functions' introduced by Mazurkiewicz (1971).

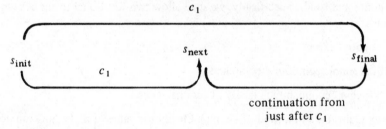

Fig. 8.9

meaning of the sequencing operator ';' shortly, but we first consider the effect of the compound command:

$$\textbf{begin } c_1 \text{ ; lab : } c_2 \textbf{ end}$$

which requires c_1 to be executed, and then, perhaps, c_2. Crucially, the compound command also introduces (that is, declares) the label lab as a point which control may reach via a **goto** command. Clearly we need to update the environment by binding the name lab to an appropriate value. This value must enable computation to start at c_2 irrespective of whether control reaches c_2 naturally by 'falling through' c_1, or unnaturally via a **goto**. The solution (in this case) is to make the value of lab a continuation, since by definition a continuation embodies the effect of running the program from a point such as c_2. This necessitates changing the value space of expressions to $V = T + (S \rightarrow S)$. Here is a clause of C-means that formalizes the above intuition:

$$C\text{-means}(\textbf{begin } c_1 \text{ ; lab : } c_2 \textbf{ end})(\text{env})(\text{cont})(s_{\text{init}})$$
$$= (\textbf{let } \text{newenv} = \text{extend}(\text{env, blockcont, lab})$$
$$\textbf{and } \text{blockcont} = C\text{-means}(c_2)(\text{newenv})(\text{cont})$$
$$\textbf{in } C\text{-means}(c_1)(\text{newenv})(\text{blockcont})(s_{\text{init}}))$$

The effect of executing **goto** lab is to discard the continuation provided, and substitute the continuation which is the value bound to lab in the environment provided:

$$C\text{-means}(\textbf{goto } \text{lab})(\text{env})(\text{cont}) = \lambda s \cdot \text{env}(\text{lab})(s)$$

We may generalize the clause for **goto** to define the meaning of a computed **goto** such as $\textbf{goto}(a < b \rightarrow \text{lab1, lab2})$.

$$C\text{-means}(\textbf{goto } e)(\text{env})(\text{cont})(s) =$$
$$(\textbf{let } E\text{-means}(e)(\text{env})(\text{cont})(s) = \langle \text{newcont}, s_{\text{next}} \rangle$$
$$\textbf{in } \text{newcont}(s_{\text{next}}))$$

Finally, we can write down the revised continuation clause defining the meaning of ';':

$$C\text{-means}(c_1 ; c_2)(\text{env})(\text{cont})(s) =$$

$$C\text{-means}(c_1)(\text{env})(\text{newcont})(s)$$

where

$$\text{newcont} = C\text{-means}(c_2)(\text{env})(\text{cont})$$

If c_1 is a non-**goto** command, $C\text{-means}(c_2)$ is applied as before. If, on the other hand, c_1 is a **goto** command, the evaluation of $C\text{-means}(c_1)$ discards newcont, so that $C\text{-means}(c_2)$ is not applied. It is now possible to prove by continuation or fixed-point induction theorems such as:

while e **do** $c \equiv$ **begin dummy** ; l : **if** e **do** $(c$; **goto** $l)$ **end**

CHECKPOINT 8.11 Write down the continuation clause defining **test** e **then** c_1 **or** c_2.

CHECKPOINT 8.12 Show how continuation semantics can be given for a language extension consisting of a **valof-resultis** construction.

Strachey and Wadsworth (1974) introduce 'expression continuations', which, intuitively, correspond to the information detailing what is to be done with the value computed for an expression. It is then possible to give a more succinct formulation of the clause required in answer to Checkpoint 8.11.

It is important to realize that continuations provide a simple and elegant model of control in the above example language, precisely because control is relatively simple. The problems that arise in implementing **goto** in ALGOL 60 stem from:

(i) **goto** leading out of a block. Blocks do not require new stack frames in ALGOL, but can be implemented as extensions to the current frame. The solution is to modify the current frame to delete the variables in the block exited. In SECD machine terms, the stack is changed but the dump is unaltered.

(ii) **goto** leading out of a procedure: a previous SECD state is substituted for the current one. In this general case, a label value corresponds to an environment, stack, and dump (see Reynolds, 1971, or Landin, 1965).

Neither blocks nor procedures were included in the example language, so problems (i) and (ii) did not arise. Indeed, an implementation of the example language would not need to resort to ALGOL-like dynamic storage allocation, but could make do with a FORTRAN-like static storage scheme (Gries, 1971, Chapter 8). An operational semantics would not need the S(tack) or D(ump) components of its state, but could make do with something simpler, something, in fact, rather like a continuation. We can 'uncurry' C-means, to define a function C-op-means:

$$C\text{-op-means}(c, \text{env}, \text{cont}, s) = C\text{-means}(c)(\text{env})(\text{cont})(s)$$

The arguments of C-op-means are strikingly similar to those of an operational semantics for a language permitting static storage: C (Control), env (Environment), cont (as we pointed out above, analogous to Stack and Dump),

252 THE THEORY OF COMPUTER SCIENCE

s (Memory). The author would argue that this amounts to postulating an abstract machine and implementation in much the same way that the operational semantics did. A close examination of Mosses's (1974) mathematical semantics of ALGOL 60 strengthens this conviction. Altogether, we would argue that the evidence is overwhelmingly against Strachey's conjecture about meaning, and the idea that there is a clear distinction between mathematical and operational semantics (see Stoy 1975, p. 13ff). Instead, we would argue that implementation questions, suitably abstracted, are an essential part of the meaning of current programming languages. It seems that what is really at issue is the level of abstraction at which implementation ideas are described, and, as we pointed out in Section 8.1, this can only be resolved against the background of reasons for wanting a formal semantics. Unfortunately, a fuller development of these arguments is not possible here, since they presuppose an extensive familiarity with the implementation of programming languages and the lattice-theoretical constructions developed by the mathematical semanticists.

Mathematical Prerequisites

A.1 Sets

The idea of a set is intuitively obvious; it is clear for example what is meant by the set *EEC* of the nine countries in the European Economic Community. In fact, as we shall indicate in Section A5, it is rather difficult to give a *precise definition* of the concept of set; nevertheless, intuition suffices for the purpose of this book. Here are some other examples of sets:

  C – the set of counties in Britiain

  H – the set of human beings currently alive in Britain

  B – the set of birth certificate numbers of British people

These examples how that sets are often dignified by a name. There is also a notation for nameless sets; thus we write {GM, Chrysler, Ford} for the set of major automobile manufacturers in the U.S.A. Instead of thinking of this set as being nameless, we can think of '{GM, Chrysler, Ford}' as a single complicated default name in contrast to the more succinct mnemonic names *C*, *EEC*, *B*, and *H*. A similar default naming mechanism can be seen in several places throughout the book, most notably in the discussion of the λ-notation in Section 6.2. We have:

  EEC = {Ireland, Belgium, Netherlands, Britain, France, West Germany, Luxembourg, Italy, Denmark}

Writing a set out in full such as {GM, Chrysler, Ford} is called specifying it *in extension*. Sometimes it is inconvenient to specify a set in extension; for example there are about 58 million human beings currently living in Britain. More significantly, it is impossible to specify in extension an infinite set such as the set *N* of natural numbers. In such cases, there are two main approaches to specifying sets.

  (1) 'Pretend' to specify it in the extension by means of the 'three dot trick', otherwise known as ellipsis notation:

  $$N = \{0, 1, 2, 3, \ldots\}$$

Crucially, we can only understand such a specification if we know a process for incrementally generating the rest of the set. An old schoolboy teaser is to 'specify' the set {M, V, E, . . .} and ask for it in full (solution at end of Appendix).

  (2) Give a property that is necessary and sufficient to determine membership in the set. Thus the property "x is a whole number which is at least zero" precisely specifies N; but "x is a major automobile manufacturer" includes Fiat as well as GM, Chrysler, and Ford. The set specified by a property p is denoted by:

$\{x \mid p(x)\}$

We say that the set is specified *in intension*.

If x is a member of a set S, we write $x \in S$; otherwise we write $x \notin S$. Thus $27 \in N$ and Italy $\in EEC$ but China $\notin EEC$ and Datsun $\notin \{$GM, Chrysler, Ford$\}$. There is a set E distinguished by the fact that it has no members; we can specify E in extension as follows:

$E = \{\ \}$

E is often called the null set, since a common notation for it is $\emptyset$, which is the Scandinavian letter null. We can use $\in$ to define new sets in terms of ones we already know:

$$Ev = \{2 * n \mid n \in N\} \qquad //\text{Even numbers}$$
$$Od = \{2 * n + 1 \mid n \in N\} \qquad //\text{Odd numbers}$$
$$Q = \{m/n \mid m, n \in N, and\ n \neq 0\} \quad //\text{Rational numbers}$$

Notice that we are indulging in a bit of mathematical licence in these intensional definitions. For example, the definition of Ev should more properly read:

$$Ev = \{m \mid m = 2 * n\ for\ some\ n \in N\}$$

In the remainder of this section we describe a number of important operations for constructing new sets out of old.

A.1.1 *Subset*

A set S is a subset of a set T, written $S \subseteq T$, if every member of S is also a member of T. That is:

$$S \subseteq T \equiv for\ all\ x\ (x \in S\ implies\ x \in T)$$

For example:

$\{$GM$\} \subseteq \{$GM, Chrysler, Ford$\}$

$Ev \subseteq N$

Notice that, if S and T are specified in intension, $S \subseteq T$ iff the property specifying S is more restrictive than that specifying T. It is customary to write $N \subseteq Q$, although strictly speaking N is *not* a subset of Q, because the elements of Q, as defined above, are syntactic constructs of the form m/n where m and n are members of N. What is meant by saying $N \subseteq Q$ is that '/' is to be *interpreted* as division and $n \in N$ is to be *identified* with $n/1 \in Q$. This identification of n with $n/1$ is an example of the familiar process of *type transfer*, say from integers to reals in ALGOL 60. Mathematicians have often been slack with regard to explicit recognition of type transfers; computer scientists cannot afford to be, because of the different representations of objects of different types within a computer.

A.1.2 *Intersection and union*

If S and T are sets, the intersection of S and T, written $S \cap T$, is the set consisting of those members that belong both to S and to T. The union of S and T, written $S \cup T$, is the set consisting of those members that belong either to S or to T (or to both if the intersection of S and T is non-empty). We have:

$$Ev \cap Od = \{\ \}$$
$$Ev \cup Od = N$$

CHECKPOINT A1   Prove that $S \subseteq T$ iff $S \cap T = S$ iff $S \cup T = T$.

A.1.3 *Complement*

If $S \subseteq T$, the complement $(T - S)$ of S in T is defined to be the set of members of T that do not belong to S:

$$(T - S) = \{x \mid x \in T \text{ and } x \notin S\}$$

CHECKPOINT A2
   (i) Show that $(N - Ev) = Od$ and $(N - Od) = Ev$, so that $(N - (N - Ev)) = Ev$.
   (ii) More generally, prove that, if $S \subseteq T, (T - (T - S)) = S$.

A.1.4 *Strings*

If S is a set, $S*$ is the set of finite strings of members of S. Thus $\{x,y\}* = \{x, y, xy, yx, \dots, xyxx, \dots\}$. If *Dict* is the set of words in the Oxford Dictionary:

$$Dict \subseteq \{a, \dots, z\}*$$

similarly

$$N \subseteq \{\emptyset, \dots, 9\}*$$

CHECKPOINT A3   We observed above that ellipsis notation implicitly implies an incremental generation process. Write programs to generate the elements of $\{x,y\}*$ and $\{a, b, \dots, z\}*$. Do you think that it is possible to write a program to generate $S*$ for an arbitrary set S?

A.1.5 *Cartesian product*

If S and T are sets, the Cartesian product $S \times T$ is the set of ordered pairs of the form (s, t) with $s \in S, t \in T$. We shall see in Section A.2 how the Cartesian product can be used to define functions of several variables. The etymology of the name Cartesian will be given in Section A.3. In the meantime, $S \times T$ is called a 'product' set for the following reason: denote the number of members of a set

S by $|S|$, so that $|\{\text{GM, Chrysler, Ford}\}| = 3$; it is easy to see that:

$$|S \times T| = |S| * |T|$$

We shall consider what $|N|$ might mean in Section A.4.

A.1.6 *Power set*

The power set $P(S)$ of a set S is the set whose members are the subsets of S. That is:

$$P(S) = \{x \mid x \subseteq S\}$$

For example:

$$P(\{\text{GM, Chrysler, Ford}\}) = \{E, \{\text{GM}\}, \{\text{Chrysler}\}, \{\text{Ford}\}, \{\text{GM, Ford}\},$$
$$\{\text{GM, Chrysler}\}, \{\text{Ford, Chrysler}\}, \{\text{GM,}$$
$$\text{Ford, Chrysler}\}\}$$

The name 'power set' derives not from the fact that it is a very powerful operation (a gruesome pun) but from the observation in the following checkpoint.

CHECKPOINT A4 Prove that if $|S| = n$, then $|P(S)| = 2^n$.

A.1.7 *Choice set*

Our final operation is very important, though rather bizarre. It derives from the apparently common or garden observation that, if one visits a greengrocer's stall (say) where there are separate non-empty baskets of apples, cabbages, oranges, and so on, one can take an initially empty basket and *choose* a piece of produce from each of the baskets to end up with a set of pieces of produce. We can make this process more precise: suppose we have sets S_i indexed by a set I (the point being that the same set may occur several times as S_i, S_j, S_k), and we choose an element x_i out of each S_i; then $\{x_i \mid i \in I\}$ is itself a set – a choice set from the family of S_i's. A number of mathematicians in the past have been worried about such a general notion, which in no way restricts the individual sets S_i or the indexing set I. In fact, a great deal of effort has been expended on trying to show that the operation was implied by, or at least consistent with, or even independent of, the rest of set theory. Cohen and Hersh (1967) give a lucid account of the problems. Nowadays the overwhelming majority of mathematicians feel completely happy about using the choice operation, or, as they say, appealing to the *axiom of choice*.

A.2 Functions

A *total function* from a set S to a set T is an association or pairing of a member of T with each element of S. Several members of S may be paired with the same member of T, but no single member of S may be paired with more than one member of T. If f is such a function, we write $f : S \rightarrow T$, and if $s \in S$, we denote by $f(s)$ the unique member of T paired with s. S is called the domain of f, and T the range. For example, if $S = T = N$, we can define the factorial function fac $: N \rightarrow N$ under which n is paired with:

$$\text{fac}(n) = 1 * 2 * \ldots * n$$

As another example, let $S = \{\text{Fred, Joe}\}$ and $T = \{\text{Mary, Ellen, Jane}\}$. We can define a function loves $: S \rightarrow T$ by:

$$\text{loves(Fred)} = \text{Ellen, loves(Joe)} = \text{Jane}$$

If $f : S \rightarrow T$ and $U \subseteq S$, we can define a function from U to T by considering only those pairings of f which relate to elements of U. We call this function the *restriction of f to U*, and denote it by $f \mid U : U \rightarrow T$. Clearly, for any $u \in U$:

$$f \mid U(u) = f(u) \in T$$

If we have sets S and T and a pairing f which has all the properties of being a function except that there are some elements of S that are not paired with any element of T, we call f a *partial function*, and write $f : S \tilde{\rightarrow} T$. As an example, consider half $: N \tilde{\rightarrow} N$ defined by half$(2 * n) = n$. Half is partial, but not total, since half$(3) \notin N$. Partial functions are very important for computer science as a way of modelling nonterminating computations.

If $f : S \tilde{\rightarrow} T$ is a partial function, there is a subset U of S consisting of those members of S that *are* paired with some member of T. Clearly $f \mid U$ is a total function from U to T.

In Section A.3 we shall show how a function $f : S \rightarrow T$ can be defined as a subset of the Cartesian product $S \times T$, and shall explain what is meant formally by the 'graph' of a function.

So far in this section we appear to have restricted our attention to functions of a single variable s. There are many well-known functions such as the greatest common divisor, as well as the logic functions AND, NAND, and so on, that have several inputs or arguments. In fact, a function of several variables can be thought of as a function whose domain is an appropriate Cartesian product. Thus if $Bool = \{\text{True, False}\}$ we can define

$$\text{AND} : (Bool \times Bool) \rightarrow Bool$$

by setting:

$$\text{AND}(x) = \begin{cases} \text{true} & x = \text{(true, true)} \\ \text{false} & \text{otherwise} \end{cases}$$

We close this section by defining two important special kinds of function.

A.2.1 *One-one*

A function $f : S \to T$ is said to be *one-one* if different members of S are paired with different members of T. That is:

$$f \text{ is one-one} \equiv \textit{for all } s_1, s_2 \in S, (f(s_1) = f(s_2)$$
$$\textit{implies } s_1 = s_2)$$

Of the example functions given above, both fac and loves are one-one, but the AND function is not.

A.2.2 *Onto*

A function $f : S \to T$ is onto if every member of T is paired with some member of S.

CHECKPOINT A5   Give examples of functions that are: (i) one-one and onto; (ii) one-one but not onto; (iii) onto but not one-one; and (iv) neither one-one nor onto.

The following lemma relates the concepts onto and one-one.

LEMMA A1   Let S and T be sets.
(i) If $f : S \to T$ is one-one, we can define an onto function $g : T \to S$ such that for all $s \in S, g(f(s)) = s$. That is, g inverts, or unpicks, the effect of f.
(ii) If $g : T \to S$ is onto, we can define a one-one function $f : S \to T$ so that for all $s \in S, g(f(s)) = s$.

Proof. (i) We may suppose that S is not empty. Since f is one-one, each member t of T is either paired with a single element s of S [so that $f(s) = t$], or with no element of S (since f may not be onto). Choose any s_0 in S, and define g as follows:

$$g(t) = \begin{cases} s & f(s) = t \\ s_0 & \text{otherwise} \end{cases}$$

Since f is one-one, g really does define a function. It is easy to check that g is onto and that $g(f(s)) = s$ for all $s \in S$.

(ii) This is more difficult. For each $s \in S$, define a subset T_s of T as follows:

$$T_s = \{t \mid t \in T \textit{ and } g(t) = s\}$$

Since g is onto, each T_s is a non-empty subset of T. We now apply the choice operation to the family of sets T_s indexed by S; that is to say, we choose an element t_s from each T_s and set $f(s) = t_s$. It is easy to see that f is one-one and that $g(f(s)) = s$ for each $s \in S$.

A.3 Relations

We have already defined a function $f : S \to T$ to be an association of members of S with members of T subject to the restriction that a member of S may only be paired with at most one member of T. This restriction is too severe for many interesting applications. For example, a single English word is generally associated with several different meanings, and an ALGOL 60 identifier is generally associated by scope rules with several different storage locations at different points in a program. The concept of 'relation' generalizes that of 'function' by allowing a single member of S to be associated with several members of T. If r is a relation from S to T, we write $r : S - \times T$.

We now give more precise definitions of relation and function based on the idea of a graph. Suppose $r : S - \times T$ is a relation from S to T. We can define a subset G_r of $S \times T$, called the *graph* of r, as follows:

$$G_r = \{(s, t) \mid (s, t) \in S \times T \text{ and } r(s) = t\}$$

Conversely, if $U \subseteq S \times T$, we can define a relation $\mathrm{rel}_U : S - \times T$ by:

$$\mathrm{rel}_U(s) = t \text{ iff } (s, t) \in U$$

CHECKPOINT A6 Show that $r = \mathrm{rel}_{G_r}$ and $U = G_{\mathrm{rel}_U}$, for any relation r and any subset U.

Since the Cartesian product $S \times T$ of two sets S and T is easy to define precisely, we can drop all appeal to intuition regarding 'associations' and formally define a relation to be a subset of $S \times T$, thus identifying r with G_r. Since the relations on S to T are then precisely the subsets of $S \times T$, and since the set of all such subsets is the power set $P(S \times T)$, we see that the collection $(S - \times T)$ of relations on S to T itself forms a set.

Identifying a relation r with its graph G_r leads to the alternative definition of a (partial) function $f : S \rightleftharpoons T$ as a subset G_f of $S \times T$ having the property that for all $s \in S$, the set $\{t \mid f(s) = t\}$ has at most one member.

CHECKPOINT A7 Show that the collection $S \rightleftharpoons T \, (S \to T)$ of partial functions (functions) on S to T forms a set.

CHECKPOINT A8 Prove that, if S and T are finite sets, $|S \rightleftharpoons T| = |T|^{|S|}$.

There is in fact a serious consequence of this conventional mathematical definition of a function as a set of ordered pairs which we shall illustrate with reference to the factorial function. Any programmer, and most mathematicians, would naively believe that the definition:

$$\mathrm{fac}(n) = 1 * 2 * \ldots * n$$

involves a *method* for computing $n!$ for any argument n. However, according to the definition given above, fac is nothing other than the set:

$$\{(1, 1), (2, 2), (3, 6), (4, 24), \ldots\}$$

so that discussions about how the number paired with n is obtained are simply not relevant! This issue is discussed further in Section 6.2.

If r_1 is a relation on S to T, and r_2 is a relation on T to U, we can *compose* r_1 with r_2 to define a new relation $(r_1 \circ r_2) : S - \times U$, as follows:

$$G_{(r_1 \circ r_2)} = \{(s, u) \mid for\ some\ t \in T, (s, t) \in G_{r_1}\ and\ (t, u) \in G_{r_2}\}$$

CHECKPOINT A9 Prove that if r_1 and r_2 are both functions (onto functions, one-one functions) so is $(r_1 \circ r_2)$.

G_f is called the 'graph' of a function $f : S \to T$ because it is in fact a formaliz- ation of the graphs familiar from schoolroom mathematics. Consider for example the function succ : $N \to N$ defined by $\operatorname{succ}(n) = n + 1$. Formally, succ is identified with its graph $G_{\operatorname{succ}} \subseteq N \times N$. We can represent the Cartesian product set $N \times N$ pictorially by the usual Cartesian coordinate grid (hence the name Cartesian) shown in Fig. A.1, in which G_{succ} is the set of points marked '·'.

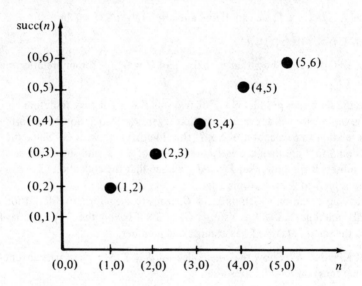

Fig. A.1

CHECKPOINT A10 How does the graph of a function differ from the graph of a general relation? What is special about the graph of an onto or one-one function?

In the case $S = T$, there is a special kind of relation called an *equivalence relation*, which generalizes the familiar mathematical idea of equality or con- gruence. There are many examples of equivalence relations in this book; each of them arises because we choose to think of certain members of a set as being indistinguishable for certain pruposes. Sections 3.4 and 6.4 consider the problem of proving two programs equivalent. The definition of 'equivalence relation' demonstrates an important mathematical process: in order to define an intuitive concept precisely, discover a set of properties that always hold for instances of that concept, and then define the concept in terms of those properties. Of course the difficult part is deciding which set of properties to choose! In the case of equivalence relations, the properties of reflexivity, symmetry, and transitivity have been found in practice to be satisfactory.

DEFINITION A1 A relation $r : S - \times S$ is an *equivalence relation* if the following three conditions are satisfied:
 (i) (reflexivity) $(s, s) \in G_r$ for all $s \in S$
 (ii) (symmetry) $(s_1, s_2) \in G_r$ iff $(s_2, s_1) \in G_r$
 (iii) (transitivity) $(s, t) \in G_r$ and $(t, u) \in G_r$ implies $(s, u) \in G_r$

CHECKPOINT A11 In FORTRAN, two variables are 'equivalent' if they share the same storage unit. Prove that this defines an equivalence relation.

Suppose r is an equivalence relation on a set S. For each element $s \in S$ we define the subset S_x of members of S equivalent to x:

$$S_x = \{y \mid y \in S \text{ and } (x, y) \in G_r\}$$

THEOREM A2 For all $x, y \in S$, either $S_x \cap S_y = \{\ \}$ or $S_x = S_y$. Indeed, $S_x = S_y$ iff $(x, y) \in G_r$, that is x is equivalent to y.

Proof. Suppose $S_x \cap S_y \neq \{\ \}$, say $z \in S_x$ and $z \in S_y$. By definition, $(x, z) \in G_r$ and $(y, z) \in G_r$. By symmetry and transitivity of r, $(x, y) \in G_r$, that is x is equivalent to y. Now, if u is *any* element of S_y, $(y, u) \in G_r$, and by transitivity, $(x, u) \in G_r$, so that $u \in S_x$. Hence $S_y \subseteq S_x$. Similarly $S_x \subseteq S_y$.

Theorem A2 implies that, if r is an equivalence relation on a set S, then S can be partitioned into a set of disjoint subsets consisting of pairwise equivalent members of S. The disjoint subsets are called *equivalence classes*.

A.4 Counting

In Section 3.2 we prove a number of theorems which show that programs can be written to enumerate, or mechanically count, many different sets, including all finite ones. The property of being 'mechanically countable' is stronger than the more established mathematical notion of 'countable' on which it is based, since, whereas 'mechanically countable' implies 'mathematically countable', there are sets that are mathematically but not mechanically countable (see Corollary 3.13). This section introduces mathematical countability as a background to the discussions in Section 3.2.

We shall work towards a mathematical formalization of counting with reference to the set *Lib* of books in the National Library. Counting a set such as *Lib* involves pairing numbers with members of the set, for example:

1st   Fanny Hill

2nd Kama Sutra

3rd Das Kapital

4th The Perfumed Garden

and so on

Such a pairing of numbers with books defines a subset, say G, of the product set $N \times \textbf{\textit{Lib}}$ with the following two properties:

(i) There is at most one book paired with each number, so that G is the graph of a function $f : N \to \textbf{\textit{Lib}}$.

(ii) In order to count the *whole* of **Lib**, we must insist that every book $b \in \textbf{\textit{Lib}}$ should appear in some pair $(n, b) \in G$. That is, we insist that f should be an onto function.

DEFINITION A2   A set S is *'countable'* if there is an onto function $f : N \to S$.

Actually, the more usual definition of countability requires that there should be a one-one function $g : S \to N$. Lemma A1 asserts that (modulo the axiom of choice) these definitions are equivalent. We have chosen to define 'countable' in terms of an onto function to be consistent with the discussion in Section 3.3.

Clearly any finite set is countable, but there are some infinite countable sets too.

CHECKPOINT A12   Prove that Ev and Od are countable.

It is not really surprising that Ev and Od are countable since they are both subsets of N, and one can always define an onto function from a set to a subset. Indeed, if $f : N \to S$ is an onto function counting S, Lemma A1 implies that there is a one-one function $g : S \to N$, so that S can be identified with a subset $g(S)$ of N. For this reason, the following result of the great German mathematician Georg Cantor (1845–1918) is truly surprising.

THEOREM A3   The set Q of rationals is countable.

Proof. We shall prove in detail in Section 3.3 that Q is even mechanically countable. The basic idea of the proof is to display the members of Q as in Fig. A2, and count along the arrows.

CHECKPOINT A13   Try to anticipate the analysis in Section 3.2 by defining the function $f : N \to Q$ (and its inverse) implicit in the sketched proof of Theorem A3.

CHECKPOINT A14   Sketch a generalization of Cantor's method to show that the product set N^r is countable for any finite r.

Theorem A3 naturally leads one to conjecture that all sets are countable. Cantor again confounded the mathematical community by showing that this was not the case: the set R of real numbers is not countable. The ramifications of

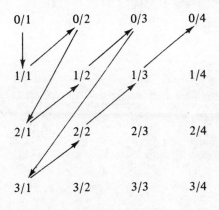

Fig. A.2

this result are considerable. If every set were countable, a single notion of infinity could adequately cater for all non-finite sets. But we have to admit at least *two* notions of infinity: a countable infinity like N and an uncountable infinity like R. In fact, by generalizing Cantor's result it becomes clear that an infinite number of different notions of infinity are needed!

Real numbers are infinite decimals of the form:

$$n \cdot d_1 d_2 d_3 \ldots$$

where $n \in N$ and each d_i is a decimal digit (that is, a member of $\{0, 1, \ldots, 9\}$). Clearly any rational number is real, so that $Q \subseteq R$; but there are real numbers such as $\sqrt{2}$ which it can be proved are not rational. (Prove it!)

CHECKPOINT A15 Show that R can be defined to be $N \times (N \to \{0, 1, \ldots, 9\})$.

THEOREM A4 The set R of real numbers is not countable. Indeed, even $R_1 = \{x \mid x \in R \text{ and } 0 \leqslant x \leqslant 1\}$ is not countable.

Proof. Since there is obviously an onto function from R to its subset R_1, and since the composition of two onto functions is onto (see Checkpoint A9), it suffices to show that R_1 is uncountable. We shall prove this by *reductio ad absurdum*: suppose R_1 is countable, say $f : N \to R_1$ is an onto function. Denote the real number $f(i)$ by r_i. Since $r_i \in R_1$, it has a unique decimal expansion of the form:

$$r_i = 0 \cdot d_{i1} d_{i2} d_{i3} \ldots$$

We now lay out the decimal expansions of r_1, r_2, and so on in turn, and fasten attention on the diagonal digits d_{11}, d_{22}, as shown in Fig. A3.

The diagonal digits can be used to 'construct' a new real number $r \in R_1$ as follows:

$$r = 0 \cdot d_1 d_2 d_3 \ldots$$

$$r_1 = 0 \cdot d_{11} \; d_{12} \; d_{13} \; d_{14} \; \cdots$$

$$r_2 = 0 \cdot d_{21} \; d_{22} \; d_{23} \; d_{24} \; \vdots \cdots$$

$$r_3 = 0 \cdot d_{31} \; d_{32} \; d_{33} \; d_{34} \; \cdots$$

$$r_4 = 0 \cdot d_{41} \; d_{42} \; d_{43} \; d_{44} \; \cdots$$

$$\vdots$$

Fig. A.3

where for $i \geqslant 1$:

$$d_i = \begin{cases} d_{ii} + 1 & d_{ii} \neq 9 \\ 0 & d_{ii} = 9 \end{cases}$$

The contradiction we seek comes from analysing r. First notice that, since $r \in R_1$ and $f : N \to R_1$ is onto, there must be some n such that:

$$r = f(n) = r_n$$

But if we expand r and r_n we find that in the nth position $d_n \neq d_{nn}$, by definition of r, and so $r \neq r_n$.

COROLLARY A5   The set $(N \to N)$ of functions from N to N is uncountable.

Proof. We construct an onto function $g : (N \to N) \to R_1$. If $(N \to N)$ *were* countable, there would be an onto function $f : N \to (N \to N)$; composing f with g would imply the countability of R_1, contradicting Theorem A4.

. Suppose $h \in (N \to N)$; then h defines a sequence $h(0), h(1), h(2), \ldots$ of natural numbers. Denoting the first digit of $h(i)$ by h_i, we put $g(h) = 0 \cdot h_1 h_2 \ldots$. It is easy to prove that g defines an onto function.

CHECKPOINT A16   Show that the set of functions $(N^r \to N)$ with r arguments is uncountable.

We conclude this section with a result whose 'enumerability' counterpart in Section 3.2 is false.

LEMMA A6   If S is a subset of T, and T is countable, so is S.

Proof. We observed above that, by Lemma A1, T is countable if and only if there is a one-one function, say g, from T to N. Clearly $S \subseteq T$ implies that there is a one-one function, say f, from S to T. Composing f with g gives a function $f \circ g : S \to N$, which, by Checkpoint A9, is also one-one. Hence S is countable.

A.5 Some proof techniques

We proved Theorem A4 in considerable detail, since the proof introduces a technique known as 'Cantor's diagonal argument', which is used frequently in Chapter 3. This section introduces two other important proof techniques known as *mathematical induction* and *Russell's paradox argument*.

The author believes that an understanding of proof techniques, including some idea of how and when it is appropriate to use them, is at least as important for *doing* mathematics as is knowing a large number of theorems. If this were not the case, there would be little point in mathematicians reading the proofs in research papers: it would be sufficient to memorize the statements of theorems proved. The argument applies even more strongly to computer science: knowing *what* a process does is not nearly so important as knowing *how* it does it.

A.5.1 *Mathematical induction*

Mathematical induction is a useful technique for proving that a property P holds for all but some initial segment of numbers. For example, it can be applied to prove:

(i) *all* $n \geqslant 0, 0 + 1 + \ldots + n = \frac{1}{2} * n * (n + 1)$

(ii) *all* $n \geqslant 3, 2 * n + 1 < 2^n$

(iii) *all* $n \geqslant 5, n^2 < 2^n$

In order to prove '*all* $n \geqslant k, P(n)$', we proceed in two steps as follows:

(a) *base step*: Prove (somehow) that $P(k)$ is true.

(b) *inductive step*: Assume that $P(n)$ is true, and on the basis of that assumption prove that $P(n + 1)$ is also true.

Having shown (a) and (b), we claim that we have indeed proved by mathematical induction that $P(n)$ is true for all $n \geqslant k$. The justification for this claim is quite simple: (a) shows that $P(k)$ is true; (b) then shows that $P(k + 1)$ is true, so (b) shows that $P(k + 2)$ is true, and so on.

EXAMPLE A1 *all* $n \geqslant 0, 0 + 1 + \ldots + n = \frac{1}{2} * n * (n + 1)$. The base step is trivial: $0 = \frac{1}{2} * 0 * 1$.

Suppose that we have already proved $P(n)$, that is:

$$0 + 1 + \ldots + n = \frac{1}{2} * n * (n + 1)$$

It follows that

$$0 + 1 + \ldots + n + (n + 1) = (0 + 1 + \ldots + n) + (n + 1)$$
$$= \frac{1}{2} * n * (n + 1) + (n + 1)$$
$$//\text{inductive assumption}$$
$$= \frac{1}{2} * (n + 1) * (n + 2)$$

so that $P(n + 1)$ is true.

CHECKPOINT A17 Prove by mathematical induction that:

(i) *all* $n \geqslant 3, 2 * n + 1 < 2^n$

(ii) *all* $n \geqslant 5, n^2 < 2^n$

There is in fact a generalization of mathematical induction known as *structural induction*. We point out in Chapter 4 that the natural numbers can be thought of as a special case of a class of structured objects: there is a single primitive object zero, and a single strategy, the successor function. Suppose more generally that $C(F)$ is a class of structured objects. In order to prove that:

$$all\ f \in C(F), P(f)$$

proceed by structural induction in two steps analogous to the base and inductive steps given above:

(a′) Prove that P holds for the primitive objects in F.

(b′) Prove that for each strategy c in C if P holds for $f_1, f_2, \ldots$, then it also holds for $c(f_1, f_2, \ldots)$.

A.5.2 *Russell's paradox argument*

The first sentence of this Appendix suggested that "the idea of a set is intuitively obvious". In the late nineteenth century, Bertrand Russell pointed out a difficulty with the intuitive approach given above, specifically with regard to intensional definitions of sets. Recall [Section A.1(2)] that one way to specify a set S is to "give a property that is necessary and sufficient to determine membership in [it]". If p is the property, we write:

$$S = \{x \mid p(x)\}$$

for example:

$$Ev = \{n \mid n \in N \ and \ 2 \ \text{divides} \ n\}$$

Notice that:

$$y \in S \ \text{iff} \ p(y)$$

No restrictions were placed on properties p. Russell showed that this is unsatisfactory by considering the property:

$$\text{russ}(x) \equiv x \ \text{is a set and} \ x \notin x$$

(This is not as artificial and contrived as it first appears: each library has a catalogue of the books in the library, and can be thought of as a set whose members are the titles of those books. The National Library has a master catalogue which lists all catalogues. Does it contain itself or not?) Let R be the set specified intensionally by the property russ:

$$R = \{x \mid \text{russ}(x)\}$$

Then for any set y:

$y \in R$ iff russ(y) //definition of R

iff $y \notin y$ //definition of russ

In particular, in the special case $y = R$:

$R \in R$ iff $R \notin R$

which is a contradiction.

We use Russell's argument in several places in Chapter 3, most notably to prove the unsolvability of the Halting problem for Turing machines.

We cannot go into the mathematical ramifications of Russell's paradox here. Suffice it to say that a great deal of effort was expended in the years 1900–1940 to give a precise axiomatic definition of set theory which evaded the paradox. The interested reader is referred to Cohen and Hersh (1967) or Nagel and Newman (1956).

Solution to teaser in Section A.1(1). The set is:

{M, V, E, M, J, S, U, N, P}

since they are the initial letters of the planets in order of increasing orbit size!!

APPENDIX B

Programming Prerequisites

This book is about the theory of computer science, which is the science based on computers and programming. Not surprisingly, descriptions of algorithms appear in many places throughout the book. As far as computer scientists are concerned (and it was primarily for their benefit that the book was written), the most natural and understandable expression of an algorithm is in a suitable programming language. There is no programming language that is simultaneously universally known, used, and useful, although some languages such as FORTRAN and ALGOL 60 might claim to satisfy the first two conditions. Unfortunately, both FORTRAN and ALGOL 60 have severely limited stocks of linguistic structures, so many of the descriptions of the algorithms in the book would be opaque and involve **gotos** and **if** commands. This would rather defeat the aim of programming to communicate algorithms.

Accordingly, we have denoted the algorithms in a notation that is based on BCPL (which itself was based on the influential CPL project).[*] It is not necessary to understand BCPL in order to read the book. This appendix is intended to provide the necessary background. Our descriptions are much less formal than those in the ALGOL 60 report. We expect that the reader is familiar with at least one high-level programming language.

We discuss expressions, commands, declarations, and, finally, the **valof-resultis** construct.

B.1 Expressions

Expressions are written as in FORTRAN or ALGOL 60, with the exception of conditional expressions (see Section 6.1) whose syntax is:

$$(p1 \rightarrow e1, p2 \rightarrow e2, \ldots, pn \rightarrow en, e_{n+1})$$

The tests $p1, p2$, etc. are evaluated in turn until one of them, say pi, yields true; then the value of ei is returned as the value of the entire expression. If none of the pi's yields true, the value of e_{n+1} is returned.

In various places in Part 1 of the book, we assume the existence of a data structure say D, which has a selector, say sel. The component of D selected by sel is denoted either by $D!$sel or sel!D.

Many of the expressions that we write require an algorithmic process to be

---

[*] D.W. Barron *et al.* (1963) 'The main features of cpl', *Comp. Journal*, **6**, 134–143.

carried out before a result can be returned as the value of the entire expression. We use BCPL's **valof** construction to achieve this effect. It is the major reason for using BCPL notation.

The main liberty we have taken with expressions is in Chapter 2 (page 26), where we aid readability by defining functions to produce sequences of states of finite state machines. We also suppose that it is possible to define functions to produce ordered pairs.

B.2 Commands

Some of the commands will be familiar to the reader. Thus:

$$x := y + z$$

is our notation for assignment commands, while:

> **if** $x < 3$ **do** $x := y$

and

> **test** $x < 3$ **then** $x := y$
>
> > **or** $x := z$

are typical one- and two-armed conditional commands. We separate commands written on the same line by ';' as in ALGOL 60. The precedence of ';' is very low, so that:

> **if** $x < 3$ **do** $x := y$; $y := z$

is equivalent to:

> (**if** $x < 3$ **do** $x := y$) ; $y := z$

There are two ways to introduce compound commands into **if** and **test** commands. One way is to use brackets as follows:

> **if** $x < 3$ **do** \$($x := y; y := z$ \$)

The other way is to introduce a high precedence sequencing operator '⟨ ⟩' whose effect is otherwise the same as ';':

> **if** $x < 3$ **do** $x := y$ ⟨ ⟩ $y := z$

The latter approach is more readable, and is used in preference to brackets as far as is reasonable.

We use a variety of iterative constructs to articulate different repetitive processes directly. The most useful ones are:

(a) **while** b **do** cmd. (i) The test expression b is evaluated. (ii) If the result is true, the command cmd is executed, and control returned to (i). Otherwise the **while** command is terminated.

(b) **until** b **do** com. This is equivalent to **while not** b **do** cmd

(c) cmd **repeat**. The command cmd is repeatedly executed. This construction is used in conjunction with the command **break,** which usually forms one arm of a conditional command. **Break** causes the execution of the repeat command to terminate, and control to pass to the point immediately following it.

(d) **for** ident = startexp **to** stopexp **do** cmd. startexp and stopexp are evaluated to yield $v1$ and $v2$ (say), and the identifier ident is assigned the value $v1$. The following iterative command is then executed:

> **untill** ident $> v2$ **do** cmd $\langle\ \rangle$ ident := ident $+ 1$

Occasionally we use a **goto** command as in ALGOL 60.

B.3 Declarations

Many of the declarations appearing in the book assume the simple form:

> **let** ident = expression

which introduces a new variable called ident and initializes its value to that of the expression on the right-side. In Chapter 3, we take liberties such as:

> **let** $\langle x, y \rangle = f(u)$

where $f(u)$ is supposed to return an ordered pair as its value.

The remaining declarations introduce either functions or routines. A function application delivers a value. For example:

> **let** $f(x, y) = x + y + 1$

declares a function f with two parameters x and y. Subsequently, an application of f forms part of an expression:

> $(x < 3 \rightarrow f(x + 3, y - 1), f(3, y)) + 1$

Functions can be recursive. Most of the functions declared in the book involve the **valof** construction described in Section B.4.

A routine defines a complicated command, and is analogous to a FORTRAN subroutine or ALGOL 60 typeless procedure. For example:

> **let** zeroize(v, k) **be**
>
> out('zeroizing') $\langle\ \rangle$ //this is a comment
>
> **for** $i = 1$ **to** k **do** $v!i := 0$

A block is a sequence of declarations, followed by a sequence of commands, and enclosed in the brackets $( )$.

B.4 valof-resultis

The value of a **valof** expression:

> **valof** command

is determined by executing the command (which is usually a block or compound command) until a command of the form:

resultis expression

is encountered. This causes the execution of the **valof** to terminate, and the value of the expression in the **resultis** command to be returned as the value of the entire expression.

For example, the following function returns the first value greater than m in a data structure V having k components, or 0 if there is no such:

```
let firstbigger(V, k, n) = valof
   $( for i = 1 to k do
          if V!i > m do resultis V!i
      resultis 0
   $)
```

References

Ackermann, W. (1928) 'On Hilbert's construction of the real numbers', in van Heijenoort (1967).

Allen, C.D., Chapman, D.N. and Jones, C.B. (1972) 'A formal definition of Algol 60', TR 12.105, IBM Hursley, U.K.

Allison, D.C.S. (see Hoare, C.A.R.)

Amarel, S. (1970) 'Representation and modelling in problems of program formation', *Machine Intelligence*, 6 (ed. Meltzer and Michie). Edinburgh Univ. Press.

Arbib, M.A. (1969) *Theories of Abstract Automata*, Prentice-Hall.

Ashcroft, E.A. and Manna, Z. (1960) 'Formalization of properties of parallel programs', Stanford AIM-110; also in *Machine Intelligence*, 6 (ed. Meltzer and Michie), Edinburgh Univ. Press (1970), 17–42.

Barron, D.W. (1969) *Recursive Techniques in Programming*, Macdonald-Elsevier.

Bernays, P. (see Hilbert, D.)

Bledsoe, W.W. (see Good, D.I.)

Bornat, R. and Brady J.M. (1976) The dimensions of programming languages. (in press)

Boyer, R.S., Elspas, B. and Levitt, K.N. (1975) 'SELECT – a formal system for testing and debugging programs by symbolic execution', Proc. Int. Conf. Reliable Software, Los Angeles, 234–245.

Boyer, R.S. and Moore, J.S. (1975) 'Proving theorems about LISP functions', *Journal ACM*, 22, 129–41.

Brady, J.M. (1976) 'A programming approach to some results and concepts in the theory of computation', *Comp. Journal,*

Brady, J.M. (see also Bornat, R)

Brady, J.M. (see also Laski, J.G.)

Bundy, A. (1975) 'Analysing mathematical proofs (or reading between the lines)', Proc. 4th IJCAI, Tblisi.

Burstall, R.M. (1972) 'Some techniques for proving correctness of programs which alter data structures', *Machine Intelligence*, 7, Edinburgh Univ. Press.

Burstall, R.M. (1969) 'Proving properties of programs by structural induction', *Comp. Journal*, 12, 41–48.

Burstall, R.M. (1974) 'Program proving as hand simulation with a little induction', Proc. IFIP, Stockholm.

Burstall, R.M. (see also Topor, R.W.)

Burstall, R.M., Collins, J.S. and Popplestone, R.J. (1971) *Programming in POP-2*, Edinburgh Univ. Press.

Caplain, M. (1975) 'Finding invariant assertions for proving programs', Proc. Int. Conf. Reliable Software, Los Angeles, 165–170.

Chapman, D.N. (see Allen, C.D.)

Chomsky, N. (1956) 'Three models for the description of language', IREE Trans. Inform. Theory, IT2, 113–124.

Church, A. (1941) 'The calculi of lambda-conversion', *Annals of Math. Studies*, **6**, Princeton.

Clint, M. and Hoare, C.A.R. (1972) 'Program proving: jumps and functions', *Acta Informatica*, **1**, 214–224.

Cohen, P.J. and Hersh, R. (1967) 'Non-Cantorian set theory', *Scientific American* (December, 217)

Colby, K.M. (see Schank, R.C.)

Collins, J.S. (see Burstall, R.M.)

Cooper, D.C. (1966) 'Theorem proving in computers', *Advances in Programming and Non-numerical Computation* (ed. Fox), Pergamon.

Cooper, D.C. (1971) 'Programs for mechanical program verification', *Machine Intelligence*, **6** (ed. Meltzer and Michie), Edinburgh Univ. Press 43–59.

Curry, H.B. and Feys, R. (1958) *Combinatory Logic*, Vol. 1, North-Holland.

Dahl, O.-J., Dijkstra, E.W. and Hoare, C.A.R. (1972) *Structured Programming*, Academic Press.

Davis, M. and Hersh, R. (1973) 'Hilbert's 10th problem', *Scientific American* (November, 229).

Deutsch, L.P. (1973) 'An interactive program verifier', PhD thesis, Univ. California at Berkeley.

Dijkstra, E.W. (1968) 'Goto statement considered harmful', *Comm. ACM*, **11**, 147–148.

Dijkstra, E.W. (1972) 'Notes on structured programming', in Dahl, Dijkstra, and Hoare (1972).

Dijkstra, E.W. (see also Dahl, O.-J.)

Elcock, E.W., *et al.* (1971) 'ABSET: a programming language based on sets; motivation and examples', *Machine Intelligence*, **6** (ed. Meltzer and Michie), Edinburgh Univ. Press.

Elgot, C.C. and Robinson, A. (1964) 'Random-access stored-program machines; an approach to programming languages', *Journal ACM*, **11**, 365–399.

Elspas, B. (1974) 'The semiautomatic generation of inductive assertions for program correctness proofs', SRI report.

Elspas, B. (see also Boyer, R.S.)

Elspas, B., Levitt, K.N., Waldinger, R.J. and Waksman, A. (1972), 'An assessement of techniques for proving program correctness', *ACM Computing Surveys*, **4**, 97–147.

Engeler, E. (1971) *Symposium on Semantics of Algorithmic Languages*, Springer.

Evans, A. (1968) 'PAL – a language designed for teaching program linguistics', Proc. ACM 23rd Nat. Conf., 395–4.

Farber, D.J., Griswold, R.E. and Polonsky, I.P. (1964) 'SNOBOL – a string manipulation language', *Journal ACM*, **11**, 21–30.

Feys, R. (see Curry, H.B.)

Fischer, P.C. (1965) 'On formalisms for Turing machines', *Journal ACM*, **12**, 570–580.

Floyd, R.W. (1962) 'On the non-existence of a phrase-structure grammar for Algol 60', *comm. ACM*, **5**, 483–484.

Floyd, R.W. (1967) 'Assigning meanings to programs', *Proc. Symp. Applied Math.*, **19** (ed. Schwarz), Amer. Math. Soc., 19–32.

Foley, M. (see Hoare, C.A.R.)

Foster, J.M. (1966) 'Artificial languages', in *Advances in Programming and Non-numerical Computation* (ed. Fox).

Foster, J.M. (1967) *List Processing*, Macdonald-Elsevier.

German, S.M. (1974) 'A program verifier that generates inductive assertions', BA thesis, Harvard.

Gimpel, J.F. (1973) 'A theory of discrete patterns and their implementation in SNOBOL 4', *Comm. ACM*, 16, 91–100.

Gödel, K. (1930) 'The completeness of the axioms of the functional calculus', in van Heijenoort (1967).

Gödel, K. (1931) 'Uber formal unentscheidbare Sätze der Principia Mathematica und verwandter Systeme I', reproduced in English in van Heijenoort (1967).

Good, D.I., London, R.L. and Bledsoe, W.W. (1975) 'An interactive program verification system', Proc. Int. Conf. Reliable Software, Los Angeles, 482–492.

Greif, I. and Waldinger, R.J. (1974) 'A more mechanical approach to program verification', SRI report.

Gries, D. (1971) *Compiler Construction for Digital Computers*, John Wiley.

Griswold, R.E. (see Farber, D.J.)

Grzegroczyk, A. (1953) 'Some classes of recursive functions', *Rozprawy Matematczyne* (Warsaw), 4, 1–45.

Halmos, P.R. (1960) *Naive Set Theory*, Van Nostrand.

Hardy, S. (1976) 'Synthesis of LISP programs', PhD thesis, University of Essex; see also Proc. 4th IJCAI, Tblisi (1975).

Hayes, P.J. (1974) 'Computation and deduction', Proc. 2nd Symp. Math. Foundations of Computer Science, Slovak Academy of Sciences, Prague, 105–118.

van Heijenoort, J. (1967) *From Frege to Gödel: A Source Book in Mathematical Logic*, 1879–1931, Cambridge, Mass.

von Henke, F.C. and Luckham, D.C. (1975) 'Automatic program verification III: a methodology for verifying programs', Proc. Int. Conf. Reliable Software, Los Angeles, 156–164.

Henkin, L. (1969) 'The completeness of the first order functional calculus', in Hintikka (1969).

Hermes, H. (1965) *Enumerability, Decidability and Computability*, Springer.

Hersh, R. (see Cohen, P.J.)

Hersh, R. (see Davis, M.)

Hetzel, W.C. (1974) *Program Test Methods*, Prentice-Hall.

Hewitt, C (1969) 'PLANNER: a language for proving theorems in a robot', Proc. IJCAI, 1 (ed. Walker and Norton), Mitre Corp.

Hilbert, D. (1925) 'On the infinite', in van Heijenoort (1967).

Hilbert, D. and Bernays, P. (1934) *Grundlagen der Mathematik*, Springer.

Hindley, J.R. Lercher, B. and Seldin, J.P. (1972) *Introduction to Combinatory Logic*, London Math. Soc. Lecture Note Series, 7, Cambridge.

Hintikka, J. (1969) *The Philosophy of Mathematics*, Univ. Press.

Hoare, C.A.R. (1969) 'An axiomatic basis for computer programming', *Comm. ACM*, 12, 576–583.

Hoare, C.A.R. (1971a) 'Proof of a program: FIND', *Comm. ACM*, 12, 576–580.

Hoare, C.A.R. (1971b) 'Procedures and parameters: an axiomatic approach', in Engeler (1971), 102–116.

Hoare, C.A.R. (1972a) 'Proof of a structured program: the sieve of Eratosthenes', *Comp. Journal*, **15**, 321–325.

Hoare, C.A.R. (1972b) 'Notes on data structuring', in Dahl, Dijkstra, and Hoare (1972).

Hoare, C.A.R. (1973) 'Recursive data structures', AI memo 223, Stanford.

Hoare, C.A.R. (see also Clint, M.)

Hoare, C.A.R. (see also Dahl, O.-J.)

Hoare, C.A.R. and Allison, D.C.S. (1972) 'Incomputability', *ACM Computing Surveys*, **4**, 169–178.

Hoare, C.A.R. and Foley, M. (1971) 'Proof of a recursive program', *Comp. Journal*, **14**, 391–395.

Hoare, C.A.R. and Wirth, N. (1972) 'An axiomatic definition of the programming language PASCAL', *Acta Informatica*, **2**, 335–355.

Hooper, P.K. (1966) 'The undecidability of the Turing machine immortality problem', *Journal Symbolic Logic*, **31**, 219–234.

Hopcroft, J. and Ullman, J (1969) *Formal Languages and Their Relation to Automata*, Addison-Wesley.

Igarishi, S., London, R.L. and Luckham, D.C. (1973) 'Automatic verification, of programs I: a logical basic and implementation', Stanford report CS-365, AIM-200; to appear in *Acta Informatica*.

Jackson, P.C. (1974) *An Introduction to Artificial Intelligence*, Petrocelli.

Jones, C.B. (see Allen, C.D.)

Karras, A. (see Magnus, W.)

Katz, S.M. and Manna, Z. (1973) 'A heuristic approach to program verification', Proc. 3rd IJCAI, Stanford, 500–512.

King, J.C. (1969) 'A program verifier', PhD thesis, CMU.

King, J.C. (1975) 'A new approach to program testing' Proc. Int. Conf. Reliable Software, Los Angeles, 228–233.

Kleene, S.C. (1936) 'General recursive functions of natural numbers', *Math. Annalen*, **112**, 340–353.

Kleene, S.C. (1956) 'Representation of events in nerve nets and finite automata', in *Automata Studies* (ed. Shannon and McCarthy), Princeton.

Knuth, D.E. (1967) 'The remaining trouble spots in ALGOL 60', *Comm. ACM*, **10**, 611–617.

Knuth, D.E. (1968a) 'Semantics of context-free languages', *Math. System Theory*, **2**, 127–145.

Knuth, D.E. (1968b) *The Art of Computer Programming*, vol. 1, Addison-Wesley.

Knuth, D.E. (1971a) 'Mathematical analysis of algorithms' Stanford memo contains text of addresses to Int. Congress of Mathematicians (1970), IFIP congress (1971).

Knuth, D.E. (1971b) 'Examples of formal semantics', in Engeler (1971).

Knuth, D.E. (1974) 'Structured programming with goto statements', *ACM Computing Surveys*, **6**, 261–301.

Koster, C.H.A. (see van Wijngaarden, A.)

Kuhn, T, (1962) *The Structure of Scientific Revolutions*, Chicago University Press.

Landin, P.J. (1964) 'The machanical evaluation of expressions', *Comp. Journal*, **6**, 308–320.

Landin, P.J. (1965) 'A correspondence between Algol 60 and Church's lambda notation', *Comm. ACM*, **8**, 89–101, 158–165.

Landin, P.J. (1966a) 'A formal description of Algol 60' in *Formal Language Description Languages* (ed. Steel), North-Holland, 266–294.

Landin, P.J. (1966b) 'The next 700 programming languages', *Comm. ACM*, **9**, 157–166.

Laski, J.G. and Brady, J.M. (1975) 'The meaning of programming languages', Essex University technical report.

Lauer, P. (see Lucas, P.)

Leavenworth, B. (1970) Review of a paper by P. Naur, *Comp. Reviews*, **11**, review 19,420.

Lercher, B. (see Hindley, J.R.)

Levitt, K.N. (see Boyer, R.S.)

Levitt, K.N. (see Elspas, B.)

London, R.L. (1970) 'Computer programs can be proved correct', in *Theoretical Approaches to Non-numerical Problem Solving* (ed. Banerji and Mesarovic) Springer, 281–302.

London, R.L. (1975) 'A view of program verification', Proc. Int. Conf. Reliable Software, Los Angeles, 534–545.

London, R.L. (see also Good, D.I.)

London, R.L, (see also Igarishi, S.)

Lucas, P. (1971) 'Formal definition of programming languages and systems', Proc. IFIP Congress.

Lucas, P., Lauer, P. and Stigleitner, H. (1968) 'Method and notation for the formal definition of programming languages', TR 25.087, IBM lab., Vienna.

Lucas, P. and Walk, K. (1969) 'On the formal description of PL/1', *Ann. Rev. Aut. Prog.*, **6**, 105–152.

Luckham, D.C., Park, D.M.R. and Paterson, M.S. (1970) 'On formalised computer programs', *Journal Comp. Syst. Sciences*, **4**, 220–249.

Luckham, D.C. (see also von Henke, F.C.)

Luckham, D.C. (see also Igarishi, S.)

Lyons, J. (1970) *Chomsky*, Fontana modern masters.

Magnus, W., Karras, A. and Solitar, D. (1966) *Combinatorial Group Theory*, Prentice-Hall.

Mailloux, B.J. (see van Wijngaarden, A.)

Manna, Z. (1969a) 'The correctness of programs', *Journal Computer and System Sciences*, **3**, 119–127.

Manna, Z. (1969b) 'Properties of programs and the first order predicate calculus', *Journal ACM*, **16**, 244–255.

Manna, Z. (1970a) 'Mathematical theory of partial correctness', in Engeler (1971).

Manna, Z. (1970b) 'Second order mathematical theory of computation', Proc. 2nd Annual ACM Symp. on Theory of Computing, 158–168.

Manna, Z. (1970c) 'The correctness of non-deterministic programs', *Artificial Intelligence Journal*, 1–26.

Manna, Z. (1974) *Mathematical Theory of Computation*, McGraw-Hill.

Manna, Z. (see also Ashcroft, E.A.)

Manna, Z. (see also Katz, S.M.)

Manna, Z. and McCarthy, J. (1970) 'Properties of programs and partial function logic', *Machine Intelligence*, 5 (ed. Meltzer and Michie), Edinburgh Univ. Press, 27–37.

Manna, Z. and Pnueli, A. (1970) 'Formalisation of properties of functional programs', *Journal ACM*, 17, 555–569.

Manna, Z. and Waldinger, R.J. (1971) 'Toward automatic program synthesis', in Engeler (1971).

Mazurkiewicz, A. (1971) 'Proving algorithms by tail functions', *Info. and Control*, 220–226.

McCarthy, J. (1959a) *Programs with Common Sense; Mechanisation of Human Thought Processes*, H.M. Stationary Office.

McCarthy, J. (1959b) Letter to the editor, *Comm. ACM*, 2, 92.

McCarthy, J. (1960) 'Recursive functions of symbolic expressions and their computation by machine', *Comm. ACM*,

McCarthy, J. (1962a) 'Towards a mathematical science of computation', Proc. IFIP 62, North-Holland, 21–28.

McCarthy, J. (1962b) 'Computer programs for checking mathematical proofs', Proc. Symp. Recursive Function Theory, Amer. Math. Soc., 219–227.

McCarthy, J. (1963) *A Basis for a Mathematical Theory of Computation, Computer Programming and Formal Systems* (ed. Braffort and Hirschberg), North-Holland, 33–69.

McCarthy, J. (1966) 'A formal description of a subset of Algol 60', in *Formal Language Description Languages* (ed. Steel), North-Holland, 1–12.

McCarthy, J. (see also Manna, Z.)

McCarthy, J. and Painter, J. (1967) 'Correctness of a compiler for arithmetic expressions', Proc. Symp. Applied Maths., 19, Mathematical Aspects of Computer Science (ed. Schwarz), Amer. Math. Soc., 33–41.

McCarthy, J., *et al.* (1962) *LISP 1.5 Programmer's Manual*, Mass. Inst. Technol.

McDermott, D.V. (see Sussman, G.J.)

Mendelson, E. (1964) *Introduction to Mathematical Logic*, Van Nostrand.

Meyer, A. and Ritchie, D.M (1967) 'The complexity of loop programs', Proc. ACM 22nd Nat. Conf., 465–470; see also 'A classification of functions by computational complexity', Proc. Hawaiian Conf. on Syst. Sciences (1968), 17–19.

Milne, R. and Strachey, C. (1976) *A Theory of Programming Language Semantics*, Chapman and Hall.

Milner, R. (1971) 'A formal notion of simulation between programs', memo 14, Computers and Logic Research Group, Univ. College Swansea.

Milner, R. (1972) 'Implementation and application of Scott's logic for computable functions', Proc. ACM on Proving Assertions about Programs, Las Cruces, 1–5.

Milner, R. (1973) 'An approach to the semantics of parallel programs', Proc. Convegno di Informatica Teorica, Pisa.

Milner, R. (1975) 'Processes: a mathematical model of computing agents', Technical Report, Edinburgh University.

Minsky, M.L. (1963) 'Steps toward artificial intelligence', reproduced in Feigenbaum and Feldman (1963).

Minsky, M.L. (1967) *Computation: Finite and Infinite Machines*, Prentice-Hall.

Minsky, M.L. and Papert, S. (1969) *Perceptrons*, Mass. Inst. Technol. Press.

Moore, E.F. (1956) *Gedanken Experiments on Sequential Machines; Automata Studies* (ed. Shannon and McCarthy), Princeton, 129–153.

Moore, J.S. (see Boyer, R.S.)

Moses, J. (1970) 'Algebraic simplification: a guide for the perplexed', *Comm. ACM*, 14, 527–537.

Mosses, P. (1974) 'The mathematical semantics of Algol 60', PRG-12, Oxford Univ.

Nagel, E. and Newman, J.R. (1956) 'Gödel's proof',

Naur, P. (1963) 'Revised report on the algorithmic language Algol 60', *Comm. ACM*, 6, 1–17.

Naur, P. (1966) 'Proof of algorithms by general snapshots', *BIT*, 9, 250–258.

Naur, P. (1969) 'Programming by action clusters', *BIT*, 9, 250–258.

Newell, A., Shaw, J.C. and Simon, H.A. (1956) 'The logic theory machine', *IRE Trans. on Inform. Theory*, 3, 61–79.

Newell, A. and Simon, H.A. (1963) 'GPS: a program that simulates human thought', in *Computers and Thought* (ed. Fiegenbaum and Feldman), McGraw-Hill.

Newman, J.R. (see Nagel, E.)

Painter, J. (see McCarthy, J.)

Papert, S. (see Minsky, M.L.)

Parikh, R.J. (1966) 'On context-free languages', *Journal ACM*, 13, 570–581.

Park, D.M.R. (see Luckham, D.C.)

Paterson, M.S. (1968) 'Program schemata', *Machine Intelligence*, 3, (ed. Michie), Edinburgh Univ. Press, 19–31.

Paterson, M.S. (see also Luckham, D.C.)

Peano, G. (1889) 'On the concept of number', in van Heijenoort (1967).

Peck, J.E.L. (see van Wijngaarden, A.)

Pnueli, A. (see Manna, Z.)

Polonsky, I.P. (see Farber, D.J.)

Popplestone, R.J. (see Burstall, R.M.)

Ragland, L.C. (1973) 'A verified program verifier', PhD thesis, Univ. of Texas at Austin.

Raphael, B. (1976) *The Thinking Computer*, Freeman, San Francisco.

Reynolds, J.C. (1971) 'GEDANKEN – a simple typeless language based on the principle of completeness and the reference concept', *Comm. ACM*, 13, 308–319.

Reynolds, J.C. (1972) 'Definitional interpreters for higher order programming languages', Proc. ACM 25th Nat. Conf., Boston.

Ritchie, D.M. (see Meyer, A.)

Robinson, A. (see Elgot, C.C.)

Rogers, H., Jr. (1959) 'The present theory of Turing machine computability, *Journal SIAM*, 7, 114–130.

Rogers, H., Jr. (1967) *Theory of Recursive Functions and Effective Computability*, McGraw-Hill.

Rotman, J.J. (1965) *The Theory of Groups: An Introduction*, Allyn and Bacon.

Schank, R.C. and Colby, K.M. (1973) *Computer Models of Thought and languages*, Freeman, San Francisco.

Scott, D. (1967) 'Some definitional suggestions for automata theory', *Journal Comp. Syst. Sciences*, **1**, 187–212.

Scott, D. (1970) 'Outline of a mathematical theory of computation', Proc. 4th Annual Princeton Conf. on Inf. Sciences and Systems, 169–176; also PRG-2, Oxford Univ.

Scott, D. (1971) 'The lattice of flow diagrams', in Engeler (1971), 311–366.

Scott, D. and Strachey, C. (1971) 'Toward a mathematical semantics for computer languages', PRG-6, Oxford Univ.

Seldin, J.P. (see Hindley, J.R.)

Shannon, C.E. (1956) 'A universal Turing machine with two internal states', *Automata Studies* (ed. Shannon and McCarthy), Princeton.

Shaw, J.C. (see Newell, A.)

Shepherdson, J.C. and Sturgis, H.E. (1963) 'Computability of recursive functions', *Journal ACM*, **10**, 217–255.

Siekmann, J. (1975) forthcoming PhD thesis, Essex University, also: string unification part 1, CSM 7, Essex University.

Simon, H.A. (see Newell, A)

Sites, R.L. (1974) 'Proving that computer programs terminate cleanly', PhD thesis, Stanford.

Solitor, D. (see Magnus, W.)

Stigleitner, H. (see Lucas, P.)

Stoy, J. (1975) 'Mathematical semantics of programming languages', project MAC, Mass. Inst. Technol.

Strachey, C. (1966) 'Towards a formal semantics', in *Formal Language Description Languages* (ed. Steel), North-Holland, 198–220.

Strachey, C. (1967) 'Fundamental concepts', lectures delivered at NATO summer school, Copenhagen (privately circulated).

Strachey, C. (see Scott, D.)

Strachey, C. and Wadsworth, C.P. (1974) 'Continuations: a mathematical semantics for handling full jumps', PRG-11, Oxford Univ.

Sturgis, H.E. (see Sheperdson, J.C.)

Sussman, G.J. and McDermott, D.V. (1973) 'Why conniving is better than planning', AI memo 255A, MIT AI lab.; also available as 'From PLANNER to CONNIVER, a genetic approach', Proc. FJCC, **41**, 1171.

Suzuki, N. (1975) 'Automatic program verification II: verifying programs by algebraic and logical reduction, Proc. Int. Conf. Reliable Software, Los Angeles, 473–481.

Teitelman, W., *et al.* (1974) *Interlisp Reference Manual*, Xerox Corporation, Palo-Alto, California.

Thomas, A.J. (see Weyrauch, R.W.)

Thue, A. (1914) 'Probleme über Veranderungen von Zeichenreihen nach gegebenen Regeln', *Skr. Vidensk. Selsk.*, **10**, 34 pp.

Topor, R.W. (1975) 'Interactive program verification using virtual programs', PhD thesis, Edinburgh University.

Topor, R.W. and Burstall, R.M. (1973) 'Proving programs by symbolic execution working', note 1, University of Edinburgh.

Turing, A.M. (1936) 'On computable numbers with an application to the Entscheidungsproblem', *Proc. London Math. Soc.*, Ser. 2-42, 230-265.

Turing, A.M. (1950) 'Computing machinery and intelligence', in Feigenbaum and Feldman (1963).

Ullman, J. (see Hopcroft, J.)

Wadsworth, C.P. (see Strachey, C.)

Waksman, A. (see Elspas, B.)

Waldinger, R.J. (see Elspas, B.)

Waldinger, R.J. (see Greif, I.)

Waldinger, R.J. (see Manna, Z.)

Walk, K. (see Lucas, P.)

Wang, H. (1957) 'A variant to Turing's theory of computing machines', *Journal ACM*, **4**,

Weber, H. (see Wirth, N.)

Wegbreit, B. (1973) 'Heuristic methods for mechanically deriving inductive assertions', Proc, 3rd IJCAI, Stanford, 524-536.

Wegbreit, B. (1974) 'The synthesis of loop predicates', *Comm. ACM*, **17**, 102-112.

Wegner, P. (1968) *Programming Languages, Information Structures and Machine Organisation*, McGraw-Hill.

Weissman, C. (1967) *LISP 1.5 Primer*, Dickenson Press.

Weyrauch, R.W. and Thomas, A.J. (1974) 'FOL: a proof checker for first order logic', Stanford AIM.

van Wijngaarden, A., Mailloux, B.J., Peck, J.E.L. and Koster, C.H.A. (1969) 'Report on the algorithmic language Algol 68', *Numerische Mathematik*, **14**, 79-218.

Winograd. T. (1972) *Understanding Natural Language*, Edinburgh Univ. Press.

Winograd, T. (1974) 'Five lectures on artificial intelligence', Stanford AI memo 246.

Winston, P.H. (1975) *The Psychology of Computer Vision*, McGraw-Hill.

Wirth, N. and Weber, H. (1966) 'A generalisation of Algol and its formal definition', *Comm. ACM*, **9**, 13-23, 88-99.

Wirth, N. (see also Hoare, C.A.R.)

Author Index

Subject Index